THE DESIGN AND ANALYSIS OF SCIENTIFIC EXPERIMENTS

An Introduction with Some Emphasis on Computation

K. C. PENG

Research Laboratories
General Motors Corporation

ADDISON-WESLEY PUBLISHING COMPANY

Reading, Massachusetts · Palo Alto · London · Don Mills, Ontario

To my daughter, Nancy

PREFACE

This book is an introduction to the design and analysis of experiments. It is written primarily for statisticians, computer programmers, and persons engaged in experimental work who have some background in mathematics and statistics. The mathematical background should include calculus and elementary matrix theory. The statistical background should be equivalent to a one-year course in statistics.

The essential ideas of constructing common experimental designs, estimation, and testing hypotheses as seen from the viewpoint of statistics are discussed. A number of general procedures for the numerical computations in analysis of variance are described. Basic information on analysis of covariance and some complex experiments is also presented. However, some topics are not covered or not treated in detail; the reader is encouraged to do additional reading.

An attempt has been made to introduce some techniques in such a way that they can be easily programmed for a digital computer. Several computer programs for the analysis of common experiments are included in the appendices. However, one does not need any background in computer programming in order to use this book profitably. Included in the book are a number of small-scale numerical examples, which can be followed through with only a desk calculator. These numerical examples all have hypothetical data and are designed for easy computation and verification.

No statistical tables have been included; the reader is expected to have common statistical tables already available to him, and specific references to tables of experimental designs are made in the book.

I wish to express my appreciation to Mr. D. E. Hart, head of the Computer Technology Department, Research Laboratories, General Motors Corporation, for encouragement in writing this book. Portions of the manuscript were used for special training courses for in-plant engineers at General Motors Institute. I thank Mr. W. F. Paulson for his cooperation and help in this respect.

I am very grateful to Professor Harold Freeman of Massachusetts Institute of Technology, who read an earlier draft and made detailed comments. Any remaining shortcomings are clearly my own.

I thank the staff at Addison-Wesley Publishing Company for the cooperation and efficient help during the process of completing the book.

Warren, Michigan   K. C. P.
May, 1966

CONTENTS

5 FIXED, RANDOM, AND MIXED MODELS

6 RANDOMIZED-BLOCKS, LATIN-SQUARE, AND SPLIT-PLOT DESIGNS

7 FRACTIONAL FACTORIAL DESIGNS AND CONFOUNDING

8 RESPONSE SURFACE DESIGNS

9 SPECIAL TOPICS

10 ANALYSIS OF COVARIANCE

PRELIMINARIES

0.1 THE DESIGN OF EXPERIMENTS

Scientific research usually involves the accumulation of information or the formulation of hypotheses and their verification. In general, this accumulation or verification requires the collection of observations. The design of the experiment is basically the planning of collection of data so that the desired information can be obtained with sufficient precision or that the hypothesis can be properly tested.

For a given set of objectives, several alternative experimental designs with varying amounts of information and cost may be constructed. The role of statistics comes into play in the selection and construction of a design and subsequently in the analysis of observed data. The analysis may include summary description of data, estimation of properties of the phenomena being investigated, and testing of hypotheses.

In a typical situation, the experimenter (namely, the scientist or engineer who conducts the experiment) must use his expert knowledge of the subject in which he is experimenting to determine especially the following:

1) the dependent or response variable to be measured;
2) the independent variables which should be included in the experiment and allowed to vary;
3) the way in which independent variables should be varied.

These decisions are essential for precisely defining the experiment. After having defined the experiment, the experimenter can now use his statistical skill or a statistician's assistance to select or construct an efficient experimental plan. The final success of the experiment will necessarily depend on the scientific or engineering ability of the experimenter as well as skill in statistical design.

0.2 THE CONCEPT OF ERROR VARIANCE

The result of any experiment is influenced not only by the action of controlled variables but also by extraneous conditions which tend to mask the effects of the controlled variables. That part of the variation among observations which is attributable to all types of extraneous conditions is commonly called *experimental error*. The basic quantity for measuring experimental errors is the *error*

1

variance per observation, which is defined as the expected value of the square of error that affects a single observation. The proper choice and valid estimate of the error variance in an experiment is very important in making probabilistic statements in regard to the importance of a certain controlled variable or the difference between categories or sets of conditions under which the experiment is carried out.

The body of statistical techniques to analyze observed data from a designed experiment involving several sources of variation, to partition the total variation in the data into components representing the experimental error, the controlled variables, and possibly their combined actions, to decide which components are statistically important, and to estimate the effects of the different sources is known as the *analysis of variance*.

The concept of error variance may be employed to define the *amount of information* an experiment supplies. Suppose that a mean m for the response under a particular controlled condition is obtained from an experiment and that the error variance is known exactly as σ^2; then the amount of information supplied by the experiment with respect to the true mean, of which m is an estimate, is defined to be

$$\frac{1}{\sigma^2}$$

If σ^2 is not known exactly but is estimated by s^2 with v degrees of freedom, it can be shown (Fisher [1]) that the amount of information is

$$\frac{v+1}{(v+3)s^2}$$

This leads to the notion of *relative efficiency* of experimental designs. If a design has an estimated error variance s_1^2 with v_1 degrees of freedom and if a second design has an estimated error variance s_2^2 with v_2 degrees of freedom, then the relative efficiency of the first design to the second is estimated as

$$\frac{(v_1+1)(v_2+3)s_2^2}{(v_2+1)(v_1+3)s_1^2}$$

This expression has general applicability. The two experiments may have different sets of controlled conditions being tested, while each provides an estimate of a specific effect. Also, the effect may have been estimated by different methods.

0.3 ESTIMATION

Statistical estimation deals with the problem of estimating the unknown value of a population parameter θ from a sample drawn from a population with an assumed density function $f(y, \theta)$, where y is a random variable. Both y and θ can be multidimensional. There are two important types of parametric estimates, namely, *point estimates* and *interval estimates*.

Suppose that a random variable y has a density function $f(y, \theta)$ and that a sample $(y_1, y_2, \ldots, y_n)$ of n elements is drawn. The point estimate of the true value of θ is an observable random variable which is a function of $(y_1, y_2, \ldots, y_n)$. This function is called a *statistic*. Intuitively, the distribution of the statistic should be concentrated as closely as possible around the true value of θ.

a) Principles of Estimation

Several important principles for determining good point estimates may be noted here.

i) *The Principle of Consistency*
Consistency is a limit property and is generally considered as the minimum requirement of a statistic which can be used as an estimate. If an estimate converges in probability* to the true value of the parameter θ as n approaches infinity, it is called a *consistent estimate*.

ii) *The Principle of Unbiasedness and Minimum Variance*
A statistic is called an *unbiased estimate* if its expected value, under the assumption that θ is the true value of the parameter, is equal to θ for all values of θ. Among all unbiased statistics, if a statistic has the minimum variance, it is called an unbiased *minimum variance estimate*. For any statistic T, the ratio of this minimum value to the actual variance of T is called the efficiency of T. A statistic with efficiency equal to 1 is an *efficient estimate*.

iii) If a statistic T contains all the information in the sample regarding the parameter θ, it is called a *sufficient estimate* for the true value of θ. This means that for any other statistic T', the conditional random variable T' for given T has a distribution which does not depend on the true value of θ.

b) Methods of Estimation

A few common methods of estimation will be mentioned below. Each may satisfy some of the above principles to a certain extent.

i) *Method of Moments*
This method consists of calculating the first few moments from the sample and equating the sample moments to the corresponding population moments. Since the population moments are functions of the unknown parameters, the number of moments to be used depends on the number of parameters to be estimated. The resulting equations are solved for the parameters. Under fairly general conditions, an estimate given by the method of mo-

---

* Suppose $(\hat{\theta}_1, \hat{\theta}_2, \ldots, \hat{\theta}_n, \ldots)$ is a sequence of estimates of θ such that for arbitrary $\epsilon > 0$,

$$\lim_{n \to \infty} P(\theta - \epsilon < \hat{\theta}_n < \theta + \epsilon) = 1$$

Then $(\hat{\theta}_1, \hat{\theta}_2, \ldots, \hat{\theta}_n, \ldots)$ is said to converge in probability to θ.

ments will tend to normality for large n (i.e., asymptotically normal), and its mean will differ from the true parameter by a value of order n^{-1}. This bias may often be removed to get an unbiased estimate. However, the estimates given by the method of moments are usually not efficient (see Cramér [2]).

ii) *Method of Maximum Likelihood*

Let $(y_1, y_2, \ldots, y_n)$ be n independent observations on a random variable y which has a density function $f(y, \theta)$. Define a *likelihood function* as

$$L(\theta) = \prod_{i=1}^{n} f(y_i, \theta)$$

The likelihood function $L(\theta)$ is a function of θ with $(y_1, y_2, \ldots, y_n)$ considered as constants (data). Intuitively, an estimate of θ which makes L relatively large is likely to be a good estimate. The method of maximum likelihood is based on this intuitive belief and simply seeks that value of θ which maximizes the likelihood function $L(\theta)$. This usually requires differentiating $L(\theta)$ with respect to θ, equating to zero, and solving the resulting equation. The importance of the maximum likelihood method is revealed by the following two properties (see Cramér [2]):

1) If an efficient estimate of θ exists, the method will yield it.

2) If a sufficient estimate T of θ exists, the method will produce an estimate which will be a function of T.

Another important property of the maximum likelihood method is that under certain conditions it gives estimates which tend to normality for large n (i.e., asymptotically normal) and have minimum variance in the limit (i.e., asymptotically efficient).

iii) *Method of Least Squares*

The method of least squares is basic in the theory of the design of experiments. Assume a random variable y whose value depends on parameters $\theta_1, \theta_2, \ldots$. To estimate the θ's, the method of least squares seeks those values of the θ's which minimize the sum of squares of deviations of the observed values of y from their expected values in terms of the parameters.

We shall illustrate the essentials of this method by considering a simple problem which, in particular, is typical in the subject matter of the design of experiments.

Suppose that we have t groups of independent observations:

$$y_{11}, y_{12}, \ldots, y_{1n_1}$$
$$y_{21}, y_{22}, \ldots, y_{2n_2}$$
$$\vdots$$
$$y_{t1}, y_{t2}, \ldots, y_{tn_t}$$

and suppose that the observations may be represented by a linear model:

$$y_{ij} = \beta_i + \epsilon_{ij} \quad (i = 1, 2, \ldots, t; \quad j = 1, 2, \ldots, n_i)$$

where β_i are the true means of the t groups and are considered as fixed constants, and the ϵ_{ij} are random errors independently distributed with zero means and equal variances σ^2.

In analysis of variance, it is common to use a different parametrization by defining effects:

$$\alpha_i = \beta_i - \mu$$

where μ is the true general mean.

The model equation then becomes

$$y_{ij} = \mu + \alpha_i + \epsilon_{ij} \tag{0.3.1}$$

The parameters to be estimated are $\mu, \alpha_1, \alpha_2, \ldots, \alpha_t$. The sum of squares to be minimized is

$$E = \sum_i \sum_j (y_{ij} - \mu - \alpha_i)^2$$

Taking partial derivatives of E with respect to μ and α_i and equating to zero, we have

$$\frac{\partial E}{\partial \mu} = -2 \sum_i \sum_j (y_{ij} - \mu - \alpha_i) = 0$$

$$\frac{\partial E}{\partial \alpha_i} = -2 \sum_j (y_{ij} - \mu - \alpha_i) = 0 \quad (i = 1, 2, \ldots, t)$$

From the above, we obtain the $(t + 1)$ normal equations

$$\sum_i \sum_j y_{ij} = n\hat{\mu} + \sum_i n_i \hat{\alpha}_i \tag{0.3.2}$$

$$\sum_j y_{ij} = n_i \hat{\mu} + n_i \hat{\alpha}_i \quad (i = 1, 2, \ldots, t) \tag{0.3.3}$$

where $n = \sum_i n_i$.

The equations are dependent, since (0.3.3) summed over i will yield (0.3.2). However, if the side condition $\sum_i n_i \hat{\alpha}_i = 0$ is used, the solutions $\hat{\mu}$ and $\hat{\alpha}_i$ are uniquely determined as functions of the observations y_{ij}. The side condition makes differential effects (relative to $\hat{\mu}$) of $\hat{\alpha}_1, \hat{\alpha}_2, \ldots, \hat{\alpha}_t$, and this does not constitute a genuine loss of information. The introduction of the n_i's, which are sample quantities, into the condition imposed on the $\hat{\alpha}_i$'s does not affect the basic structure of the model, and conveniently simplifies the algebra. The use of $\sum_i n_i \hat{\alpha}_i = 0$ also yields that $\hat{\mu}$ is the weighted average of the $\hat{\beta}_i$'s, namely

$$\hat{\mu} = \frac{\sum_i n_i \hat{\beta}_i}{\sum_i n_i}$$

Equation (0.3.3) can be written as

$$\frac{\sum_j y_{ij}}{n_i} = \hat{\mu} + \hat{\alpha}_i \quad (i = 1, 2, \ldots, t)$$

or

$$y_{i.} = \hat{\mu} + \hat{\alpha}_i \quad (i = 1, 2, \ldots, t) \tag{0.3.4}$$

where the convenient dot notation is employed. In general, replacing a subscript of a quantity by a dot means that the mean of the quantity has been taken over all defined values of the subscript.

Equation (0.3.2) gives

$$\hat{\mu} = \frac{\sum_i \sum_j y_{ij}}{n} = y_{..}$$

and from (0.3.4), we have

$$\hat{\alpha}_i = y_{i.} - y_{..} \quad (i = 1, 2, \ldots, t)$$

How good are the least squares estimates? This question is answered by a general theorem, the *Gauss-Markov theorem*, which is stated below.

Suppose that we have the linear model

$$y_r = \sum_{v=1}^{m} b_v x_{rv} + \epsilon_r \quad (r = 1, 2, \ldots, n)$$

where the y_r's are observable random variables, the x_{rv}'s have known fixed values, and the b_v's are unknown constants. Also assume that the random variables ϵ_r are uncorrelated with zero means and variances σ^2. Then the least squares estimates of the b_v's obtained by minimizing the sum of squares

$$\sum_{r=1}^{n} \left(y_r - \sum_{v=1}^{m} b_v x_{rv} \right)^2$$

are unbiased, minimum variance, linear estimates of the b_v's.

c) Unbiased Estimate of the Error Variance

The estimation of error variance is important yet simple. Return to the model equation (0.3.1). The error sum of squares is

$$SS_E = \sum_i^t \sum_j^{n_i} (y_{ij} - \hat{\mu} - \hat{\alpha}_i)^2$$

By (0.3.4), this can be written as

$$SS_E = \sum_i \sum_j (y_{ij} - y_{i.})^2$$

$$= \sum_i \sum_j y_{ij}^2 + \sum_i n_i \left(\frac{\sum_j y_{ij}}{n_i} \right)^2 - 2 \sum_i \left(\frac{\sum_j y_{ij}}{n_i} \right) \sum_j y_{ij}$$

$$= \sum_i \sum_j y_{ij}^2 + \sum_i \frac{(\sum_j y_{ij})^2}{n_i} - 2 \sum_i \frac{(\sum_j y_{ij})^2}{n_i}$$

$$= \sum_i \sum_j y_{ij}^2 - \sum_i \frac{(\sum_j y_{ij})^2}{n_i} \tag{0.3.5}$$

Taking expected values, we have

$$E\left[\sum_i^t \sum_j^{n_i} y_{ij}^2\right] = E\left[\sum_i \sum_j (\mu + \alpha_i + \epsilon_{ij})^2\right]$$

$$= \sum_i \sum_j E[\mu^2 + \alpha_i^2 + \epsilon_{ij}^2 + 2\mu\alpha_i + 2\mu\epsilon_{ij} + 2\alpha_i\epsilon_{ij}]$$

Since

$$E[\epsilon_{ij}] = 0, \qquad E[\epsilon_{ij}^2] = \sigma^2, \qquad E[\alpha_i] = \alpha_i, \qquad E[\alpha_i^2] = \alpha_i^2$$

and μ, α_1, and ϵ_{ij} are independent, clearly then

$$E\left[\sum_i \sum_j y_{ij}^2\right] = E\left[\sum_i \sum_j (\mu^2 + \alpha_i^2 + \sigma^2 + 2\mu\alpha_i + 2\mu\epsilon_{ij} + 2\alpha_i\epsilon_{ij})\right]$$

$$= \sum_i n_i(\mu^2 + \alpha_i^2 + \sigma^2) \qquad (0.3.6)$$

and

$$E\left[\sum_i^t \frac{(\sum_j^{n_i} y_{ij})^2}{n_i}\right] = E\left[\sum_i \frac{1}{n_i}\left(n_i\mu + n_i\alpha_i + \sum_j \epsilon_{ij}\right)^2\right]$$

$$= E\left[\sum_i \frac{1}{n_i}\left\{n_i^2\mu^2 + n_i^2\alpha_i^2 + \left(\sum_j \epsilon_{ij}\right)^2 + n_i^2\mu\alpha_i\right.\right.$$

$$\left.\left. + n_i(\mu + \alpha_i)\left(\sum_j \epsilon_{ij}\right)\right\}\right]$$

$$= \sum_i n_i(\mu^2 + \alpha_i^2) + t\sigma^2 \qquad (0.3.7)$$

Hence

$$E[SS_E] = \left(\sum_i^t n_i - t\right)\sigma^2 \qquad (0.3.8)$$

This means that $SS_E/(\sum_i n_i - t)$, or MS_E, is an unbiased estimate of the error variance σ^2 for this model.

In general, an unbiased estimate of the error variance is given by the error sum of squares divided by the degrees of freedom, n_E, in the estimated error, and

$n_E = $ (Total number of observations) $-$ (number of independent parameters to be estimated)

d) Confidence Limits

The problem of estimation by an interval is of greater importance than that of estimation by a point. In interval estimation the procedure is to find two functions, θ_L and θ_U, of the observed random variables such that the probability that the random interval $[\theta_L, \theta_U]$ will cover the true value of a parameter θ is equal to a fixed value $1 - \alpha$. This statement may be written as

$$\text{Prob } \{\theta_L \leqq \theta \leqq \theta_U \mid \theta\} = 1 - \alpha$$

where α is generally taken as 0.10, 0.05, 0.01, etc. The interval is commonly called a *confidence interval*. The quantities θ_L and θ_U are lower and upper *confidence limits*, respectively, and correspond to the *confidence coefficient* $(1 - \alpha)$ or the *confidence level* α. The risk of accepting the hypothesis that the confidence interval covers the true value θ when in fact it does not is α.

i) *Shortest Confidence Interval*

In general, for a given confidence coefficient, there are infinitely many confidence intervals, and we have the problem of choosing one among them. It is intuitively reasonable to prefer that confidence interval with minimum length. However, the length is a random variable, and often the confidence interval obtained from one procedure may be shorter than that from another procedure for some sample points but longer for other sample points. Instead of considering the length, a confidence interval for a fixed confidence coefficient may be regarded as best if it minimizes the probability of covering any false value θ_1 when the true value is θ. This condition may be stated more precisely.

Let I_0 be the interval $[\theta_L, \theta_U]$; then I_0 is a shortest confidence interval of confidence coefficient $(1 - \alpha)$, if

1) I_0 is a confidence interval of confidence coefficient $(1 - \alpha)$

2) for any other confidence interval $I = [\theta'_L, \theta'_U]$ of confidence coefficient $(1 - \alpha)$, then

$$\text{Prob } \{\theta_L \leq \theta_1 \leq \theta_U | \theta\} \leq \text{Prob } \{\theta'_L \leq \theta_1 \leq \theta'_U | \theta\}$$
for all θ_1 and θ, and $\theta_1 \neq \theta$.

Unfortunately, shortest confidence intervals exist only in rare cases, so additional principles are formulated by which one confidence interval may be preferred to another.

ii) *Unbiased Confidence Interval*

A confidence interval is unbiased if the probability that it covers θ_0 when θ_0 is the true value is $(1 - \alpha)$ and the probability that it covers a false value θ_1 is always less than or equal to $(1 - \alpha)$ for all θ_0 and θ_1. In other words, $I_0 = [\theta_L, \theta_U]$ is an unbiased confidence interval of confidence coefficient $(1 - \alpha)$ if

1) $\text{Prob } \{\theta_L \leq \theta_0 \leq \theta_U | \theta_0\} = 1 - \alpha$ for all θ_0

2) $\text{Prob } \{\theta_L \leq \theta_1 \leq \theta_U | \theta_0\} \leq \text{Prob } \{\theta_L \leq \theta_0 \leq \theta_U | \theta_0\}$
for all θ_0 and θ_1, and $\theta_1 \neq \theta_0$

iii) *Asymptotically Shortest Confidence Interval*

Consider sequences of confidence intervals $I_N = [\theta_{NL}, \theta_{NU}]$ defined for each sample size N $(N = 2, 3, \ldots)$. Then I_N is an asymptotically shortest confidence interval of confidence coefficient $(1 - \alpha)$ if

1) $\lim_{N \to \infty} \text{Prob } \{\theta_{NL} \leq \theta \leq \theta_{NU} | \theta\} = 1 - \alpha$ uniformly in θ

2) $\lim\limits_{N \to \infty}$ [least upper bound (Prob $\{\theta_{NL} \leqq \theta_1 \leqq \theta_{NU} | \theta\}$

   $- \text{Prob } \{\theta'_{NL} \leqq \theta_1 \leqq \theta'_{NU} | \theta\})] = 0$

where $I'_N = [\theta'_{NL}, \theta'_{NU}]$ is any other sequence of confidence intervals of confidence coefficient $(1 - \alpha)$.

To illustrate a common procedure for determining confidence limits, consider the model equation (0.3.1) for two groups:

$$y_{ij} = \mu + \alpha_i + \epsilon_{ij} \quad (i = 1, 2; \quad j = n_1, n_2)$$

If is often of interest not only to estimate the difference between the two effects but also to determine the confidence limits. Let

$$d = \hat{\alpha}_1 - \hat{\alpha}_2$$

Then

$$d = (y_1. - y_..) - (y_2. - y_..) = y_1. - y_2.$$
$$E[d] = \alpha_1 - \alpha_2$$

Assume that ϵ_{ij}'s are independently and normally distributed with zero means and equal variances σ^2; then

$$\text{Var }[y_1. - y_2.] = \sigma^2 \left(\frac{1}{n_1} + \frac{1}{n_2}\right)$$

Denote the estimate of σ^2 by s^2 and the sample variances by s_1^2 and s_2^2. The quantity

$$\frac{(y_1. - y_2.) - (\alpha_1 - \alpha_2)}{s\sqrt{(1/n_1) + (1/n_2)}}$$

where s is here given by

$$\sqrt{(n_1 s_1^2 + n_2 s_2^2)/(n_1 + n_2 - 2)} \qquad (0.3.9)$$

follows a t-distribution with $(n_1 + n_2 - 2)$ degrees of freedom. The confidence limits for the difference between the two effects are given by

$$(y_1. - y_2.) \pm s t_{\alpha/2} \sqrt{(1/n_1) + (1/n_2)}$$

where $t_{\alpha/2}$ is the $t_{\alpha/2}$ value corresponding to $(n_1 + n_2 - 2)$ degrees of freedom at a chosen confidence coefficient $(1 - \alpha)$.

0.4 TESTING HYPOTHESES

When an experimenter studies a random variable y with a density function $f(y, \theta)$, he is interested not only in estimating the value of the unknown parameter θ but also frequently in testing whether θ or some function of θ is equal to some given value, say θ_0. From theoretical considerations or experience, a hypothesis

$$H_0 : \theta = \theta_0$$

is set up. Observations are taken and used as a basis for either accepting or rejecting H_0. In so doing, two types of errors may be committed:

Type I error: rejecting the hypothesis although it is true;

Type II error: accepting the hypothesis although it is false.

Let α and β represent the probability of making Type I and Type II errors, respectively. The expression

$$P = 1 - \beta$$

is called *the power of a test*. A function of the parameter, P, denotes the probability of rejecting the hypothesis

$$H_0 : \theta = \theta_0$$

when θ actually equals some other value θ_1. If the power is plotted for different values of θ_1, we obtain the *power curve* for the test. Sometimes, the probability β is plotted for different values of θ_1, and the plot is called the *operating characteristic curve* of the test.

It is desirable to minimize the probabilities of making Type I and Type II errors at the same time. However, in general, for a fixed sample size, it can be shown that when P increases, then α increases, and vice versa. The general approach is to maximize P while choosing α in advance and keeping it constant.

Frequently, the experimenter may observe a random variable y with a density function characterized by k parameters $(\theta_1, \theta_2, \ldots, \theta_k)$. Consider a k-dimensional space Ω with coordinates $\theta_1, \theta_2, \ldots, \theta_k$. This space is called the *parameter space* and contains all possible values of $\theta_1, \theta_2, \ldots, \theta_k$. A certain set of values for the parameters of a density function is represented by a point in the parameter space.

A sample of n observations $(y_1, y_2, \ldots, y_n)$ is represented by a point in a space of n dimensions with coordinates $y_1, y_2, \ldots, y_n$. This space is called *the sample space*. The point representing the sample is called a *sample point*.

Testing a certain statistical hypothesis H_0 means that a decision will be made as to whether the parameters fall within a certain region ω of the parameter space Ω, where ω is defined by H_0. The hypothesis H_0 is true if the parameters fall within ω and is false if within $(\Omega - \omega)$. If ω is a single point, the hypothesis is called a *simple hypothesis*; otherwise it is a *composite hypothesis*. The hypothesis H_0 that the parameters are contained in ω is referred to as the *null hypothesis*.

On the basis of the observations $(y_1, y_2, \ldots, y_n)$, we accept or reject H_0. This is carried out by selecting a region R in the sample space such that if the sample point is in R, we reject H_0; otherwise we accept H_0. Region R is called *the critical region*. The *probabilities* of *committing Type I and Type II errors* are, respectively,

$$\alpha = \text{Prob } \{(y_1, y_2, \ldots, y_n) \text{ in } R \mid (\theta_1, \theta_2, \ldots, \theta_k) \in \omega\}$$

and

$$\beta = \text{Prob } \{(y_1, y_2, \ldots, y_n) \text{ not in } R \mid (\theta_1, \theta_2, \ldots, \theta_k) \in \Omega - \omega\}$$

The *power function* and *operating characteristic function* are functions of $(\theta_1, \theta_2, \ldots, \theta_k)$, and are represented, respectively, by

$$1 - \text{Prob} \{(y_1, y_2, \ldots, y_n) \text{ not in } R \mid (\theta_1, \theta_2, \ldots, \theta_k) \in \Omega - \omega\}$$

and

$$\text{Prob} \{(y_1, y_2, \ldots, y_n) \text{ not in } R \mid (\theta_1, \theta_2, \ldots, \theta_k) \in \Omega - \omega\}$$

If a power function of a given test is $P(\theta)$, where θ may be multidimensional and $P_1(\theta)$ is the power function of any other test, and if $P(\theta) \geqq P_1(\theta)$, then the test corresponding to $P(\theta)$ is said to be *uniformly most powerful*. Unfortunately, a uniformly most powerful test rarely exists; therefore we may have to restrict our class of tests and find a uniformly most powerful test in the restricted smaller class.

One restriction may be introduced by adopting the *principle of unbiasedness*. A test is unbiased if the power function of the test has a relative minimum for the value $\theta = \theta_0$, where θ_0 is the hypothesized value to be tested. This is a reasonable principle. For if a test is unbiased, the probability of rejecting the hypothesis is smaller if θ is really θ_0 than if θ is really some neighboring value θ_1, and this is clearly desirable.

Other principles may be used to place restriction on the class of tests.

A general procedure for testing hypotheses, called the *likelihood ratio test*, may be used to derive many of the common statistical tests. Suppose that we have a density function $f(y; \theta_1, \theta_2, \ldots, \theta_k)$, that observations $(y_1, y_2, \ldots, y_n)$ are taken, and that the *likelihood function*

$$L(\theta_1, \theta_2, \ldots, \theta_k) = \prod_{i=1}^{n} f(y_i; \theta_1, \theta_2, \ldots, \theta_k)$$

is formed. Suppose the null hypothesis is

$$H_0 : (\theta_1, \theta_2, \ldots, \theta_k) \text{ in } \omega$$

and the alternative is

$$H_1 : (\theta_1, \theta_2, \ldots, \theta_k) \text{ in } \Omega - \omega$$

Form the likelihood ratio

$$\lambda = \frac{\max L(\omega)}{\max L(\Omega)}$$

where $\max L(\omega)$ is the maximum of L with respect to $(\theta_1, \theta_2, \ldots, \theta_k)$ subject to the condition $(\theta_1, \theta_2, \ldots, \theta_k)$ in ω, and $\max L(\Omega)$ is the maximum of L with respect to $(\theta_1, \theta_2, \ldots, \theta_k)$ subject to the condition $(\theta_1, \theta_2, \ldots, \theta_k)$ in Ω. Clearly, λ must lie between 0 and 1. A small value of λ indicates that the likelihood computed within ω corresponding to the null hypothesis is relatively small, so we reject H_0. Conversely, if λ is large, we accept H_0. The critical region (for rejection of H_0) is defined as

$$0 < \lambda < \lambda_0$$

where the constant λ_0 is chosen to give the desired significance level. If a uniformly most powerful test exists, the likelihood ratio test will often yield it.

We will consider some typical problems of testing hypotheses which are of particular interest to us. Return to the model equation

$$y_{ij} = \mu + \alpha_i + \epsilon_{ij} \quad (i = 1, 2; j = n_1, n_2)$$

It may be desired to test the significance of the difference between the two effects. A null hypothesis

$$H_0 : \alpha_1 = \alpha_2$$

is set up. If H_0 is true, then, under the assumption that the ϵ_{ij} are normally distributed with zero means and equal variances, $(y_1. - y_2.)$ is normally distributed with mean zero and estimated variance

$$s^2 \left(\frac{1}{n_1} + \frac{1}{n_2} \right)$$

where s is given by Eq. (0.3.9). The quantity

$$\frac{y_1. - y_2.}{s\sqrt{(1/n_1) + (1/n_2)}}$$

follows a t-distribution with $(n_1 + n_2 - 2)$ degrees of freedom. This quantity is used for testing the significance of the null hypothesis.

Frequently, there are more than two groups for model (0.3.1), and a more general hypothesis H_0 that all α_i $(i = 1, 2, \ldots, t)$ are equal to zero is set up. The test is provided by a general procedure as described below, which, in fact, follows directly from the likelihood ratio test criterion.

First, we compute the error sum of squares in the usual way, that is,

$$SS_E = \sum_i^t \sum_j^{n_i} (y_{ij} - \hat{\mu} - \hat{\alpha}_i)^2$$

Next, we compute the error sum of squares under the restricted model obtained from the original model (0.3.1) by setting

$$\alpha_1 = \alpha_2 = \cdots = 0$$

That is,

$$SS_{E'} = \sum_i^t \sum_j^{n_i} (y_{ij} - \hat{\mu})^2 \tag{0.4.1}$$

Then if H_0 is true, the ratio

$$\frac{(SS_{E'} - SS_E)/(t - 1)}{SS_E/n_E}$$

follows an F-distribution with $(t - 1)$ and n_E degrees of freedom. We shall derive the expected value of $(SS_{E'} - SS_E)$ in the following.

For the detailed calculations, we need Eq. (0.3.5), which gives

$$SS_E = \sum_i^t \sum_j^{n_i} y_{ij}^2 - \sum_i \frac{(\sum_j y_{ij})^2}{n_i}$$

Now consider $SS_{E'}$. There is only one normal equation:

$$-2 \sum_i \sum_j (y_{ij} - \hat{\mu}) = 0$$

So

$$\sum_i \sum_j y_{ij} = n\hat{\mu}$$

where

$$n = \sum_i n_i$$

Hence

$$\hat{\mu} = \frac{\sum_i \sum_j y_{ij}}{n}$$

It follows that

$$SS_{E'} = \sum_i \sum_j (y_{ij} - \hat{\mu})^2$$

$$= \sum_i \sum_j \left(y_{ij} - \frac{1}{n} \sum_i \sum_j y_{ij} \right)^2$$

$$= \sum_i \sum_j y_{ij}^2 - \frac{1}{n} \left(\sum_i \sum_j y_{ij} \right)^2$$

and

$$SS_{E'} - SS_E = \sum_i \frac{(\sum_j y_{ij})^2}{n_i} - \frac{1}{n} \left(\sum_i \sum_j y_{ij} \right)^2 \tag{0.4.2}$$

We recall that the expected value of SS_E is given by (0.3.8), that is,

$$E[SS_E] = \left(\sum_i n_i - t \right) \sigma^2$$

and that (0.3.7) gives

$$E\left[\sum_i \frac{(\sum_j y_{ij})^2}{n_i} \right] = \sum_i n_i(\mu^2 + \alpha_i^2) + t\sigma^2$$

To compute the expected value of $(SS_{E'} - SS_E)$, we consider

$$E\left[\frac{1}{n} \left(\sum_i \sum_j y_{ij} \right)^2 \right] = E\left[\frac{1}{n} \left\{ \sum_i \sum_j (\mu + \alpha_i + \epsilon_{ij}) \right\}^2 \right]$$

$$= E\left[\frac{1}{n} \left\{ n\mu + \sum_i n_i\alpha_i + \sum_i \sum_j \epsilon_{ij} \right\}^2 \right]$$

Since $\sum_i n_i \alpha_i = 0$,

$$E\left[\frac{1}{n}\left(\sum_i \sum_j y_{ij}\right)^2\right] = \sum_i n_i \mu^2 + \sigma^2$$

Combining results, we have

$$E[SS_{E'} - SS_E] = \sum_i n_i \alpha_i^2 + (t-1)\sigma^2$$

or

$$E\left[\frac{SS_{E'} - SS_E}{t-1}\right] = \frac{1}{t-1}\sum_i n_i \alpha_i^2 + \sigma^2 \qquad (0.4.3)$$

Under the null hypothesis, the ratio

$$\frac{(SS_{E'} - SS_E)/(t-1)}{SS_E/(n-t)} \qquad (0.4.4)$$

is distributed as F with $(t-1)$ and $(n-t)$ degrees of freedom. We will discuss the above ratio again in the next section.

The method we used to calculate SS_E and $SS_{E'}$ is straightforward but slow. In Chapters 1 and 2, a speedier technique commonly employed in analysis of variance will be described.

0.5 NONCENTRAL X^2, F, THE POWER OF THE F-TEST, AND THE DETERMINATION OF SAMPLE SIZES

a) Noncentral X^2

It is well known that if $y_1, y_2, \ldots, y_v$ are independent normal random variables with zero means and unit variances, then $\sum_1^v y_i^2$ is distributed as $\chi^2(v)$, that is, as a chi-square variable with v degrees of freedom. However, if the means are not zero, the distribution of $\sum_1^v y_i^2$ is not the ordinary chi-square. We shall state the following theorem.

If $y_1, y_2, \ldots, y_v$ are independently normally distributed with means $\mu_1, \mu_2, \ldots, \mu_v$, respectively, and with variances equal to unity, then

$$U = \sum_1^v y_i^2$$

is distributed as the noncentral chi-square with v degrees of freedom and *noncentrality parameter*

$$\delta = \frac{1}{2}\sum_1^v \mu_i^2$$

and the frequency function of U is given by

$$f(U) = e^{-\delta}\sum_{i=0}^{\infty}\frac{\delta^i U^{(1/2)(v+2i)-1}e^{-U/2}}{i!2^{(1/2)(v+2i)}\Gamma[(v+2i)/2]} \qquad (0 \le U < \infty) \qquad (0.5.1)$$

The ordinary or central chi-square distribution is a special case of the noncentral chi-square distribution when $\delta = 0$, that is, when $\mu_1 = \mu_2 = \cdots = 0$.

The mean of the noncentral chi-square distribution is $v + 2\delta$ and the variance is $2v + 8\delta$. The noncentral chi-square distribution, like the central chi-square, has the *reproductive property*. If independent random variables U_1 and U_2 are distributed according to noncentral chi-square distributions with degrees of freedom v_1 and v_2, and parameters δ_1 and δ_2, respectively, then $(U_1 + U_2)$ has again a noncentral chi-square distribution with degrees of freedom $(v_1 + v_2)$ and noncentrality parameter $(\delta_1 + \delta_2)$.

b) Noncentral F

If a random variable W_1 is distributed as $\chi^2(v_1)$, and W_2 is distributed as $\chi^2(v_2)$, and if W_1 and W_2 are independent, then

$$Z = \frac{v_2}{v_1} \frac{W_1}{W_2}$$

is distributed as the well-known F-distribution with v_1 and v_2 degrees of freedom, or $F(v_1, v_2)$. However, if W_1 is a noncentral chi-square, we obtain what is called the *noncentral F-distribution*. We state the related theorem as follows.

If a random variable W_2 is distributed as the central chi-square with v_2 degrees of freedom and another random variable W_1 is distributed as the noncentral chi-square with v_1 degrees of freedom and noncentrality parameter δ, and if W_1 and W_2 are independent, then

$$Z = \frac{v_2}{v_1} \frac{W_1}{W_2}$$

is distributed as the noncentral F-distribution with v_1 and v_2 degrees of freedom and *noncentrality parameter* δ. The frequency function of Z is given by

$$f(Z) = \sum_{i=0}^{\infty} \frac{\Gamma[(2i + v_1 + v_2)/2](v_1/v_2)^{(1/2)(2i+v_1)} \delta^i e^{-\delta}}{\Gamma(v_2/2)\Gamma[(2i + v_1)/2]i!}$$

$$\times \frac{Z^{(1/2)(2i+v_1-2)}}{[1 + (v_1 Z)/v_2]^{(1/2)(2i+v_1+v_2)}} \quad (0 \le Z < \infty) \quad (0.5.2)$$

A noncentral F is usually denoted by F'. When $\delta = 0$, then $f(Z)$ becomes the frequency function of a central F.

c) The Power of the F-Test

Noncentral F plays an important role in the theory of the power of significance tests in analysis of variance. We shall discuss the essential ideas by again considering the model equation (0.3.1):

$$y_{ij} = \mu + \alpha_i + \epsilon_{ij} \quad (i = 1, 2, \ldots, t; \quad j = 1, 2, \ldots, n_i)$$

and the related equation (0.4.2):

$$SS_{E'} - SS_E = \sum_i \frac{(\sum_j y_{ij})^2}{n_i} - \frac{1}{n}\left(\sum_i \sum_j y_{ij}\right)^2$$

It can be shown easily by direct expansion that (0.4.2) can be written as

$$SS_{E'} - SS_E = \sum_i \sum_j (y_{i.} - y_{..})^2$$

$$= \sum_i n_i(y_{i.} - y_{..})^2 \qquad (0.5.3)$$

Now consider

$$\frac{SS_{E'} - SS_E}{\sigma^2} = \sum_i \sum_j \left(\frac{y_{i.} - y_{..}}{\sigma}\right)^2 \qquad (0.5.4)$$

The $(y_{i.} - y_{..})/\sigma$ are independently normally distributed with mean α_i/σ and unit variance. Then by the theorem on noncentral χ^2, (0.5.4) is distributed as noncentral χ^2 with degrees of freedom $(t - 1)$ and noncentrality parameter

$$\delta = \frac{1}{2}\sum \left(\frac{n_i\alpha_i^2}{\sigma^2}\right) \qquad (0.5.5)$$

Hence the ratio (0.4.4), that is,

$$\frac{(SS_{E'} - SS_E)/(t - 1)}{SS_E/(n - t)} = F'$$

must be a noncentral F with degrees of freedom $(t - 1)$ and $(n - t)$ and noncentrality parameter δ.

However, under the null hypothesis

$$\alpha_1 = \alpha_2 = \cdots = 0$$

$\delta = 0$, and so the above ratio is distributed as a central F.

If we wish to test the hypothesis $\delta = 0$ in the noncentral F distribution with a type I error α, then

$$F_\alpha \leq F' < \infty$$

is the critical region, where F_α may be read from a table of the F-distribution. We reject the hypothesis $(\delta = 0)$, if the computed ratio F' falls in this interval. The *power of the test*, $P(\delta)$, is the probability that the computed F' falls in the critical region when $\delta \neq 0$, and is determined by the integral

$$P(\delta) = \int_{F_\alpha}^\infty f(F'; v_1, v_2, \delta)\, dF' \qquad (0.5.6)$$

For certain values of F_α, Tang [4] calculated tables which can be used to evaluate

$$\int_0^{F_\alpha} f(F')\, dF' \qquad (0.5.7)$$

These tables are tabulated in terms of E^2, where

$$E^2 = \frac{v_1 F'}{v_2 + v_1 F'} \tag{0.5.8}$$

The frequency function of E^2 is

$$g(E^2; v_1, v_2, \delta) = \sum_{i=0}^{\infty} \frac{\Gamma[(2i + v_1 + v_2)/2]}{\Gamma(v_2/2)\Gamma[(2i + v_1)/2]} \frac{\delta^i}{i!} e^{-\delta}(E^2)^{(1/2)(2i+v_1-2)}$$

$$\times (1 - E^2)^{(1/2)(v_2-2)} \quad (0 \le E^2 \le 1) \tag{0.5.9}$$

If $\delta = 0$, then $g(E^2)$ is the *beta distribution*. When $\delta \ne 0$, then $g(E^2)$ is called the *noncentral beta distribution*.

Transforming F' to E^2 in Eq. (0.5.6), we obtain

$$P(\delta) = \int_{E_\alpha^2}^{1} g(E^2; v_1, v_2, \delta)\, dE^2 \tag{0.5.10}$$

We are interested in evaluating the integral

$$\int_{0}^{E_\alpha^2} g(E^2; v_1, v_2, \delta)\, dE^2 = 1 - P(\delta) \tag{0.5.11}$$

which is the probability of type II error. The quantity E_α^2 is obtained from the integral

$$\alpha = \int_{E_\alpha^2}^{1} g(E^2; v_1, v_2, \delta = 0)\, dE^2$$

$$= \int_{F_\alpha}^{\infty} f(F'; v_1, v_2, \delta = 0)\, dF' \tag{0.5.12}$$

where

$$F_\alpha = \frac{v_2 E_\alpha^2}{v_1 - v_1 E_\alpha^2}$$

If $\alpha = 0.05$ or $\alpha = 0.01$, we can read F_α from the ordinary F tables.

Tang evaluated the integral

$$\beta = 1 - P(\delta) = \int_{0}^{E_\alpha^2} g(E^2; f_1, f_2, \phi)\, dE^2$$

for various values of f_1, f_2, ϕ, and E_α^2, where $f_1 = v_1$, $f_2 = v_2$,

$$\phi = \sqrt{\frac{2\delta}{v_1 + 1}} \tag{0.5.13}$$

and E_α^2 is obtained from Eq. (0.5.12) for $\alpha = 0.05$ and $\alpha = 0.01$.

Tang's tables have been reprinted in several books, for example, Mann [3].

Now consider an example. If, for the ratio (0.4.4), α is given as 0.05, $v_1 = t - 1 = 5$, $v_2 = n - t = 18$ and $\delta = 12$, then Tang's tables give

$E^2_{0.05} = 0.435$. Since

$$\phi = \sqrt{\frac{2(12)}{5+1}} = 2$$

Tang's tables give the probability of type II error (which is denoted by P_{II} in Tang's notation) as 0.078. Hence the power of the test is

$$P(\delta) = 1 - 0.078 = 0.922$$

In other words, when $\delta = 12$, the probability of rejecting the hypothesis that $\delta = 0$ is equal to 0.922 when a type I error probability of 0.05 is used.

Pearson and Hartley [5] constructed charts from these tables. These charts are somewhat easier to use, and give the power of the test directly.

d) The Determination of Sample Sizes

The calculation of the power of a statistical test is closely related to the problem of determining the number of observations (or the sample size) required in an experiment. Consider the experiment represented by the model equation (0.3.1), where the observations are classified into t-groups (or categories). Assuming that we shall take an equal number of observations, r, for each group, we wish to determine r for testing the hypothesis that all α_i are equal to zero.

Before estimating r, we need to specify the type I error and to have a reasonably good estimate of the error variance σ^2. Next, we may decide that it is important to discover differences among the t-groups as a given multiple of σ. This means that we may set

$$\sum \left(\frac{\alpha_i}{\sigma}\right)^2$$

in the following formula:

$$\delta = \frac{r}{2} \sum \left(\frac{\alpha_i}{\sigma}\right)^2$$

which is obtained from Eq. (0.5.5) by putting $n_i = r$.

Now we can compute δ for trial values of r. For any δ, we proceed to calculate

$$\phi = \sqrt{\frac{2\delta}{v_1 + 1}}$$

Then turn to Tang's tables to find E^2_α and the size of type II error, or read the power from Pearson-Hartley charts.

Note that for a specified value of

$$\sum \left(\frac{\alpha_i}{\sigma}\right)^2$$

δ increases with r, ϕ increases with δ, and the power of the test increases with δ. On the other hand, for a given r, δ increases with

$$\sum \left(\frac{\alpha_i}{\sigma}\right)^2$$

Therefore, in planning an experiment, it may be useful to list several combinations of r and α_i/σ together with the powers of the test in order to select a feasible sample size among a number of possible alternatives.

The estimation of sample sizes for other experimental designs are similar to the procedure described above.

0.6 METHODS OF MULTIPLE COMPARISONS

The application of an F-test may reject the hypothesis that in (0.3.1) all α_i are equal to zero or, equivalently, that all means

$$\beta_i = \alpha_i + \mu$$

are equal. The experimenter may then wish to know which β_i are significantly different from others. Several procedures have been proposed for the problem of making multiple comparisons within a set of means. We shall discuss two of these general procedures.

a) Scheffé's Method

Scheffé's method [6] is very general. It can be used to judge all contrasts. A *contrast* ψ is a linear function of a set of true means with known constant coefficients c_i subject to the condition that the sum of these coefficients is equal to zero. The simplest contrast is the difference of any pair of means. Interactions defined in Chapter 2 can also be called contrasts.

For a contrast such as

$$\psi = \sum_i c_i \beta_i \quad \left(\sum_i c_i = 0 \right)$$

the unbiased estimate is

$$\hat{\psi} = \sum c_i \hat{\beta}_i = \sum c_i y_i.$$

with variance

$$\sigma_{\hat{\psi}}^2 = \sum_i c_i^2 \operatorname{Var}[y_i.] = \sigma^2 \sum_i \left(\frac{c_i^2}{n_i} \right)$$

which is estimated by

$$\hat{\sigma}_{\hat{\psi}}^2 = MS_E \sum_i \left(\frac{c_i^2}{n_i} \right)$$

Scheffé's method is based on the following theorem on *simultaneous confidence intervals*.

The probability that the values of all contrasts simultaneously satisfy the inequalities

$$\hat{\psi} - S\hat{\sigma}_{\hat{\psi}} \leq \psi \leq \hat{\psi} + S\hat{\sigma}_{\hat{\psi}}$$

is $(1 - \alpha)$, with the constant S calculated from

$$S^2 = (t - 1)F_\alpha$$

where F_α is obtained from the ordinary F-table with $(t - 1)$ and $(n - t)$ degrees of freedom.

b) Tukey's Method

Tukey's method [7] is similar to Scheffé's, but it requires that estimates of the true means have equal variances. Thus if we apply the method to the means β_i, the sample sizes n_i must be equal. Tukey's method is based on the following theorem.

The probability that the values of all contrasts

$$\psi = \sum_i c_i \beta_i$$

simultaneously satisfy the inequalities

$$\hat{\psi} - T\sqrt{MS_E} \left(\frac{1}{2} \sum_{i=1}^{t} |c_i| \right) \leq \psi \leq \hat{\psi} + T\sqrt{MS_E} \left(\frac{1}{2} \sum_{i=1}^{t} |c_i| \right)$$

is $1 - \alpha$, with

$$T = \frac{1}{\sqrt{r}} q_\alpha$$

where r is the equal sample sizes of the means and q is the studentized range for a sample of t and $(n - t)$ degrees of freedom.

The distribution of q is defined as follows. Let $y_1, y_2, \ldots, y_n$ be independently and normally distributed with mean μ and variance σ^2; let the range

$$R = \max y - \min y$$

and let σ^2 be independently estimated by s^2 with v degrees of freedom. Then the distribution of studentized range $q(n, v)$ is that of R/s. Tables of upper α-points of studentized range are available from several sources, for example, [8] and [10].

REFERENCES

1. FISHER, R. A., *The Design of Experiments.* Hafner, New York, 1960.

2. CRAMÉR, H., *Mathematical Methods of Statistics.* Princeton University Press, Princeton, N. J., 1946.

3. MANN, H. B., *Analysis and Design of Experiments.* Dover, New York, 1949.

4. TANG, P. C., "The Power Function of the Analysis of Variance Tests with Tables and Illustrations of their Use," *Stat. Research Memoirs*, Vol. 2, pp. 126–149 (1938).

5. PEARSON, E. S., and H. O. HARTLEY, "Charts of the Power Function of the Analysis of Variance Tests, Derived from the Noncentral *F*-distribution," *Biometrika*, Vol. 38, pp. 112–130 (1951).

6. SCHEFFÉ, H., "A Method for Judging all Contrasts in the Analysis of Variance," *Biometrika*, Vol. 40, pp. 87–104 (1953).

7. TUKEY, J. W., "The Problem of Multiple Comparisons," dittoed notes of 396 pages, Princeton University, Princeton, N. J., 1953.

8. PEARSON, E. S., and H. O. HARTLEY, *Biometrika Tables for Statisticians.* Cambridge University Press, New York, 1958.

9. FREEMAN, H. A., *Introduction to Statistical Inference.* Addison-Wesley, Reading, Mass., 1963.

10. OWEN, D. B., *Handbook of Statistical Tables.* Addison-Wesley, Reading, Mass., 1962.

11. WILKS, S. S., *Mathematical Statistics.* Wiley, New York, 1962.

1 TWO-WAY ARRANGEMENTS

1.1 EXPERIMENTAL SITUATION AND SOME TERMINOLOGY

An experimenter may wish to study two variables which he can control and to investigate their effect or influence on a response or dependent variable which he can observe and measure. Under these conditions, he may use a two-way arrangement.

The variables an experimenter controls are commonly called *factors* in experimental design. The number of forms or categories of a factor appearing in an experiment is called the number of *levels* of that factor. A particular combination with one level from each factor is a *treatment*. If all possible treatments, or a definite portion of them, is of interest, the experiment is called a *factorial* experiment.

A factor can be *quantitative*, such as different temperatures, different concentrations of a reactant, different doses of a drug, etc., or it can be *qualitative*, such as different methods of testing, different chemical solutions, etc. There is usually no natural order established among the different levels of a qualitative factor, but the different levels of a quantitative factor correspond to well-defined values of some numerical quantity.

The response (or dependent variable) to be measured can be the output or yield of a system or a process either of variable type (such as weight gain or amount of wear) or of attribute type (such as percent defective).

1.2 COMBINATORIAL CONFIGURATION

In a factorial experiment, if all possible treatments are included, the experiment is called a *complete factorial*. In a complete two-way arrangement with factor A at a levels and factor B at b levels, there are ab treatments. Each level of A appears b times and each level of B appears a times. For example, if $a = 3$, $b = 4$, the first level is denoted by 0, second level by 1, third level by 2, and fourth level by 3, then the 12 treatments are as follows:

A	0	1	2	0	1	2	0	1	2	0	1	2
B	0	0	0	1	1	1	2	2	2	3	3	3

This is often called the *design matrix* and corresponds to the following two-way layout.

	B_0	B_1	B_2	B_3
A_0	(00)	(01)	(02)	(03)
A_1	(10)	(11)	(12)	(13)
A_2	(20)	(21)	(22)	(23)

It is natural to call each treatment a *cell*.

If A and B are quantitative factors, the ab combinations of levels of A and B are simply lattice points in the AB plane as shown in Fig. 1.2.1. If repeated measurements or observations are made for each treatment in a factorial design, it is called *factorial with replicates*. In a factorial design with the same number of replicates in each cell, every level of a factor or every combination of levels of any given number of factors appears the same number of times. The design is *balanced*. Furthermore, the levels of one factor occur with each of the levels of any other factor with equal frequency, and the design is said to be *orthogonal*.

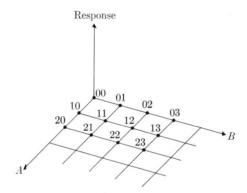

FIG. 1.2.1

1.3 RANDOMIZATION

The smallest division of the experimental material is called an *experimental unit* if any two units may receive different treatments in the actual experiment. The assignment of treatments to experimental units requires particular care. A seemingly reasonable and convenient way of handling treatments may continually favor or handicap a certain treatment in successive replications because of some extraneous source of variation, known or unknown. In order to avoid biases which may occur from a subjective personal procedure, a device known as *randomization* should be used. It arranges the allocation of treatments in a random order such that each treatment has an equal chance of being tested under the more favorable conditions, and possible variations in space, in time, between different experimental units, etc., may not cause systematic error.

Randomization may be carried out by drawing numbered balls from a well-shaken container or other similar devices. A more reliable way is to use the tables of random numbers. For example, if three replications are going to be tested for each treatment of the 3×4 factorial listed in Section 1.2, and if there are 36 experimental units, randomization can be done as follows:

1) Order the experimental units in any convenient way.

2) Number the treatments. Assign numbers 1, 2, 3 to treatment $(0, 0)$; 4, 5, 6 to $(1, 0)$; and so on.

3) Use a table of random numbers. Start at a point of the table in a haphazard way.

4) Read off pairs of digits as they occur. List those numbers between 1 and 36.

5) The first number in the list determines the particular treatment to be applied to the first experimental unit, the second number to the second experimental unit, and so on.

In some experimental situations, all treatments may be applied to the same experimental material; then the above procedure produces a random ordering of the treatments to be received by the same experimental material.

Another important application of randomization is in situations where a considerable amount of variation may come from subjective effects due to personal attitudes or emotions of the individuals participating in the experiment. In such cases randomization avoids the personal biases by concealing the identity of the treatments from the persons taking part in the experiment.

1.4 DESCRIPTIVE INFORMATION

Some common descriptive statistics from experimental data are useful. Let y_{ijk} be the value of the response for the ith level of factor A, jth level of factor B, and kth replication, in a two-way arrangement with a levels for A, b levels for B, and r replications for each cell. Then we have the following definitions:

Mean of the ith level of $A = y_{i..} = \dfrac{1}{br} \sum_{j} \sum_{k} y_{ijk}$

Mean of the jth level of $B = y_{.j.} = \dfrac{1}{ar} \sum_{i} \sum_{k} y_{ijk}$

Mean of (i, j) cell $= y_{ij.} = \dfrac{1}{r} \sum_{k} y_{ijk}$

Standard deviation of the ith level of $A = s_{A_i} = \sqrt{\dfrac{\sum_{j} \sum_{k} (y_{ijk} - y_{i..})^2}{br - 1}}$

Standard deviation of the jth level of $B = s_{B_j} = \sqrt{\dfrac{\sum_{i} \sum_{k} (y_{ijk} - y_{.j.})^2}{ar - 1}}$

Standard deviation of the (i, j) cell $= s_{A_i B_j} = \sqrt{\dfrac{\sum_k (y_{ijk} - y_{ij.})^2}{r - 1}}$

General mean $= y_{...} = \dfrac{1}{abr} \sum_i \sum_j \sum_k y_{ijk}$

General standard deviation $= s = \sqrt{\dfrac{\sum_i \sum_j \sum_k (y_{ijk} - y_{...})^2}{abr - 1}}$

We need additional definitions. Let Y_{ij} be the true mean of the (i, j) cell, and let us adopt the convention of using capital letters for true values. The *main effect of the ith level of A* is defined as the excess of $Y_{i.}$ over the general mean

$$\alpha_i = Y_{i.} - Y_{..}$$

and the α_i's satisfy the condition

$$\sum_i \alpha_i = 0$$

Similarly, *the main effect of the jth level of B* is defined as

$$\beta_j = Y_{.j} - Y_{..}$$

and

$$\sum_j \beta_j = 0$$

The effect of ith level of A specific to the jth level of B is the excess of the cell mean Y_{ij} over the mean of the jth level of B:

$$\alpha_{i(j)} = Y_{ij} - Y_{.j}$$

But α_i is actually the average of $\alpha_{i(j)}$ over the j levels of B. Hence the excess of $\alpha_{i(j)}$ over α_i is called the *interaction effect of the ith level of A with the jth level of B*, that is,

$$\gamma_{ij} = \alpha_{i(j)} - \alpha_i = Y_{ij} - Y_{.j} - Y_{i.} + Y_{..}$$

and the ab interaction effects satisfy the conditions:

$$\sum_i \gamma_{ij} = 0 \text{ for all } j, \qquad \sum_j \gamma_{ij} = 0 \text{ for all } i$$

Since

$$Y_{i.} = \alpha_i + Y_{..}, \qquad Y_{.j} = \beta_j + Y_{..}$$

we have

$$Y_{ij} = \mu + \alpha_i + \beta_j + \gamma_{ij}$$

where

$$\mu = Y_{..}$$

A graphical representation of cell means in a two-factor experiment may reveal some apparent interaction. However, to determine whether any such interaction is a real characteristic of the response, we usually need to apply the proper significance test.

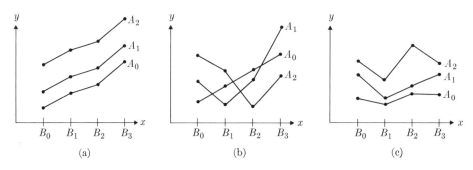

FIG. 1.4.1

Returning to the 3×4 factorial experiment with 3 replications in each cell, we can choose factor B to be represented on the x-axis and plot the cell means by a series of lines—one for each level of the other factor A. The parallel lines in Fig. 1.4.1(a) indicate no interaction, and the lines in Fig. 1.4.1(b) and (c) indicate some apparent interaction.

1.5 STATISTICAL ANALYSIS

In the planning stages of an experiment, it is important to decide whether levels of the factors are to be set at fixed values or to be chosen at random from a large number of possible values. For instance, if an experimenter studies the effect of temperature on the yield of a chemical process, he may set the temperature at 100°F, 150°F, and 200°F, and he uses an approach known as *fixed model* or *model I*. In many similar situations in which the factors are quantitative (such as pressure, time, chemical concentration, etc.), it is often desirable to select fixed levels near practical extremes and, at some intermediate points, to ensure that the experiment covers the range of interest. When an experimenter studies all categories of a qualitative factor (such as all available methods of testing a certain material), the mathematical model of the experiment is also called model I.

However, in some experiments it is reasonable to select at random the levels of some factors, because the interest is in the estimation of variances of the infinite populations from which the samples are drawn. For example, suppose that n animals are chosen randomly from a large population of a given species and that some physical characteristic of each animal is measured on each of m days selected randomly from a long period of time. In such an experiment it is clearly of interest to estimate a component of variation due to days in general and a component of variation due to animals in general, and the experimenter uses an approach called *random model* or *model II*.

When several factors are involved in an experiment in which some factors are at fixed levels and others are at random levels, the model is known as *mixed model* or *model III*.

We will confine our discussions in the early chapters to the fixed model. A detailed study of the various models is given in Chapter 5.

The method of analysis described here will take advantage of the pattern of data and use the well-known *Cochran's theorem*, which is stated as follows:*

Let Z_1, Z_2, ..., Z_n be normally and independently distributed random variables with unit variances. Let

$$\sum_i^n Z_i^2 = Q_1 + Q_2 + \cdots + Q_m$$

where Q_j, $j = 1, 2, \ldots, m$ are sums of squares with n_j degrees of freedom. The Q_j are independently distributed as χ^2 with n_j degrees of freedom if and only if

$$n_1 + n_2 + \cdots + n_m = n$$

a) Analysis of Two-Way Arrangements With *r* Observations Per Cell: Fixed Model

Using the notations defined in Section 1.4 and assuming that the ab sets of r observations in the cells represent random samples of size r drawn from ab separate populations (each distributed independently and normally with mean Y_{ij} and the same variance σ^2), we can write the model as

$$y_{ijk} = \mu + \alpha_i + \beta_j + \gamma_{ij} + \epsilon_{ijk}$$
$$(i = 1, 2, \ldots, a; \quad j = 1, 2, \ldots, b; \quad k = 1, 2, \ldots, r) \quad (1.5.1)$$

where the ϵ_{ijk} are independently $N(0, \sigma^2)$.

The *total variation* or *total sum of squares* is $\sum_i \sum_j \sum_k (y_{ijk} - y_{...})^2$. Motivated by discussions in the preceding section, we form the decomposition

$$\sum_i \sum_j \sum_k (y_{ijk} - y_{...})^2$$

$$= \sum_i \sum_j \sum_k [(y_{i..} - y_{...}) + (y_{.j.} - y_{...}) + (y_{ij.} - y_{i..} - y_{.j.} + y_{...})$$

$$+ (y_{ijk} - y_{ij.})]^2$$

$$= \sum_i \sum_j \sum_k (y_{i..} - y_{...})^2 + \sum_i \sum_j \sum_k (y_{.j.} - y_{...})^2$$

$$+ \sum_i \sum_j \sum_k (y_{ij.} - y_{i..} - y_{.j.} + y_{...})^2 + \sum_i \sum_j \sum_k (y_{ijk} - y_{ij.})^2$$

$$= rb \sum_i (y_{i..} - y_{...})^2 + ra \sum_j (y_{.j.} - y_{...})^2$$

$$+ r \sum_i \sum_j (y_{ij.} - y_{i..} - y_{.j.} + y_{...})^2 + \sum_i \sum_j \sum_k (y_{ijk} - y_{ij.})^2$$

$$(1.5.2)$$

---

*This is a restricted form of the theorem. A more general form and its proof can be found in Graybill [7] and Scheffé [12].

which is valid, since all cross-products vanish. The first three sums of squares at the right of (1.5.2) measure the variation due to the α's, β's, and γ's, respectively, and the last one corresponds to error. The quantities

$$y_{i..} - y_{...}, \qquad y_{.j.} - y_{...}, \qquad \text{and} \qquad y_{ij.} - y_{i..} - y_{.j.} + y_{...}$$

are, in fact, the least squares estimates of the α_i, β_j, and γ_{ij}.

Now consider the identities

$$\sum_i \sum_j \sum_k (y_{ijk} - Y_{ij})^2$$
$$= \sum_i \sum_j \sum_k (y_{ijk} - y_{ij.})^2 + r \sum_i \sum_j (y_{ij.} - Y_{ij})^2 \qquad (1.5.3)$$

and

$$r \sum_i \sum_j (y_{ij.} - Y_{ij})^2$$
$$= r \sum_i \sum_j (y_{ij.} - y_{i..} - y_{.j.} + y_{...} - \gamma_{ij})^2$$
$$+ rb \sum_i (y_{i..} - y_{...} - \alpha_i)^2 + ra \sum_j (y_{.j.} - y_{...} - \beta_j)^2$$
$$+ rab(y_{...} - \mu)^2 \qquad (1.5.4)$$

The left-hand side of (1.5.3) is distributed as $\sigma^2\chi^2(abr)$ and the two terms on the right-hand side are distributed independently as $\sigma^2\chi^2(ab(r-1))$ and $\sigma^2\chi^2(ab)$. Since the left-hand side of (1.5.4) is distributed as $\sigma^2\chi^2(ab)$, and the four terms on the right-hand side have degrees of freedom $(a-1)(b-1)$, $(a-1)$, $(b-1)$, and 1, respectively, hence, by Cochran's theorem, they are distributed independently as

$$\sigma^2\chi^2((a-1)(b-1)), \qquad \sigma^2\chi^2(a-1), \qquad \sigma^2\chi^2(b-1), \qquad \sigma^2\chi^2$$

The sums of squares in (1.5.2) divided by their respective degrees of freedom are referred to as mean squares. The expected values of mean squares are called expected mean squares, or $E[MS]$. They are used as an aid to form the F-tests. Consider

$$MS_E = \frac{\sum_i \sum_j \sum_k (y_{ijk} - y_{ij.})^2}{ab(r-1)}$$

Its expected value is

$$E[MS_E] = \sigma^2$$

To derive the expected value of

$$MS_{AB} = \frac{r\sum_i \sum_j (y_{ij.} - y_{i..} - y_{.j.} + y_{...})^2}{(a-1)(b-1)}$$

we use the identity

$$r \sum_i \sum_j (y_{ij.} - y_{i..} - y_{.j.} + y_{...} - \gamma_{ij})^2$$

$$= r \sum_i \sum_j (y_{ij.} - y_{i..} - y_{.j.} + y_{...})^2$$

$$- 2r \sum_i \sum_j \gamma_{ij}(y_{ij.} - y_{i..} - y_{.j.} + y_{...})$$

$$+ r \sum_i \sum_j \gamma_{ij}^2 \qquad (1.5.5)$$

Since the left-hand side of (1.5.5) is distributed as $\sigma^2 \chi^2((a-1)(b-1))$, its expected value is $(a-1)(b-1)\sigma^2$. We also have

$$E[y_{ij.} - y_{i..} - y_{.j.} + y_{...}] = \gamma_{ij}$$

Therefore, taking expected values of (1.5.5), we find

$$(a-1)(b-1)\sigma^2 = E\left[r \sum_i \sum_j (y_{ij.} - y_{i..} - y_{.j.} + y_{...})^2\right] - r \sum_i \sum_j \gamma_{ij}^2$$

Consequently,

$$E[MS_{AB}] = \sigma^2 + \frac{r\sum_i \sum_j \gamma_{ij}^2}{(a-1)(b-1)}$$

To find the expected value of

$$MS_A = \frac{rb\sum_i (y_{i..} - y_{...})^2}{a-1}$$

we use a similar identity

$$rb \sum_i (y_{i..} - y_{...} - \alpha_i)^2$$

$$= rb \sum_i (y_{i..} - y_{...})^2 - 2rb \sum_i \alpha_i(y_{i..} - y_{...}) + rb \sum_i \alpha_i^2 \qquad (1.5.6)$$

Since the left-hand side of (1.5.6) is distributed as $\sigma^2 \chi^2(a-1)$, its expected value is $(a-1)\sigma^2$. Also,

$$E[y_{i..} - y_{...}] = \alpha_i$$

Hence

$$(a-1)\sigma^2 = E\left[rb \sum_i (y_{i..} - y_{...})^2\right] - rb \sum_i \alpha_i^2$$

It follows that

$$E[MS_A] = \sigma^2 + \frac{rb\sum_i \alpha_i^2}{a-1}$$

Similarly, the expected value of

$$MS_B = \frac{ra\sum_j (y_{.j.} - y_{...})^2}{b - 1}$$

is

$$E[MS_B] = \sigma^2 + \frac{ra\sum_j \beta_j^2}{b - 1}$$

The results are summarized in a tabular form (Table 1.5.1), commonly called *analysis-of-variance table*.

TABLE 1.5.1

Source	SS	d.f.	MS	E[MS]
A	$br \sum_i (y_{i..} - y_{...})^2$	$a - 1$	MS_A	$\sigma^2 + \dfrac{rb\sum_i \alpha_i^2}{a - 1}$
B	$ar \sum_j (y_{.j.} - y_{...})^2$	$b - 1$	MS_B	$\sigma^2 + \dfrac{ra\sum_j \beta_j^2}{b - 1}$
AB	$r \sum_i \sum_j (y_{ij.} - y_{i..} - y_{.j.} + y_{...})^2$	$(a-1)(b-1)$	MS_{AB}	$\sigma^2 + \dfrac{r\sum_i \sum_j \gamma_{ij}^2}{(a-1)(b-1)}$
Error	$\sum_i \sum_j \sum_k (y_{ijk} - y_{ij.})^2$	$ab(r-1)$	MS_E	σ^2
Total	$\sum_i \sum_j \sum_k (y_{ijk} - y_{...})^2$	$abr - 1$		

The usual hypotheses and their corresponding F-tests as seen from the expected mean squares are

$$H_A: \text{all } \alpha_i = 0, \quad F((a-1), ab(r-1)) = MS_A/MS_E$$
$$H_B: \text{all } \beta_j = 0, \quad F((b-1), ab(r-1)) = MS_B/MS_E$$
$$H_{AB}: \text{all } \gamma_{ij} = 0, \quad F((a-1)(b-1), ab(r-1)) = MS_{AB}/MS_E$$

The right-hand tail of F is used, since in all $E[MS]$ the terms added to σ^2 are nonnegative.

Power of these F-tests can be calculated by using the following:

for H_A,

$$\phi = \sqrt{\frac{br}{a\sigma^2} \sum_i \alpha_i^2}, \quad v_1 = a - 1, \quad v_2 = ab(r-1)$$

for H_B,

$$\phi = \sqrt{\frac{ar}{b\sigma^2} \sum_j \beta_j^2}, \quad v_1 = b - 1, \quad v_2 = ab(r-1)$$

for H_{AB},

$$\phi = \sqrt{\frac{r}{[(a-1)(b-1)+1]\sigma^2} \sum_i \sum_j \gamma_{ij}^2} \, ,$$

$$v_1 = (a-1)(b-1),$$
$$v_2 = ab(r-1)$$

where the notations ϕ, v_1, and v_2 are derived from Section 0.5(c).

In general, if H_{AB} is rejected, we would be interested in the cell means. Then, Scheffé's method may be used to investigate, for example, contrasts of the type

$$\psi = Y_{ij} - Y_{i'j'}$$

among all cell means, where ψ is estimated by

$$\hat{\psi} = y_{ij.} - y_{i'j'.}$$

Suppose that $y_{ij.}$ is larger than $y_{i'j'.}$. Then $\hat{\psi}$ is significantly different from zero with confidence coefficient $(1-\alpha)$ if

$$\hat{\psi} > S\hat{\sigma}_{\hat{\psi}}$$

with

$$S^2 = (ab-1)F(\alpha; ab-1, ab(r-1)), \qquad \sigma_{\hat{\psi}}^2 = MS_E(2/r)$$

If Tukey's method is applied to these comparisons, then $\hat{\psi}$ is significantly different from zero with confidence coefficient $(1-\alpha)$ if

$$\hat{\psi} > (\sqrt{MS_E}) \frac{1}{\sqrt{r}} q(\alpha; ab, ab(r-1))$$

If H_{AB} is accepted, we usually would proceed to test H_A and H_B. If H_A or H_B is rejected, Scheffé's method or Tukey's method may be used to study contrasts among the A means or the B means. For example, contrasts among the A means may take the form

$$\psi = \sum_{i=1}^{a} c_i Y_{i.}$$

which is estimated by

$$\hat{\psi} = \sum_{i=1}^{a} c_i y_{i..}$$

For Scheffé's method, we have

$$S^2 = (a-1)F(\alpha; a-1, ab(r-1)), \qquad \sigma_{\hat{\psi}}^2 = \frac{MS_E}{br} \sum_i c_i^2$$

For Tukey's method, we have

$$T = \frac{1}{\sqrt{br}} q(\alpha; a, ab(r-1))$$

TABLE 1.5.2

Source	SS	d.f.	MS	E[MS]
A	$b \sum_i (y_i. - y..)^2$	$a - 1$	MS_A	$\sigma^2 + \dfrac{b \sum_i \alpha_i^2}{a - 1}$
B	$a \sum_j (y._j - y..)^2$	$b - 1$	MS_B	$\sigma^2 + \dfrac{a \sum_j \beta_j^2}{b - 1}$
Error	$\sum_i \sum_j (y_{ij} - y_i. - y._j + y..)^2$	$(a-1)(b-1)$	MS_E	σ^2
Total	$\sum_i \sum_j (y_{ij} - y..)^2$	$ab - 1$		

b) Analysis of Two-Way Arrangements with One Observation Per Cell: Fixed Model

When there is only one observation in every cell of a two-way arrangement, we have to assume that there is no true interaction between factors A and B; that is, A and B effects combine *additively*. The model is written as

$$y_{ij} = \mu + \alpha_i + \beta_j + \epsilon_{ij} \quad (i = 1, 2, \ldots, a; \quad j = 1, 2, \ldots, b)$$

To perform the F-tests on A-effects or B-effects, the quantity

$$\frac{1}{(a-1)(b-1)} \sum_i \sum_j (y_{ij} - y_i. - y._j + y..)^2$$

is used as the error mean square. This is done out of necessity, because there is no longer the estimate of error variance from within cell replications. The analysis-of-variance table is shown in Table 1.5.2.

1.6 COMPUTATIONS

The calculation of sums of squares in analysis of variance for two-way arrangements may be more conveniently done by using the following list of formulas, which can be obtained by the repeated application of the basic relation

$$\sum_{v=1}^{n} (y_v - y.)^2 = \sum_{v=1}^{n} y_v^2 - \frac{\left(\sum_{v=1}^{n} y_v\right)^2}{n}$$

a) Two-Factor Experiment with r Observations Per Cell

$$SS_A = br \sum_i (y_{i..} - y_{...})^2$$

$$= \frac{1}{br} \sum_i \left[\left(\sum_j \sum_k y_{ijk}\right)^2\right] - \frac{1}{abr}\left(\sum_i \sum_j \sum_k y_{ijk}\right)^2$$

$$SS_B = ar \sum_j (y_{.j.} - y_{...})^2$$

$$= \frac{1}{ar} \sum_j \left[\left(\sum_i \sum_k y_{ijk}\right)^2\right] - \frac{1}{abr}\left(\sum_i \sum_j \sum_k y_{ijk}\right)^2$$

$$SS_{AB} = r \sum_i \sum_j (y_{ij.} - y_{i..} - y_{.j.} + y_{...})^2$$

$$= \frac{1}{r} \sum_i \sum_j \left[\left(\sum_k y_{ijk}\right)^2\right] - \frac{1}{br}\sum_i \left[\left(\sum_j \sum_k y_{ijk}\right)^2\right]$$

$$- \frac{1}{ar} \sum_j \left[\left(\sum_i \sum_k y_{ijk}\right)^2\right] + \frac{1}{abr}\left(\sum_i \sum_j \sum_k y_{ijk}\right)^2$$

$$SS_E = \sum_i \sum_j \sum_k (y_{ijk} - y_{ij.})^2 = SS_T - SS_A - SS_B - SS_{AB}$$

$$SS_T = \sum_i \sum_j \sum_k (y_{ijk} - y_{...})^2 = \sum_i \sum_j \sum_k y_{ijk}^2 - \frac{(\sum_i \sum_j \sum_k y_{ijk})^2}{abr}$$

b) Two-Factor Experiment with One Observation Per Cell

$$SS_A = b \sum_i (y_{i.} - y_{..})^2 = \frac{1}{b} \sum_i \left[\left(\sum_j y_{ij}\right)^2\right] - \frac{1}{ab}\left(\sum_i \sum_j y_{ij}\right)^2$$

$$SS_B = a \sum_j (y_{.j} - y_{..})^2 = \frac{1}{a} \sum_j \left[\left(\sum_i y_{ij}\right)^2\right] - \frac{1}{ab}\left(\sum_i \sum_j y_{ij}\right)^2$$

$$SS_E = \sum_i \sum_j (y_{ij} - y_{i.} - y_{.j} + y_{..})^2 = SS_T - SS_A - SS_B$$

$$SS_T = \sum_i \sum_j (y_{ij} - y_{..})^2 = \sum_i \sum_j y_{ij}^2 - \frac{1}{ab}\left(\sum_i \sum_j y_{ij}\right)^2$$

1.7 A NUMERICAL EXAMPLE

Suppose that we have a 2-factor experiment with A at 3 fixed levels, B at 4 fixed levels, and 2 observations per cell. Data are shown in Table 1.7.1. The A means, B means, and cell means are shown in Table 1.7.2. The general mean is estimated by

$$y_{...} = 12.90$$

Now we can estimate α_i, β_j, γ_{ij} as shown in Table 1.7.3. Note that

$$\sum_i \hat{\alpha}_i = 0, \qquad \sum_j \hat{\beta}_j = 0$$

and

$$\sum_i \hat{\gamma}_{ij} = 0, \qquad \sum_j \hat{\gamma}_{ij} = 0$$

The errors $\hat{\epsilon}_{ijk}$ are computed in Table 1.7.4.

TABLE 1.7.1

A		B 1	2	3	4
1		0.3	5.3	10.7	15.5
		0.1	5.1	10.6	15.6
2		5.7	10.0	15.4	20.6
		5.8	10.6	15.0	20.1
3		10.9	15.0	20.3	25.8
		10.2	15.2	20.4	25.4

TABLE 1.7.2

	Cell means: $y_{ij.}$ 1	2	3	4	A means: $y_{i..}$
1	0.20	5.20	10.65	15.55	7.90
2	5.75	10.30	15.20	20.35	12.90
3	10.55	15.10	20.35	25.60	17.90
B means: $y_{.j.}$	5.50	10.20	15.40	20.50	

TABLE 1.7.3

	$\hat{\gamma}_{ij}: y_{ij.} - y_{i..} - y_{.j.} + y_{...}$ 1	2	3	4	$\hat{\alpha}_i: y_{i..} - y_{...}$
1	-0.30	0.00	0.25	0.05	-5
2	0.25	0.10	-0.20	-0.15	0
3	0.05	-0.10	-0.05	0.10	5
$\hat{\beta}_j: y_{.j.} - y_{...}$	-7.4	-2.7	2.5	7.6	

TABLE 1.7.4

		$\hat{\epsilon}_{ijk}: y_{ijk} - y_{ij.}$ 1	2	3	4
1		0.1	0.1	0.05	-0.05
		-0.1	-0.1	-0.05	0.05
2		-0.05	-0.3	0.2	0.25
		0.05	0.3	-0.2	-0.25
3		0.35	-0.1	-0.05	0.2
		-0.35	0.1	0.05	-0.2

TABLE 1.7.5

Source	SS	d.f.	MS
A	400.000	2	200.000
B	756.360	3	252.120
AB	0.630	6	0.105
Error	0.790	12	0.066
Total	1157.780	23	

Using the values in Table 1.7.3 and Table 1.7.4 or the data in Table 1.7.1 and following the computational formulas in Section 1.6 to calculate the sums of squares, we obtain the results in Table 1.7.5. The F-ratios are

$$A: \frac{200.000}{0.066} > F(0.05; 2, 12)$$

$$B: \frac{252.120}{0.066} > F(0.05; 3, 12)$$

$$AB: \frac{0.105}{0.066} < F(0.05; 6, 12)$$

Hence the null hypothesis that the interaction is zero is acceptable. The A effect and the B effect are highly significant.

Suppose that we are interested in comparing pairs of B means. Using Scheffé's method, we have

$$S^2 = (b - 1)F(0.05; b - 1, ab(r - 1)) = 3(3.49) = 10.47$$

$$\sigma_{\hat{\psi}}^2 = \frac{MS_E}{ar} \sum_i c_i^2 = \frac{0.066}{6} [(1)^2 + (-1)^2] = 0.022$$

$$S\sigma_{\hat{\psi}} = \sqrt{(10.47)}\sqrt{(0.022)} = 3.23574(0.148324) = 0.4799$$

Clearly, all differences of pairs of B means are significantly different from zero. If we use Tukey's method, we obtain

$$T = \frac{1}{\sqrt{ar}} q(0.05; b, ab(r - 1)) = \frac{1}{\sqrt{6}} (4.20) = 1.7146$$

$$T\sqrt{MS_E} \left(\frac{1}{2} \sum_i |c_i| \right) = 1.7146\sqrt{0.066}\tfrac{1}{2}(2) = 1.7146(0.2569) = 0.4405$$

This gives a slightly shorter interval but leads to the same conclusion. Scheffé's method or Tukey's method can be applied to other types of contrast to calculate confidence intervals. For example, consider the contrast

$$\psi = Y_{.1} - Y_{.2} - Y_{.3} + Y_{.4}$$

which is estimated by

$$\hat{\psi} = y_{.1.} - y_{.2.} - y_{.3.} + y_{.4.} = 0.40$$

Scheffé's method gives

$$S^2 = (b - 1)F(0.05; b - 1, ab(r - 1))$$
$$= 3(3.49)$$
$$= 10.47$$

$$\sigma_{\hat{\psi}}^2 = \frac{MS_E}{ar} \sum_i c_i^2$$

$$= \frac{0.066}{6} (4)$$

$$= 0.044$$

$$S\sigma_{\hat{\psi}} = \sqrt{(10.47)}\sqrt{(0.044)}$$
$$= 0.6783$$

so that the confidence interval is

$$0.40 - 0.6783 \leqq \psi \leqq 0.40 + 0.6783$$
$$-0.2783 \leqq \psi \leqq 1.0783$$

Clearly, $\hat{\psi}$ is not significantly different from zero. Again, Tukey's method gives

$$T = \frac{1}{\sqrt{ar}} q(0.05; b, ab(r - 1))$$

$$= \frac{1}{\sqrt{6}} (4.20)$$

$$= 1.7146$$

$$T\sqrt{MS_E} \left(\frac{1}{2} \sum_i |c_i| \right) = 1.7146\sqrt{0.066}\tfrac{1}{2}(4)$$

$$= 0.8810$$

Hence the confidence interval is

$$0.40 - 0.8810 \leqq \psi \leqq 0.40 + 0.8810$$
$$-0.4810 \leqq \psi \leqq 1.2810$$

which is larger than the one obtained by Scheffé's method. We again conclude that $\hat{\psi}$ is not significant.

In general, for paired comparisons, Tukey's method is more sensitive and is often used in practice. For more complex contrasts, Scheffé's method is more sensitive and is generally applied in practice.

In order to fix ideas on the meaning of various effects and sums of squares, let us eliminate first the main effects of one factor from the data in Table 1.7.1

and then the main effects of the other factor and the interaction effects. Suppose that we eliminate the A effects first. Using the values of $\hat{\alpha}_i$: $-5, 0, 5$, in Table 1.7.3, we simply add 5 to the observations related to the first level of A, keep those related to the second level of A unchanged, and subtract 5 from those related to the third level of A. Now, applying the same analysis to the adjusted data, we find that the sum of squares due to A is zero, but the sums of squares due to B, AB, and error remain the same as in Table 1.7.5. The new estimates of α_i are zero, but those of β_j and γ_{ij} remain unchanged. If we use the values of $\hat{\beta}_j$ to eliminate the main effects of B from the A-adjusted data, we shall find that the sum of squares due to B is also zero, but those due to AB and error remain the same, and the estimates of γ_{ij} are not changed. Continuing to eliminate the AB effects in a similar way, we shall discover that the sum of squares due to error still remains the same but that those due to A, B, and AB are all zero.

The order of elimination is immaterial. The important fact is that the elimination of A effects or B effects or AB effects will not change the other effects. In other words, the estimates of main effects, interaction effects, and error are mutually independent.*

REFERENCES

1. COCHRAN, W. G., "The Distribution of Quadratic Forms in a Normal System, with Applications to the Analysis of Covariance," *Proc. Cambridge Philos. Soc.,* **30**, pp. 178–191 (1934).

2. ANDERSON, R. L., and T. A. BANCROFT, *Statistical Theory in Research.* McGraw-Hill, New York, 1952.

3. BROWNLEE, K. A., *Statistical Theory and Methodology in Science and Engineering,* 2nd Ed. Wiley, New York, 1965.

4. COCHRAN, W. G. and G. M. COX, *Experimental Designs,* 2nd Ed. Wiley, New York, 1957.

---

* The fact that the total variation from observations of a balanced experiment can be decomposed into several components which are sums of squares of mutually independent linear combinations of observations is basically an algebraic or geometric property. Indeed, the sums of squares are squared lengths of projections of the vector of observations in mutually orthogonal spaces. The *abr*-dimensional space in which the vector of observations lies is decomposed into these mutually orthogonal spaces. These orthogonal spaces are spanned by the linear forms

$$y_{...}$$
$$y_{i..} - y_{...}$$
$$y_{.j.} - y_{...}$$
$$y_{ij.} - y_{i..} - y_{.j.} + y_{...}$$
$$y_{ijk} - y_{ij.}$$

and have corresponding dimensions 1, $a - 1$, $b - 1$, $(a - 1)(b - 1)$, and $ab(r - 1)$.

5. Cox, D. R., *Planning of Experiments*. Wiley, New York, 1958.

6. Fisher, R. A., *The Design of Experiments*. Hafner, New York, 1960.

7. Graybill, F. A., *An Introduction to Linear Statistical Models*, Vol. 1. McGraw-Hill, New York, 1961.

8. Hicks, C. R., *Fundamental Concepts in the Design of Experiments*. Holt, Rinehart and Winston, New York, 1964.

9. Johnson, N. L., and F. C. Leone, *Statistics and Experimental Design in Engineering and the Physical Sciences*, Vol. II. Wiley, New York, 1964.

10. Li, C. C., *Introduction to Experimental Statistics*. McGraw-Hill, New York, 1964.

11. Kempthorne, O., *The Design and Analysis of Experiments*. Wiley, New York, 1952.

12. Scheffé, H., *The Analysis of Variance*. Wiley, New York, 1959.

13. Guenther, W. C., *Analysis of Variance*. Prentice-Hall, Englewood Cliffs, N. J., 1964.

14. Davies, O. L. (Ed.), *The Design and Analysis of Industrial Experiments*. Hafner, New York, 1960.

15. Bennett, C. A., and N. L. Franklin, *Statistical Analysis in Chemistry and the Chemical Industry*. Wiley, New York, 1954.

16. Snedecor, G. W., *Statistical Methods*. Iowa State University Press, 1956.

2 THREE-WAY AND MULTIWAY ARRANGEMENTS

2.1 THREE-WAY ARRANGEMENTS

Frequently (especially in exploratory experiments) an experimenter may wish to study more than two variables; then a three-way or multiway arrangement, depending on the number of variables, may be in order. The concepts and definitions discussed in Chapter 1 apply to the multiway case after simple generalization.

a) Three-Way Arrangements With r Observations Per Cell

Denote the three factors by A, B, and C; A has a levels, B has b levels, and C has c levels. Let y_{ijkm} be the mth observation on the i, j, k treatment combination or in the (i, j, k) cell where A is at the ith level, B is at the jth, and C at the kth. Let Y_{ijk} be the true mean of the (i, j, k) cell.

We shall generalize two-factor concepts by considering a two-way table of A and B for each level of C. The *interaction of the ith level of A and the jth level of B specific to the kth level of C* is

$$\delta_{ij(k)} = Y_{ijk} - Y_{i.k} - Y_{.jk} + Y_{..k}$$

The average of these over all the levels of C is called the *interaction of the ith level of A and the jth level of B*, and is represented by

$$\delta_{ij} = Y_{ij.} - Y_{i..} - Y_{.j.} + Y_{...}$$

Similarly, from the two-way table, we have the *main effects* for ith level of A, jth level of B, kth level of C, respectively:

$$\alpha_i = Y_{i..} - Y_{...}$$
$$\beta_j = Y_{.j.} - Y_{...}$$
$$\gamma_k = Y_{..k} - Y_{...}$$

The *general mean* is

$$\mu = Y_{...}$$

The remaining two-factor interactions are defined similarly as

$$\delta_{jk} = Y_{.jk} - Y_{.j.} - Y_{..k} + Y_{...}$$
$$\delta_{ik} = Y_{i.k} - Y_{i..} - Y_{..k} + Y_{...}$$

39

Consider how the AB interactions, $\delta_{ij(k)}$, specific to the kth level of C differ for the different levels of C. These differential values of the AB interaction may be expressed as the specific value, $\delta_{ij(k)}$, minus the average value, δ_{ij}. The difference

$$\zeta_{ijk} = Y_{ijk} - Y_{i.k} - Y_{.jk} + Y_{..k} - Y_{ij.} + Y_{i..} + Y_{.j.} - Y_{...}$$

is called the *three-factor interaction* between the ith level of A, the jth of B, and the kth of C.

The two-factor interactions are also called *first-order interactions*, and the three-factor interactions are *second-order interactions*. The concept of interaction and related terminology can be carried over to multifactor experiments.

With the definitions of main effects and interactions, we have

$$Y_{ijk} = \mu + \alpha_i + \beta_j + \gamma_k + \delta_{ij} + \delta_{ik} + \delta_{jk} + \zeta_{ijk}$$

Clearly,

$$\sum \alpha_i = \sum \beta_j = \sum \gamma_k = 0$$

By using the definitions and performing the summations, we can see that

$$\sum_i \delta_{ij} = \sum_j \delta_{ij} = \sum_i \delta_{ik} = \sum_k \delta_{ik} = \sum_j \delta_{jk} = \sum_k \delta_{jk} = 0$$

$$\sum_i \zeta_{ijk} = \sum_j \zeta_{ijk} = \sum_k \zeta_{ijk} = 0$$

Now let us turn to two simple numerical examples which will render the notions of interactions more concrete. Consider a three-factor experiment with factors A, B, and C at 2, 2, and 3 levels, respectively. Suppose that the true means Y_{ijk} of the 12 cells and means $Y_{i.k}$, $Y_{.jk}$, and $Y_{..k}$ are those given in Table 2.1.1. The values of $\delta_{ij(k)}$ and the interaction of the ith level of A, and the jth level of B specific to the kth level of C are calculated easily by substitution. The results are shown in Table 2.1.2. Thus A and B interact at each

TABLE 2.1.1

			C								
		1			2			3			
		B			B			B			
		1	2	$Y_{i.1}$	1	2	$Y_{i.2}$	1	2	$Y_{i.3}$	
A	1	4	-2	1	4	0	2	4	2	3	
	2	0	-2	-1	0	4	2	6	-8	-1	
$Y_{.jk}$		2	-2		2	2		5	-3		
$Y_{..k}$		0			2			1			

TABLE 2.1.2   TABLE 2.1.3

		1st level of C		2nd level of C		3rd level of C	
		B		B		B	
		1	2	1	2	1	2
A	1	1	-1	2	-2	-3	3
	2	-1	1	-2	2	3	-3

		B		
		1	2	$Y_{i..}$
A	1	4	0	2
	2	2	-2	0
$Y_{.j.}$		3	-1	1

level of C. However, the averages of these values over all levels of C become zero. Calculating δ_{ij} directly from $Y_{ij.}$, $Y_{i..}$, $Y_{.j.}$, and $Y_{...}$ in Table 2.1.3 also immediately verifies that all δ_{ij} equal zero.

Now consider the differences between $\delta_{ij(k)}$ and their averages δ_{ij}. Since the averages are zero, the differences have the same values as the $\delta_{ij(k)}$ themselves. Therefore the values of $\delta_{ij(k)}$ in Table 2.1.2 become, what we mean by ABC, three-factor interaction.

As a second example, the data in Table 2.1.4 represent the true means of the 12 cells together with means $Y_{i.k}$, $Y_{.jk}$, and $Y_{..k}$.

It can be easily verified that the data in Table 2.1.4 have the same A, B, C main effects and the same AC, BC interactions as those in Table 2.1.1. However, the AB interaction is no longer zero, but the ABC interaction becomes zero. The values of $\delta_{ij(k)}$ are shown in Table 2.1.5.

It is seen that at all levels of C, $\delta_{ij(k)}$ are the same. Hence their averages are equal to $\delta_{ij(k)}$ for any k, and give a nonzero AB interaction. This fact also obviously leads to the conclusion that the ABC interaction is zero.

The assumptions for a three-way arrangement are that the abc sets of r observations represent random samples of size r drawn from abc populations and

TABLE 2.1.4

		C								
		1			2			3		
		B			B			B		
		1	2	$Y_{i.1}$	1	2	$Y_{i.2}$	1	2	$Y_{i.3}$
A	1	4	-2	1	3	1	2	8	-2	3
	2	0	-2	-1	1	3	2	2	-4	-1
$Y_{.jk}$		2	-2		2	2		5	-3	
$Y_{..k}$		0			2			1		

TABLE 2.1.5

		1st level of C		2nd level of C		3rd level of C	
		B		B		B	
		1	2	1	2	1	2
A	1	1	-1	1	-1	1	-1
	2	-1	1	-1	1	-1	1

that each of these populations is normally distributed with mean Y_{ijk} and the same variance σ^2. The model is written as

$$y_{ijkm} = \mu + \alpha_i + \beta_j + \gamma_k + \delta_{ij} + \delta_{ik} + \delta_{jk} + \zeta_{ijk} + \epsilon_{ijkm}$$
$$(i = 1, 2, \ldots, a; \quad j = 1, 2, \ldots, b; \quad k = 1, 2, \ldots, c; \quad m = 1, 2, \ldots, r)$$
$$(2.1.1)$$

where the ϵ_{ijkm} are independently $N(0, \sigma^2)$.

The total sum of squares is $\sum_i \sum_j \sum_k \sum_m (y_{ijkm} - y_{....})^2$. We can write the identity

$$
\begin{aligned}
y_{ijkm} - y_{....} =\ & (y_{i...} - y_{....}) + (y_{.j..} - y_{....}) + (y_{..k.} - y_{....}) \\
& + (y_{ij..} - y_{i...} - y_{.j..} + y_{....}) \\
& + (y_{i.k.} - y_{i...} - y_{..k.} + y_{....}) \\
& + (y_{.jk.} - y_{.j..} - y_{..k.} + y_{....}) \\
& + (y_{ijk.} + y_{i...} + y_{.j..} + y_{..k.} - y_{ij..} - y_{i.k.} - y_{.jk.} - y_{....}) \\
& + (y_{ijkm} - y_{ijk.}) \quad\quad\quad (2.1.2)
\end{aligned}
$$

The successive terms at the right of (2.1.2) are estimates of the parameters in the model (2.1.1). Performing operations of squaring and summing (2.1.2), we obtain the decomposition of the total sum of squares into the eight sums of squares given in Table 2.1.6, since all the cross-product terms are equal to zero. It can be shown that the expected mean squares are those given in the last column of Table 2.1.6.

In the fixed model all mean squares are tested against the mean square for error. When the null hypothesis about a certain main effect or interaction is rejected, Scheffé's method or Tukey's method may be used to investigate contrasts of interest.

The parameter ϕ needed for calculating power of each of the F-tests can be obtained by using the second term of each corresponding $E[MS]$ in Table 2.1.6. To get ϕ, we simply add 1 to the denominator of the second term of each $E[MS]$, divide it by σ^2, and finally take square root, with v_1 equal to the related degrees of freedom in the d.f. column of the same table and v_2 equal to $abc(r - 1)$. For example, for the test of the null hypothesis that the interaction AB is zero,

TABLE 2.1.6

Source	SS	d.f.	MS	E[MS]
A	$SS_A = bcr \sum_i (y_{i...} - y_{....})^2$	$a - 1$	$\dfrac{SS_A}{a-1}$	$\sigma^2 + rbc \sum_i \dfrac{\alpha_i^2}{a-1}$
B	$SS_B = acr \sum_j (y_{.j..} - y_{....})^2$	$b - 1$	$\dfrac{SS_B}{b-1}$	$\sigma^2 + rac \sum_j \dfrac{\beta_j^2}{b-1}$
C	$SS_C = abr \sum_k (y_{..k.} - y_{....})^2$	$c - 1$	$\dfrac{SS_C}{c-1}$	$\sigma^2 + rab \sum_k \dfrac{\gamma_k^2}{c-1}$
AB	$SS_{AB} = cr \sum_i \sum_j (y_{ij..} - y_{i...} - y_{.j..} + y_{....})^2$	$(a-1)(b-1)$	$\dfrac{SS_{AB}}{(a-1)(b-1)}$	$\sigma^2 + rc \sum_i \sum_j \dfrac{\delta_{ij}^2}{(a-1)(b-1)}$
AC	$SS_{AC} = br \sum_i \sum_k (y_{i.k.} - y_{i...} - y_{..k.} + y_{....})^2$	$(a-1)(c-1)$	$\dfrac{SS_{AC}}{(a-1)(c-1)}$	$\sigma^2 + rb \sum_i \sum_k \dfrac{\delta_{ik}^2}{(a-1)(c-1)}$
BC	$SS_{BC} = ar \sum_j \sum_k (y_{.jk.} - y_{.j..} - y_{..k.} + y_{....})^2$	$(b-1)(c-1)$	$\dfrac{SS_{BC}}{(b-1)(c-1)}$	$\sigma^2 + ra \sum_j \sum_k \dfrac{\delta_{jk}^2}{(b-1)(c-1)}$
ABC	$SS_{ABC} = r \sum_i \sum_j \sum_k (y_{ijk.} + y_{i...} + y_{.j..} + y_{..k.}$ $- y_{ij..} - y_{i.k.} - y_{.jk.} - y_{....})^2$	$(a-1)(b-1)(c-1)$	$\dfrac{SS_{ABC}}{(a-1)(b-1)(c-1)}$	$\sigma^2 + r \sum_i \sum_j \sum_k \dfrac{\zeta_{ijk}^2}{(a-1)(b-1)(c-1)}$
Error	$SS_E = \sum_i \sum_j \sum_k \sum_m (y_{ijkm} - y_{ijk.})^2$	$abc(r-1)$	$\dfrac{SS_E}{abc(r-1)}$	σ^2
Total	$SS_T = \sum_i \sum_j \sum_k \sum_m (y_{ijkm} - y_{....})^2$	$abc - 1$		

we have

$$\phi = \sqrt{\frac{rc}{[(a-1)(b-1)+1]\sigma^2} \sum_i \sum_j \delta_{ij}^2}, \qquad \begin{aligned} v_1 &= (a-1)(b-1), \\ v_2 &= abc(r-1) \end{aligned}$$

The following formulas may be used to calculate the sums of squares:

$$SS_A = \frac{1}{bcr} \sum_i \left[\left(\sum_j \sum_k \sum_m y_{ijkm} \right)^2 \right] - \frac{1}{abcr} \left(\sum_i \sum_j \sum_k \sum_m y_{ijkm} \right)^2$$

$$SS_B = \frac{1}{acr} \sum_j \left[\left(\sum_i \sum_k \sum_m y_{ijkm} \right)^2 \right] - \frac{1}{abcr} \left(\sum_i \sum_j \sum_k \sum_m y_{ijkm} \right)^2$$

$$SS_C = \frac{1}{abr} \sum_k \left[\left(\sum_i \sum_j \sum_m y_{ijkm} \right)^2 \right] - \frac{1}{abcr} \left(\sum_i \sum_j \sum_k \sum_m y_{ijkm} \right)^2$$

$$SS_{AB} = \frac{1}{cr} \sum_i \sum_j \left[\left(\sum_k \sum_m y_{ijkm} \right)^2 \right] - \frac{1}{bcr} \sum_i \left[\left(\sum_j \sum_k \sum_m y_{ijkm} \right)^2 \right]$$
$$- \frac{1}{acr} \sum_j \left[\left(\sum_i \sum_k \sum_m y_{ijkm} \right)^2 \right] + \frac{1}{abcr} \left(\sum_i \sum_j \sum_k \sum_m y_{ijkm} \right)^2$$

$$SS_{AC} = \frac{1}{br} \sum_i \sum_k \left[\left(\sum_j \sum_m y_{ijkm} \right)^2 \right] - \frac{1}{bcr} \sum_i \left[\left(\sum_j \sum_k \sum_m y_{ijkm} \right)^2 \right]$$
$$- \frac{1}{abr} \sum_k \left[\left(\sum_i \sum_j \sum_m y_{ijkm} \right)^2 \right] + \frac{1}{abcr} \left(\sum_i \sum_j \sum_k \sum_m y_{ijkm} \right)^2$$

$$SS_{BC} = \frac{1}{ar} \left[\sum_j \sum_k \left(\sum_i \sum_m y_{ijkm} \right)^2 \right] - \frac{1}{acr} \sum_j \left[\left(\sum_i \sum_k \sum_m y_{ijkm} \right)^2 \right]$$
$$- \frac{1}{abr} \sum_k \left[\left(\sum_i \sum_j \sum_m y_{ijkm} \right)^2 \right] + \frac{1}{abcr} \left(\sum_i \sum_j \sum_k \sum_m y_{ijkm} \right)^2$$

$$SS_{ABC} = \frac{1}{r} \sum_i \sum_j \sum_k \left[\left(\sum_m y_{ijkm} \right)^2 \right] - \frac{1}{cr} \sum_i \sum_j \left[\left(\sum_k \sum_m y_{ijkm} \right)^2 \right]$$
$$- \frac{1}{br} \sum_i \sum_k \left[\left(\sum_j \sum_m y_{ijkm} \right)^2 \right] - \frac{1}{ar} \sum_j \sum_k \left[\left(\sum_i \sum_m y_{ijkm} \right)^2 \right]$$
$$+ \frac{1}{bcr} \sum_i \left[\left(\sum_j \sum_k \sum_m y_{ijkm} \right)^2 \right] + \frac{1}{acr} \sum_j \left[\left(\sum_i \sum_k \sum_m y_{ijkm} \right)^2 \right]$$
$$+ \frac{1}{abr} \sum_k \left[\left(\sum_i \sum_j \sum_m y_{ijkm} \right)^2 \right] - \frac{1}{abcr} \left(\sum_i \sum_j \sum_k \sum_m y_{ijkm} \right)^2$$

$$SS_E = SS_T - SS_A - SS_B - SS_C - SS_{AB} - SS_{AC} - SS_{BC} - SS_{ABC}$$

$$SS_T = \sum_i \sum_j \sum_k \sum_m y_{ijkm}^2 - \frac{\left(\sum_i \sum_j \sum_k \sum_m y_{ijkm} \right)^2}{abcr}$$

TABLE 2.1.7

Source	SS	d.f.	MS	E[MS]
A	$SS_A = bc \sum_i (y_{i..} - y_{...})^2$	$a-1$	$\dfrac{SS_A}{a-1}$	$\sigma^2 + bc \sum_i \dfrac{\alpha_i^2}{a-1}$
B	$SS_B = ac \sum_j (y_{.j.} - y_{...})^2$	$b-1$	$\dfrac{SS_B}{b-1}$	$\sigma^2 + ac \sum_j \dfrac{\beta_j^2}{b-1}$
C	$SS_C = ab \sum_k (y_{..k} - y_{...})^2$	$c-1$	$\dfrac{SS_C}{c-1}$	$\sigma^2 + ab \sum_k \dfrac{\gamma_k^2}{c-1}$
AB	$SS_{AB} = c \sum_i \sum_j (y_{ij.} - y_{i..} - y_{.j.} + y_{...})^2$	$(a-1)(b-1)$	$\dfrac{SS_{AB}}{(a-1)(b-1)}$	$\sigma^2 + c \sum_i \sum_j \dfrac{\delta_{ij}^2}{(a-1)(b-1)}$
AC	$SS_{AC} = b \sum_i \sum_k (y_{i.k} - y_{i..} - y_{..k} + y_{...})^2$	$(a-1)(c-1)$	$\dfrac{SS_{AC}}{(a-1)(c-1)}$	$\sigma^2 + b \sum_i \sum_k \dfrac{\delta_{ik}^2}{(a-1)(c-1)}$
BC	$SS_{BC} = a \sum_j \sum_k (y_{.jk} - y_{.j.} - y_{..k} + y_{...})^2$	$(b-1)(c-1)$	$\dfrac{SS_{BC}}{(b-1)(c-1)}$	$\sigma^2 + a \sum_j \sum_k \dfrac{\delta_{jk}^2}{(b-1)(c-1)}$
ABC (Error)	$SS_{ABC} = \sum_i \sum_j \sum_k (y_{ijk} + y_{i..} + y_{.j.} + y_{..k} - y_{ij.} - y_{i.k} - y_{.jk} - y_{...})^2$	$(a-1)(b-1)(c-1)$	$\dfrac{SS_{ABC}}{(a-1)(b-1)(c-1)}$	σ^2
Total	$SS_T = \sum_i \sum_j \sum_k (y_{ijk} - y_{...})^2$	$abc-1$		

The quantity

$$\frac{(\text{total})^2}{\text{total number of observations}}$$

is often called the *correction term*.

b) Three-Way Arrangement With One Observation Per Cell

If there is only one observation per cell in a three-way arrangement, we can not estimate the error variance from within cell replications. In this case it is necessary to make an additional assumption that certain interactions are zero. Usually we would assume that there is no *ABC* interaction and would use the corresponding mean square to estimate the error variance. Then the model is written as

$$y_{ijk} = \mu + \alpha_i + \beta_j + \gamma_k + \delta_{ij} + \delta_{ik} + \delta_{jk} + \epsilon_{ijk}$$
$$(i = 1, 2, \ldots, a; \quad j = 1, 2, \ldots, b; \quad k = 1, 2, \ldots, c)$$

We shall give the analysis-of-variance table (Table 2.1.7) and the following computational formulas:

$$SS_A = \frac{1}{bc} \sum_i \left[\left(\sum_i \sum_k y_{ijk} \right)^2 \right] - \frac{1}{abc} \left(\sum_i \sum_j \sum_k y_{ijk} \right)^2$$

$$SS_B = \frac{1}{ac} \sum_j \left[\left(\sum_i \sum_k y_{ijk} \right)^2 \right] - \frac{1}{abc} \left(\sum_i \sum_j \sum_k y_{ijk} \right)^2$$

$$SS_C = \frac{1}{ab} \sum_k \left[\left(\sum_i \sum_j y_{ijk} \right)^2 \right] - \frac{1}{abc} \left(\sum_i \sum_j \sum_k y_{ijk} \right)^2$$

$$SS_{AB} = \frac{1}{c} \sum_i \sum_j \left[\left(\sum_k y_{ijk} \right)^2 \right] - \frac{1}{bc} \sum_i \left[\left(\sum_j \sum_k y_{ijk} \right)^2 \right]$$
$$- \frac{1}{ac} \sum_j \left[\left(\sum_i \sum_k y_{ijk} \right)^2 \right] + \frac{1}{abc} \left(\sum_i \sum_j \sum_k y_{ijk} \right)^2$$

$$SS_{AC} = \frac{1}{b} \sum_i \sum_k \left[\left(\sum_j y_{ijk} \right)^2 \right] - \frac{1}{bc} \sum_i \left[\left(\sum_j \sum_k y_{ijk} \right)^2 \right]$$
$$- \frac{1}{ab} \sum_k \left[\left(\sum_i \sum_j y_{ijk} \right)^2 \right] + \frac{1}{abc} \left(\sum_i \sum_j \sum_k y_{ijk} \right)^2$$

$$SS_{BC} = \frac{1}{a} \sum_j \sum_k \left[\left(\sum_i y_{ijk} \right)^2 \right] - \frac{1}{ac} \sum_j \left[\left(\sum_i \sum_k y_{ijk} \right)^2 \right]$$
$$- \frac{1}{ab} \sum_k \left[\left(\sum_i \sum_j y_{ijk} \right)^2 \right] + \frac{1}{abc} \left(\sum_i \sum_j \sum_k y_{ijk} \right)^2$$

$$SS_{ABC} = \sum_i \sum_j \sum_k y_{ijk}^2 - \frac{1}{c} \sum_i \sum_j \left[\left(\sum_k y_{ijk} \right)^2 \right] - \frac{1}{b} \sum_i \sum_k \left[\left(\sum_j y_{ijk} \right)^2 \right]$$

$$- \frac{1}{a} \sum_j \sum_k \left[\left(\sum_i y_{ijk} \right)^2 \right] + \frac{1}{bc} \sum_i \left[\left(\sum_j \sum_k y_{ijk} \right)^2 \right]$$

$$+ \frac{1}{ac} \sum_j \left[\left(\sum_i \sum_k y_{ijk} \right)^2 \right] + \frac{1}{ab} \sum_k \left[\left(\sum_i \sum_j y_{ijk} \right)^2 \right]$$

$$- \frac{1}{abc} \left(\sum_i \sum_j \sum_k y_{ijk} \right)^2$$

2.2 OPERATOR CALCULUS AND MAPPING SCHEMES FOR PROGRAMMING MULTIFACTOR ANALYSIS OF VARIANCE

It is clear that the definitions, concepts, and analysis-of-variance table may be easily generalized to multifactor experiments. However, when the number of factors becomes large, the amount of required computational work increases rapidly. Certain mechanization of the computational procedure is very important. We shall describe here a method for programming on a digital computer.

A special *operator calculus* together with a *mapping scheme* has been found to be very useful in programming analysis of variance for multifactor experiments. The mapping scheme improves the logistics of computation and reduces memory requirements considerably.

For simplicity, the case of a three-factor experiment is used here to describe the procedure.

Let y_{ijk} denote the observed experimental result from the ith level of factor A, jth level of factor B, and kth level of factor C. The symbols a, b, and c will denote the number of levels for each factor so that

$$i = 1, 2, \ldots, a; \quad j = 1, 2, \ldots, b; \quad k = 1, 2, \ldots, c$$

We shall also need the following notations:

$$T_{.jk} = \sum_{i=1}^a y_{ijk} \quad \text{and similarly} \quad T_{i.k}, \; T_{ij.}$$

$$T_{..k} = \sum_{i=1}^a \sum_{j=1}^b y_{ijk} \quad \text{and similarly} \quad T_{.j.}, \; T_{i..}$$

The sums of squares in the analysis-of-variance table can be obtained by repeated application of the following operators:

Operator Σ_i: Sum over all levels of $i = 1, 2, \ldots, a$, while keeping the other subscripts constant.

Operator D_j: Multiply all items by a and subtract the result of Σ_i from all items.

Operator $(\ )^2$: Form the sum of the squares of the items inside the brackets and divide by the number of items.

TABLE 2.2.1

Input	y_{ijk}			
Operator	Total or deviates	d.f.	$abc(SS)$	Source
$\Sigma_k\Sigma_j\Sigma_i$	T (Grand total)			
$\Sigma_k\Sigma_j D_i$	$aT_{i..} - T$	$a - 1$	$(\ )^2$	A
$\Sigma_k D_j\Sigma_i$	$bT_{.j.} - T$	$b - 1$	$(\ )^2$	B
$\Sigma_k D_j D_i$	$abT_{ij.} - bT_{.j.} - aT_{i..} + T$	$(a - 1)(b - 1)$	$(\ )^2$	AB
$D_k\Sigma_j\Sigma_i$	$cT_{..k} - T$	$c - 1$	$(\ )^2$	C
$D_k\Sigma_j D_i$	$acT_{i.k} - cT_{..k} - aT_{i..} + T$	$(a - 1)(c - 1)$	$(\ )^2$	AC
$D_k D_j\Sigma_i$	$bcT_{.jk} - cT_{..k} - bT_{.j.} + T$	$(b - 1)(c - 1)$	$(\ )^2$	BC
$D_k D_j D_i$	$abcy_{ijk} - bcT_{.jk} - acT_{i.k}$ $+ cT_{..k} - abT_{ij.} + bT_{.j.}$ $+ aT_{i..} - T$	$(a - 1)(b - 1)(c - 1)$	$(\ )^2$	ABC

Operators Σ_j, Σ_k, D_j, and D_k can be defined similarly. For example, if we apply the first two operators to y_{ijk}, we have

$$\Sigma_i(y_{ijk}) = \Sigma_i y_{ijk} = T_{.jk}$$
$$D_i(y_{ijk}) = ay_{ijk} - T_{.jk} = a(y_{ijk} - y_{.jk})$$

The complete analysis of variance of the three-factor experiment is shown in Table 2.2.1. The fourth column in the table is obtained by applying the square operation $(\ )^2$ to the sets of deviates in column 2. It may be noted that the results in column 4 are the ordinary sums of squares multiplied by the total number of observations.

The above procedure can be easily generalized to a general K-factor experiment. The generalized computing procedure is greatly simplified by using an isomorphism between the sequences of special operators Σ, D, and a sequence of ordered, binary-valued K-tuples.

For example, consider the following sequence of ordered triples:

$$
\begin{array}{ccc}
1 & 1 & 1 \\
2 & 1 & 1 \\
1 & 2 & 1 \\
2 & 2 & 1 \\
1 & 1 & 2 \\
2 & 1 & 2 \\
1 & 2 & 2 \\
2 & 2 & 2 \\
\end{array}
$$

If we denote 1 by Σ and 2 by D and reverse the order in each triple, we obtain the sequences of operators in column 1 of Table 2.2.1 for the three-factor case.

The identification of source of variation and the computation of degrees of freedom can also be simplified by observing a similar isomorphism. For example, consider the triple, $(1, 2, 2)$. If we map it onto the set ABC and nullify the factor corresponding to 1, we have the interaction BC. Similarly, the degrees of freedom can be computed by mapping the above triple onto a set of ordered integers representing the number of levels of the factors.

In general, for a K-factor experiment a sequence of 2^K binary-valued K-tuples can be generated to control the logical sequencing of the special operators, identification of source of variation, and the computing of degrees of freedom.

In order to use the special operator calculus, the experimental data have to be arranged in a special order. For instance, if y_{ijk} denotes the data from a three-factor experiment and $i = 1, 2; j = 1, 2, 3;$ and $k = 1, 2$, then the 12 observations have to be arranged in the following order:

$$y_{111}$$
$$y_{211}$$
$$y_{121}$$
$$y_{221}$$
$$y_{131}$$
$$y_{231}$$
$$y_{112}$$
$$y_{212}$$
$$y_{122}$$
$$y_{222}$$
$$y_{132}$$
$$y_{232}$$

This arrangement can be identified by generating a sequence of K-tuples and associating each observation with respect to its proper K-tuple. Thus the storing of the index of each observation is not required. The following relation may be used in generating this sequence.

Let

$$K = \text{the number of factors}$$
$$N_i = \text{the number of the levels of the } i\text{th factor}$$
$$L_i = \text{the coded value of the levels of the } i\text{th factor}$$

For our purposes, denote L_i by $0, 1, 2, \ldots, N_i - 1$.

Consider the ordered K-tuple $L_1, L_2, \ldots, L_K$. The sequence can be constructed in the following steps:

1) Set initially all $L_i = 0$. The zero value is repeated for an ith factor for

$$N_0 \times N_1 \times \cdots \times N_{i-1} \text{ times}$$

where $i = 1, 2, \ldots, K; N_0$ is defined to be 1; and L_i is interpreted modulo N_i.

2) Then, add 1 to L_i and repeat this new L_i value for an ith factor for $N_0 \times N_1 \times \cdots \times N_{i-1}$ times, where i, N_0, and L_i are defined as in step (1).

3) Repeat step (2) until $N_1 \times N_2 \times \cdots \times N_K$ K-tuples have been constructed.

The sequence of 2^K binary-valued K-tuples used in controlling the computing procedure is a special case of the above.

The computation of group means may use a similar scheme to generate all factorial combinations in any group indicated by a parameter card.

The calculation of sums of squares of a K-way arrangement with r replications per cell can be simplified by introducing a fictitious factor corresponding to the r-fold replication of the observations in the cells. The experimental data are treated as that of a $(K + 1)$ factorial design. The error sum of squares is obtained by summing the main effect sum of squares of this fictitious factor and all sums of squares of those interactions involving the fictitious factor.

REFERENCES

1. HARTLEY, H. O., "A Plan for Programming Analysis of Variance for General Purpose Computers," *Biometrics*, **12**, 2, 110–122 (1956).

2. RALSTON, A., and H. S. WILF, (Eds.), *Mathematical Methods for Digital Computers*. Wiley, New York, 1960.

3. HEMMERLE, W. J., "Algebraic Specification of Statistical Models for Analysis of Variance Computations," *J. Assoc. for Comp. Mach.*, **11**, 2, 234–239 (1964).

4. COOLEY, W. W., and P. R. LOHNES, *Multivariate Procedures for the Behavioral Sciences*. Wiley, New York, 1962.

5. BOCK, R. D., "Programming Univariate and Multivariate Analysis of Variance," *Technometrics*, **5**, 1, 95–117 (1963).

6. DIXON, W. J. (Ed.), *Biomedical Computer Programs*, Health Sciences Computing Facility, Department of Preventive Medicine and Public Health, School of Medicine, University of California, Los Angeles, 1964.

7. BROWNLEE, K. A., *Statistical Theory and Methodology in Science and Engineering*, 2nd Ed. Wiley, New York, 1965.

8. COCHRAN, W. G. and G. M. COX, *Experimental Designs*, 2nd Ed. Wiley, New York, 1957.

9. KEMPTHORNE, O., *The Design and Analysis of Experiments*. Wiley, New York, 1952.

10. SCHEFFÉ, H., *The Analysis of Variance*. Wiley, New York, 1959.

3 METHODS OF PARTITIONING A SUM OF SQUARES

3.1 ORTHOGONAL CONTRASTS

a) Basic Concepts

Sometimes an experimenter is interested in making particular comparisons among fixed levels of a factor and wants to study the effect of that factor in more detail. For example, consider a qualitative factor such as machines. Suppose that the variation of a certain characteristic of a product made from four machines is investigated and that machines 1 and 2 were manufactured by company U and machines 3 and 4 by company W. Then it is meaningful to compare means of

machine 1 vs. machine 2

machine 3 vs. machine 4

machines 1 and 2 vs. machines 3 and 4

Each such comparison may be called a contrast. The sum of squares due to machines with 3 degrees of freedom can be partitioned into 3 components corresponding to these 3 contrasts, each of which has a single degree of freedom.

As in Section 0.6, a *contrast* is defined as

$$\psi = \sum_{i=1}^{t} c_i Y_i$$

where

$$\sum_i c_i = 0$$

and the Y_i are true means of the t levels of a factor. Suppose that the true means Y_i are estimated by $y_{i.}$ from samples of size n_i, with variances σ^2/n_i. Then ψ is estimated by

$$\hat{\psi} = \sum_i c_i y_{i.}$$

with variance

$$\sigma_{\hat{\psi}}^2 = \sigma^2 \sum_i \frac{c_i^2}{n_i}$$

51

Two contrasts

$$\hat{\psi}_1 = \sum_i c_{1i} y_{i.}, \quad \hat{\psi}_2 = \sum_i c_{2i} y_{i.}.$$

are said to be orthogonal if

$$\sum_i \frac{c_{1i} c_{2i}}{n_i} = 0$$

and when all sample sizes are the same, this expression becomes

$$\sum_i c_{1i} c_{2i} = 0$$

For the above example, suppose that $n_1 = 3$, $n_2 = 3$, $n_3 = 2$, $n_4 = 2$. We may choose

$$c_{1i} = 1, -1, 0, 0$$
$$c_{2i} = 0, 0, 1, -1$$
$$c_{3i} = 1, 1, -1, -1$$

Clearly, they are mutually orthogonal. In terms of totals T_i from which the $y_{i.}$ are computed, we have

$$\hat{\psi} = \sum_i c_i \frac{T_i}{n_i}$$

If all n_i equal r, we get

$$\hat{\psi} = \frac{1}{r} \sum_i c_i T_i$$

For given t quantities T_i, it is possible to form infinitely many sets of $(t - 1)$ mutually orthogonal contrasts. However, the experimenter must choose only those contrasts which have reasonable interpretation and are relevant to specific questions.

Consider quantities T_i. For every m and for each of the c_{mi} of a set of orthogonal contrasts ψ_m, let

$$a_{mi} = \frac{c_{mi}/\sqrt{n_i}}{\sqrt{\sum_i (c_{mi}^2/n_i)}}$$

Then the matrix

$$\mathbf{P} = \begin{bmatrix} \dfrac{\sqrt{n_1}}{\sqrt{\sum n_i}} & \dfrac{\sqrt{n_2}}{\sqrt{\sum n_i}} & \cdots & \dfrac{\sqrt{n_t}}{\sqrt{\sum n_i}} \\ a_{11} & a_{12} & \cdots & a_{1t} \\ \vdots & & & \vdots \\ a_{(t-1)1} & a_{(t-1)2} & \cdots & a_{(t-1)t} \end{bmatrix}$$

is orthogonal, since the sum of squares of the elements in any row equals 1 and the sum of products of the elements in any row with the corresponding elements in any other row equals zero. Then the orthogonal matrix $\mathbf{P}$ will transform $(T_1/\sqrt{n_1},\ T_2/\sqrt{n_2},\ \ldots,\ T_t/\sqrt{n_t})$ into

$$\left(\sum T_i/\sqrt{\sum n_i},\ \sum a_{1i}T_i/\sqrt{n_i},\ \ldots,\ \sum a_{(t-1)i}T_i/\sqrt{n_i}\right)$$

Furthermore, we have

$$\sum_i \left(\frac{T_i}{\sqrt{n_i}}\right)^2 = \left(\sum \frac{T_i}{\sqrt{\sum n_i}}\right)^2 + \left(\sum \frac{a_{1i}T_i}{\sqrt{n_i}}\right)^2 + \cdots + \left(\sum \frac{a_{(t-1)i}T_i}{\sqrt{n_i}}\right)^2$$

and each term at the right of the equality has a single degree of freedom. After subtracting the first term at the right from both sides, the left side becomes the sum of squares for the t levels of a factor with $(t-1)$ degrees of freedom which have been partitioned into components with a single degree of freedom each, corresponding to the orthogonal contrasts. We note that the sum of squares

$$SS_{\hat{\psi}_m} = \left(\sum_i \frac{a_{mi}T_i}{\sqrt{n_i}}\right)^2 = \frac{[\sum_i (c_{mi}T_i/n_i)]^2}{\sum_i (c_{mi}^2/n_i)}$$

is distributed as $\sigma^2 \chi^2(1)$ under the null hypothesis $\psi_m = 0$ and the assumption that the $y_{i.}$ are distributed normally. If σ^2 is estimated by MS_E with v degrees of freedom, then, under the null hypothesis, $SS_{\hat{\psi}_m}/MS_E$ is distributed as $F(1, v)$.

When all n_i equal r, we have

$$a_{mi} = \frac{c_{mi}}{\sqrt{\sum_i c_{mi}^2}}, \qquad SS_{\hat{\psi}_m} = \frac{(\sum_i c_{mi}T_i)^2}{r \sum c_{mi}^2}$$

and the first row of the orthogonal matrix $\mathbf{P}$ becomes

$$\frac{1}{\sqrt{t}},\ \frac{1}{\sqrt{t}},\ \ldots,\ \frac{1}{\sqrt{t}}$$

b) Example

To demonstrate these results, let us consider the following data for the example of four machines:

        Machine 1: 6, 4, 5   Machine 2: 5, 7, 6
        Machine 3: 9, 9   Machine 4: 12, 8

We have

$$T_1 = 15, \quad n_1 = 3$$
$$T_2 = 18, \quad n_2 = 3$$
$$T_3 = 18, \quad n_3 = 2$$
$$T_4 = 20, \quad n_4 = 2$$

Hence the sum of squares due to the machines is

$$\sum_i \left(\frac{T_i}{\sqrt{n_i}}\right)^2 - \left(\frac{\sum_i T_i}{\sqrt{\sum_i n_i}}\right)^2 = 545 - 504.1 = 40.9$$

Using the set of three orthogonal contrasts described earlier, we form

$$
\mathbf{P} =
\begin{bmatrix}
\dfrac{\sqrt{3}}{\sqrt{10}} & \dfrac{\sqrt{3}}{\sqrt{10}} & \dfrac{\sqrt{2}}{\sqrt{10}} & \dfrac{\sqrt{2}}{\sqrt{10}} \\[2ex]
\dfrac{1/\sqrt{3}}{\sqrt{\frac{2}{3}}} & \dfrac{-1/\sqrt{3}}{\sqrt{\frac{2}{3}}} & 0 & 0 \\[2ex]
0 & 0 & \dfrac{1/\sqrt{2}}{\sqrt{\frac{2}{2}}} & \dfrac{-1/\sqrt{2}}{\sqrt{\frac{2}{2}}} \\[2ex]
\dfrac{1/\sqrt{3}}{\sqrt{\frac{10}{6}}} & \dfrac{1/\sqrt{3}}{\sqrt{\frac{10}{6}}} & \dfrac{-1/\sqrt{2}}{\sqrt{\frac{10}{6}}} & \dfrac{-1/\sqrt{2}}{\sqrt{\frac{10}{6}}}
\end{bmatrix}
$$

or

$$
\mathbf{P} =
\begin{bmatrix}
\dfrac{\sqrt{3}}{\sqrt{10}} & \dfrac{\sqrt{3}}{\sqrt{10}} & \dfrac{\sqrt{2}}{\sqrt{10}} & \dfrac{\sqrt{2}}{\sqrt{10}} \\[2ex]
\dfrac{1}{\sqrt{2}} & \dfrac{-1}{\sqrt{2}} & 0 & 0 \\[2ex]
0 & 0 & \dfrac{1}{\sqrt{2}} & \dfrac{-1}{\sqrt{2}} \\[2ex]
\dfrac{1}{\sqrt{5}} & \dfrac{1}{\sqrt{5}} & \dfrac{-\sqrt{3}}{\sqrt{10}} & \dfrac{-\sqrt{3}}{\sqrt{10}}
\end{bmatrix}
$$

Thus

$$
\frac{\sqrt{3}}{\sqrt{10}}\frac{15}{\sqrt{3}} + \frac{\sqrt{3}}{\sqrt{10}}\frac{18}{\sqrt{3}} + \frac{\sqrt{2}}{\sqrt{10}}\frac{18}{\sqrt{2}} + \frac{\sqrt{2}}{\sqrt{10}}\frac{20}{\sqrt{2}} = \frac{71}{\sqrt{10}}
$$

$$
\frac{1}{\sqrt{2}}\frac{15}{\sqrt{3}} - \frac{1}{\sqrt{2}}\frac{18}{\sqrt{3}} = \frac{-3}{\sqrt{6}}
$$

$$
\frac{1}{\sqrt{2}}\frac{18}{\sqrt{2}} - \frac{1}{\sqrt{2}}\frac{20}{\sqrt{2}} = \frac{-2}{\sqrt{4}}
$$

$$
\frac{1}{\sqrt{5}}\frac{15}{\sqrt{3}} + \frac{1}{\sqrt{5}}\frac{18}{\sqrt{3}} - \frac{3}{\sqrt{10}}\frac{18}{\sqrt{2}} - \frac{3}{\sqrt{10}}\frac{20}{\sqrt{2}} = \frac{48}{\sqrt{60}}
$$

Squaring these quantities, we obtain

$$
\left(\frac{\sum T_i}{\sqrt{\sum n_i}}\right)^2 = 504.10
$$

$$
SS_{\hat{\psi}_1} = 1.50, \qquad SS_{\hat{\psi}_2} = 1.00, \qquad SS_{\hat{\psi}_3} = 38.40
$$

and the sum of squares due to machines equals the total of 1.50, 1.00, and 38.40.

In practice, more frequently all sample sizes n_i are equal to r. Let us consider only the first two observations for machines 1 and 2 together with the two observations for machines 3 and 4. Then

$$T_1 = 10, \quad T_2 = 12,$$
$$T_3 = 18, \quad T_4 = 20$$

and $r = 2$. Now the sum of squares due to machines is

$$\tfrac{968}{2} - \tfrac{3600}{8} = 34$$

Using the same set of coefficients as before which again form three mutually orthogonal contrasts for the case of equal sample sizes, we have

$$\mathbf{P} = \begin{bmatrix} \dfrac{1}{\sqrt{4}} & \dfrac{1}{\sqrt{4}} & \dfrac{1}{\sqrt{4}} & \dfrac{1}{\sqrt{4}} \\[2mm] \dfrac{1}{\sqrt{2}} & \dfrac{-1}{\sqrt{2}} & 0 & 0 \\[2mm] 0 & 0 & \dfrac{1}{\sqrt{2}} & \dfrac{-1}{\sqrt{2}} \\[2mm] \dfrac{1}{\sqrt{4}} & \dfrac{1}{\sqrt{4}} & \dfrac{-1}{\sqrt{4}} & \dfrac{-1}{\sqrt{4}} \end{bmatrix}$$

Thus

$$\frac{1}{\sqrt{4}}\frac{10}{\sqrt{2}} + \frac{1}{\sqrt{4}}\frac{12}{\sqrt{2}} + \frac{1}{\sqrt{4}}\frac{18}{\sqrt{2}} + \frac{1}{\sqrt{4}}\frac{20}{\sqrt{2}} = \frac{60}{\sqrt{8}}$$

$$\frac{1}{\sqrt{2}}\frac{10}{\sqrt{2}} - \frac{1}{\sqrt{2}}\frac{12}{\sqrt{2}} = -\frac{2}{\sqrt{4}}$$

$$\frac{1}{\sqrt{2}}\frac{18}{\sqrt{2}} - \frac{1}{\sqrt{2}}\frac{20}{\sqrt{2}} = -\frac{2}{\sqrt{4}}$$

$$\frac{1}{\sqrt{4}}\frac{10}{\sqrt{2}} + \frac{1}{\sqrt{4}}\frac{12}{\sqrt{2}} - \frac{1}{\sqrt{4}}\frac{18}{\sqrt{2}} - \frac{1}{\sqrt{4}}\frac{20}{\sqrt{2}} = -\frac{16}{\sqrt{8}}$$

and their squares are 450, 1, 1, 32. Finally,

$$34 = 1 + 1 + 32$$

3.2 ORTHOGONAL POLYNOMIALS

In the case where the factor is quantitative, it is often desirable to examine the numerical relationship between the response variable and fixed levels of the factor. Usually the precise mathematical function describing the relationship is not known but can be approximated by a polynomial model:

$$y_i = a_0 + a_1 x_i + a_2 x_i^2 + a_3 x_i^3 + \cdots + a_{(t-1)} x_i^{(t-1)} + \epsilon_i$$
$$(i = 1, 2, \ldots, t)$$

where x_i denote the t levels of the factor, y_i the responses, and ϵ_i random errors. Given the values of the levels and the responses, the coefficients a_0, a_1, a_2, $\ldots$ can be estimated by the least squares method. Obviously, for t levels, the degree of the polynomial cannot exceed $(t-1)$.

It can be shown that the above equation may be replaced by

$$y_i = A_0 P_{0i} + A_1 P_{1i} + A_2 P_{2i} + A_3 P_{3i} + \cdots + A_{(t-1)} P_{(t-1)i} + \epsilon_i$$
$$(i = 1, 2, \ldots, t)$$

where $P_{0i} = 1$, P_{mi} is a polynomial of degree m $(m = 1, 2, \ldots, t-1)$ in x_i, and

$$\sum_i P_{mi} = 0, \qquad \sum_i P_{mi} P_{m'i} = 0 \quad (m \neq m')$$

over a specific set of values of x_i. The polynomials P_m are called *orthogonal polynomials*.

If $x_i = i$ and $i = 1, 2, \ldots, N$, the first five of these polynomials are

$$P_{1i} = x_i - \bar{x}$$
$$P_{2i} = P_{1i}^2 - \frac{N^2 - 1}{12}$$
$$P_{3i} = P_{1i}^3 - \frac{3N^2 - 7}{20} (P_{1i})$$
$$P_{4i} = P_{1i}^4 - \frac{3N^2 - 13}{14} (P_{1i}^2) + \frac{3(N^2 - 1)(N^2 - 9)}{560}$$
$$P_{5i} = P_{1i}^5 - \frac{5(N^2 - 7)}{18} (P_{1i}^3) + \frac{15N^4 - 230N^2 + 407}{1008} (P_{1i})$$

where $\bar{x}$ is the mean of x_i and the values of P_{mi} are often conveniently scaled so as to make them integers (as small as possible) for all x_i. The P_m's can also be obtained by using the recurrence relation

$$P_{m+1} = P_1 P_m - \frac{r^2(N^2 - m^2)}{4(4m^2 - 1)} P_{m-1}$$

The coefficients A_0, A_1, A_2, $\ldots$, $A_{(t-1)}$ are calculated by least squares method so as to make

$$\sum (y_i - A_0 P_{0i} - A_1 P_{1i} - A_2 P_{2i} - \cdots - A_{(t-1)} P_{(t-1)i})^2$$

a minimum. The normal equations for determining the A_m are

$$A_0 \sum (P_{0i} P_{0i}) + A_1 \sum (P_{0i} P_{1i}) + \cdots + A_{(t-1)} \sum (P_{0i} P_{(t-1)i}) = \sum (y_i P_{0i})$$
$$A_0 \sum (P_{1i} P_{0i}) + A_1 \sum (P_{1i} P_{1i}) + \cdots + A_{(t-1)} \sum (P_{1i} P_{(t-1)i}) = \sum (y_i P_{1i})$$
$$\vdots$$

Since $P_{0i} = 1$ and $(P_{mi}P_{m'i}) = 0$, we have

$$A_0N = \sum y_i$$
$$A_1\sum(P_{1i})^2 = \sum(y_iP_{1i})$$
$$\vdots$$
$$A_{(t-1)}\sum(P_{(t-1)i})^2 = \sum(y_iP_{(t-1)i})$$

We may now write

$$\hat{y}_i = \frac{\sum y_i}{N} + \frac{\sum y_iP_{1i}}{\sum P_{1i}^2} P_{1i} + \frac{\sum y_iP_{2i}}{\sum P_{2i}^2} P_{2i} + \cdots + \frac{\sum y_iP_{(t-1)i}}{\sum P_{(t-1)i}^2} P_{(t-1)i}$$

Since the P_{mi} are orthogonal, after some simplification we have the sum of squares due to deviations between the actual values of the response and their estimated values as

$$\sum(y_i - \hat{y}_i)^2 = \sum y_i^2 - \frac{(\sum y_i)^2}{N} - \frac{(\sum y_iP_{1i})^2}{\sum P_{1i}^2} - \frac{(\sum y_iP_{2i})^2}{\sum P_{2i}^2} - \frac{(\sum y_iP_{3i})^2}{\sum P_{3i}^2} - \cdots$$

where each term $(\sum y_iP_{mi})^2/\sum P_{mi}^2$ is the sum of squares with a single degree of freedom (corresponding to a component $\sum y_iP_{mi}$) and represents the independent reduction due to the polynomial P_m. The quantities

$$\sum y_iP_{1i}, \quad \sum y_iP_{2i}, \quad \sum y_iP_{3i}, \quad \ldots$$

are called *linear, quadratic, cubic, . . . components.* If successive polynomials up to $P_{(t-1)}$ are used, then

$$\sum y_i^2 - \frac{(\sum y_i)^2}{N} = \frac{(\sum y_iP_{1i})^2}{\sum P_{1i}^2} + \frac{(\sum y_iP_{2i})^2}{\sum P_{2i}^2} + \cdots + \frac{(\sum y_iP_{(t-1)i})^2}{\sum P_{(t-1)i}^2}$$

In analysis of variance, we usually have means $y_{i.}$ computed from sums T_i with r observations each. Then $\sum y_{i.}P_{mi}$ $(i = 1, 2, \ldots, t-1)$ form a complete set of orthogonal contrasts. The sum of squares of contrast $\sum y_{i.}P_{mi}$ is $(\sum T_iP_{mi})^2/r\sum P_{mi}^2$.

The values of P_1 to P_5 for a wide range of equally spaced levels are tabulated in a number of statistical tables (see, for example, Fisher and Yates [3]).

3.3 ORTHOGONAL POLYNOMIALS FOR UNEQUAL INTERVALS

The formulas for orthogonal polynomials listed in Section 3.2 are for equally spaced levels, and tabulated tables of orthogonal polynomials are also for equally spaced intervals of a variable x. However, a simple procedure for computing orthogonal polynomials for unequally spaced levels is available.

For any set of orthogonal polynomials:

$$P_1 = L_0 + L_1x$$
$$P_2 = Q_0 + Q_1x + Q_2x^2$$
$$P_3 = C_0 + C_1x + C_2x^2 + C_3x^3$$
$$\vdots$$

TABLE 3.3.1

x, levels	Linear	Quadratic	Cubic
0	L_0	Q_0	C_0
1	$L_0 + L_1$	$Q_0 + Q_1 + Q_2$	$C_0 + C_1 + C_2 + C_3$
2	$L_0 + 2L_1$	$Q_0 + 2Q_1 + 4Q_2$	$C_0 + 2C_1 + 4C_2 + 8C_3$
4	$L_0 + 4L_1$	$Q_0 + 4Q_1 + 16Q_2$	$C_0 + 4C_1 + 16C_2 + 64C_3$

let

$\sum(L_0 + L_1 x)y_x$ be the linear component

$\sum(Q_0 + Q_1 x + Q_2 x^2)y_x$ be the quadratic component

$\sum(C_0 + C_1 x + C_2 x^2 + C_3 x^3)y_x$ be the cubic component

$\vdots$

where L_0, L_1, Q_0, Q_1, $\ldots$ are constants, x is the level of the factor, y_x is the response when the factor is at x level, and the summation carries over all levels of x.

The procedure for computing the orthogonal polynomials will be illustrated by an example.

Let the levels of the factor be 0, 1, 2, 4. The coefficients of the orthogonal polynomials are listed in Table 3.3.1. The orthogonal condition requires that the sum of each set of coefficients is zero and that the sum of product of any two sets of coefficients is zero.

For the sum of the linear set, we have

$$4L_0 + 7L_1 = 0$$

Set $L_1 = 1$, then $L_0 = -\frac{7}{4}$ or set $L_1 = 4$, then $L_0 = -7$. The results are shown in Table 3.3.2. For the sum of the quadratic set, we have

$$4Q_0 + 7Q_1 + 21Q_2 = 0. \tag{3.3.1}$$

For the sum of linear times quadratic, we have

$$-7(Q_0)$$
$$-3(Q_0 + Q_1 + Q_2)$$
$$1(Q_0 + 2Q_1 + 4Q_2)$$
$$9(Q_0 + 4Q_1 + 16Q_2)$$

so

$$35Q_1 + 145Q_2 = 0 \tag{3.3.2}$$

Set $Q_0 = 1$, and solve Eqs. (3.3.1) and (3.3.2):

$$-40Q_2 = -20, \qquad Q_2 = \tfrac{1}{2}$$

Hence

$$Q_1 = -\tfrac{29}{14}$$

TABLE 3.3.2

x	L
0	$L_0 = -7$
1	$L_0 + L_1 = -3$
2	$L_0 + 2L_1 = 1$
4	$L_0 + 4L_1 = 9$

TABLE 3.3.3

x	Q	Divided by 2
0	$Q_0 = 14$	7
1	$Q_0 + Q_1 + Q_2 = -8$	-4
2	$Q_0 + 2Q_1 + 4Q_2 = -16$	-8
4	$Q_0 + 4Q_1 + 16Q_2 = 10$	5

Multiply Q_0, Q_1, Q_2 by 14 to get

$$Q_0 = 14, \qquad Q_1 = -29, \qquad Q_2 = 7$$

and the results in Table 3.3.3. For the sum of the cubic set, we have

$$4C_0 + 7C_1 + 21C_2 + 73C_3 = 0 \tag{3.3.3}$$

For the sum of linear times cubic:

$$-7(C_0)$$
$$-3(C_0 + C_1 + C_2 + C_3)$$
$$1(C_0 + 2C_1 + 4C_2 + 8C_3)$$
$$9(C_0 + 4C_1 + 16C_2 + 64C_3)$$

so

$$35C_1 + 145C_2 + 581C_3 = 0 \tag{3.3.4}$$

For the sum of quadratic times cubic:

$$7(C_0)$$
$$-4(C_0 + C_1 + C_2 + C_3)$$
$$-8(C_0 + 2C_1 + 4C_2 + 8C_3)$$
$$5(C_0 + 4C_1 + 16C_2 + 64C_3)$$

so

$$44C_2 + 252C_3 = 0 \tag{3.3.5}$$

Set $C_0 = 1$ in (3.3.3), and calculate $10(3.3.5) - 11[(3.3.4) - 5(3.3.3)]$. Then

$$C_3 = \frac{-220}{144} = \frac{-55}{36}$$

$$C_2 = \frac{385}{44} = \frac{35}{4} = \frac{315}{36}$$

$$C_1 = \frac{-392}{36}$$

Hence

$$C_0 = 36, \qquad C_1 = -392, \qquad C_2 = 315, \qquad C_3 = -55$$

The results are shown in Table 3.3.4. Combining the results, we get Table 3.3.5.

TABLE 3.3.4

x	C	Divided by 12
0	$C_0 = 36$	3
1	$C_0 + C_1 + C_2 + C_3 = -96$	-8
2	$C_0 + 2C_1 + 4C_2 + 8C_3 = 72$	6
4	$C_0 + 4C_1 + 16C_2 + 64C_3 = -12$	-1

The coefficients of the linear component are given by $(-7 + 4x)$, and the symbol L_1 represents one unit of the linear effect of a factor when set equal to unity; L_1 was set equal to 4 in order to make the coefficients integers. Hence $\frac{1}{4}L_1$ represents one unit of the linear effect. Consequently, if we denote the scale by λ, we have $1/\lambda = \frac{1}{4}$. Similarly, the quadratic coefficients are given by

$$7 - \frac{29}{2}x + \frac{7}{2}x^2$$

hence

$$1/\lambda = \frac{2}{7}$$

The cubic coefficients are given by

$$3 - \frac{392}{12}x + \frac{315}{12}x^2 - \frac{55}{12}x^3$$

hence

$$1/\lambda = \frac{12}{55}$$

TABLE 3.3.5

x	L	Q	C
0	-7	7	3
1	-3	-4	-8
2	1	-8	6
4	9	5	-1

3.4 A NUMERICAL EXAMPLE

Suppose we have a two-factor experiment with quantitative factor A at 4 levels, quantitative factor B at 3 levels (all evenly spaced), and two replications in each cell. The data and analysis are shown in Tables 3.4.1, 3.4.2, and 3.4.3.

Note that data in this example were generated from

$$y = x_1^2 + x_2 + x_1^2 x_2 + \text{random error}$$

with $x_1 = 1, 2, 3, 4$, and $x_2 = 1, 2, 3$.

We need the coefficients of orthogonal polynomials for 3 levels in Table 3.4.4 and for 4 levels in Table 3.4.5.

For the partitioning of SS_A, we have

Linear component:
$$A_L = -3(31.1) - 1(86.0) + 1(176.4) + 3(303.1) = 906.4$$

Quadratic component:
$$B_Q = 1(31.1) - 1(86.0) - 1(176.4) + 1(303.1) = 71.8$$

Cubic component:
$$A_C = -1(31.1) + 3(86.0) - 3(176.4) + 1(303.1) = 0.8$$

TABLE 3.4.1

		B		
		2.9	5.0	7.8
		2.1	5.9	7.4
		9.2	14.8	19.2
	A	9.7	14.1	19.0
		19.7	29.5	39.2
		19.6	29.3	39.1
		33.2	50.7	67.3
		33.9	50.9	67.1

TABLE 3.4.2

Identification	Sum	Mean	Number of observations
A_1	31.1	5.18	6
A_2	86.0	14.33	6
A_3	176.4	29.40	6
A_4	303.1	50.52	6
B_1	130.3	16.29	8
B_2	200.2	25.02	8
B_3	266.1	33.26	8
A_1B_1	5.0	2.5	2
A_2B_1	18.9	9.45	2
A_3B_1	39.3	19.65	2
A_4B_1	67.1	33.55	2
A_1B_2	10.9	5.45	2
A_2B_2	28.9	14.45	2
A_3B_2	58.8	29.40	2
A_4B_2	101.6	50.80	2
A_1B_3	15.2	7.60	2
A_2B_3	38.2	19.10	2
A_3B_3	78.3	39.15	2
A_4B_3	134.4	67.20	2

TABLE 3.4.3

Source	SS	d.f.	MS
A	7061.148	3	2353.716
B	1152.935	2	576.467
AB	479.264	6	79.877
Error	1.510	12	0.126

TABLE 3.4.4

x	Linear	Quadratic
0	−1	1
1	0	−2
2	1	1
$\sum$	2	6
λ	1	3

TABLE 3.4.5

x	Linear	Quadratic	Cubic
0	−3	1	−1
1	−1	−1	3
2	1	−1	−3
3	3	1	1
$\sum$	20	4	20
λ	2	1	$\frac{10}{3}$

The sums of squares with one degree of freedom each are

$$A_L: \frac{(906.4)^2}{20 \times 6} = 6846.341$$

$$A_Q: \frac{(71.8)^2}{4 \times 6} = 214.802$$

$$A_C: \frac{(0.8)^2}{20 \times 6} = 0.005$$

For the partitioning of SS_B, we have

Linear component:
$$B_L = -1(130.3) + 0(200.2) + 1(266.1) = 135.8$$

Quadratic component:
$$B_Q = 1(130.3) - 2(200.2) + 1(266.1) = -4.0$$

The sums of squares with one degree of freedom each are

$$B_L: \frac{(135.8)^2}{2 \times 8} = 1152.602$$

$$B_Q: \frac{(-4.0)^2}{6 \times 8} = 0.333$$

It is possible for the shape of the curve which represents the effect of B to change from one level of A to another. Therefore it is useful to examine the linear and quadratic components of B at each level of A.

For the first level of A, we have

$$A_1B_1 = 5.0$$
$$A_1B_2 = 10.9$$
$$A_1B_3 = 15.2$$

Linear component of $B = -1(5.0) + 0(10.9) + 1(15.2) = 10.2$

Quadratic component of $B = 1(5.0) - 2(10.9) + 1(15.2) = -1.6$

For the second level of A, we have

$$A_2B_1 = 18.9$$
$$A_2B_2 = 28.9$$
$$A_2B_3 = 38.2$$

Linear component of $B = -1(18.9) + 0(28.9) + 1(38.2) = 19.3$

Quadratic component of $B = 1(18.9) - 2(28.9) + 1(38.2) = -0.7$

For the third level of A, we have

$$A_3B_1 = 39.3$$
$$A_3B_2 = 58.8$$
$$A_3B_3 = 78.3$$

Linear component of $B = -1(39.3) + 0(58.8) + 1(78.3) = 39$

Quadratic component of $B = 1(39.3) - 2(58.8) + 1(78.3) = 0$

For the fourth level of A, we have

$$A_4B_1 = 67.1$$
$$A_4B_2 = 101.6$$
$$A_4B_3 = 134.4$$

Linear component of $B = -1(67.1) + 0(101.6) + 1(134.4) = 67.3$

Quadratic component of $B = 1(67.1) - 2(101.6) + 1(134.4) = -1.7$

We summarize the results in Table 3.4.6.

TABLE 3.4.6

Levels of A	Component of B	
	Linear	Quadratic
1	10.2	−1.6
2	19.3	−0.7
3	39.0	0
4	67.3	−1.7
Sum	135.8	−4.0

The linear and quadratic components vary from one level of A to another. These components may be analyzed in the same way as were responses. Thus for the linear components of B with respect to levels of A, we have

Linear $B \times$ linear A:

$$A_L B_L = -3(10.2) - 1(19.3) + 1(39.0) + 3(67.3) = 191.0$$

Linear $B \times$ quadratic A:

$$A_Q B_L = 1(10.2) - 1(19.3) - 1(39.0) + 1(67.3) = 19.2$$

Linear $B \times$ cubic A:

$$A_C B_L = -1(10.2) + 3(19.3) - 3(39.0) + 1(67.3) = -2.0$$

Similarly, we have

Quadratic $B \times$ linear A:

$$A_L B_Q = -3(-1.6) - 1(-0.7) + 1(0) + 3(-1.7) = 0.4$$

Quadratic $B \times$ quadratic A:

$$A_Q B_Q = 1(-1.6) - 1(-0.7) - 1(0) + 1(-1.7) = -2.6$$

Quadratic $B \times$ cubic A:

$$A_C B_Q = -1(-1.6) + 3(-0.7) - 3(0) + 1(-1.7) = -2.2$$

The sums of squares with one degree of freedom each are obtained by dividing the squares of the above quantities by the appropriate divisors, which are the products of the corresponding sums of squares of the orthogonal coefficients used to derive the components times the number of observations contained in a cross-over sum:

$$A_L B_L: \frac{(191)^2}{(20)(2)(2)} = 456.012$$

$$A_Q B_L: \frac{(19.2)^2}{(4)(2)(2)} = 23.04$$

$$A_C B_L: \frac{(-2.0)^2}{(20)(2)(2)} = 0.05$$

$$A_L B_Q: \frac{(0.4)^2}{(20)(6)(2)} = 0.001$$

$$A_Q B_Q: \frac{(-2.6)^2}{(4)(6)(2)} = 0.141$$

$$A_C B_Q: \frac{(-2.2)^2}{(20)(6)(2)} = 0.020$$

A simple scheme for computing these interaction components uses the cell totals directly. The coefficients for the cell totals are obtained by multiplying

TABLE 3.4.7

A_Q $\downarrow$	$B_L \to -1$	0	1
1	-1 5.0	0 10.9	1 15.2
-1	1 18.9	0 28.9	-1 38.2
-1	1 39.3	0 58.8	-1 78.3
1	-1 67.1	0 101.6	1 134.4

the corresponding coefficients of the main effects. For example, consider the $A_Q B_L$ component. In Table 3.4.7, the cell totals (from Table 3.4.2) are shown in the lower right-hand corner of the cells, and the coefficients in the upper left-hand corner of the cells are products of the coefficients of A_Q and B_L. Applying these coefficients to the totals and summing, we get $A_Q B_L = 19.2$. We can find the other interaction components by exactly the same scheme with the proper corresponding main-effect coefficients.

The analysis-of-variance table shown in Table 3.4.3 can now be expanded into Table 3.4.8. This complete analysis shows that A_L, A_Q, B_L, $A_L B_L$, and $A_Q B_L$ are significant.

TABLE 3.4.8

Source		SS		d.f.	MS
A		7061.148		3	
	A_L		6846.341	1	6846.341
	A_Q		214.802	1	214.802
	A_C		0.005	1	0.005
B		1152.935		2	
	B_L		1152.602	1	1152.602
	B_Q		0.333	1	0.333
AB		479.264		6	
	$A_L B_L$		456.012	1	456.012
	$A_Q B_L$		23.040	1	23.040
	$A_C B_L$		0.050	1	0.050
	$A_L B_Q$		0.001	1	0.001
	$A_Q B_Q$		0.141	1	0.141
	$A_C B_Q$		0.020	1	0.020
Error		1.510		12	0.126

REFERENCES

1. MILNE, W. E., *Numerical Calculus*. Princeton University Press, Princeton, N. J., 1949.
2. GRANDAGE, A., "Orthogonal Coefficients for Unequal Intervals," *Biometrics*, **14**, 2, 287–289, 1958.
3. FISHER, R. A. and F. YATES, *Statistical Tables for Biological, Agricultural, and Medical Research*. Stechert-Hafner, New York, 1963.

4 NESTED EXPERIMENTS

4.1 NESTED TWO-FACTOR EXPERIMENT

In some two-factor experiments, the levels of one factor, say B, are similar but not identical for different levels of the other factor, say A; and the experiment is called nested, with factor B nested under factor A. For example, if in order to study a certain characteristic of a product, samples of size 3 are taken from each of 4 stations within each of 3 machines, the stations are nested under the machines. Each separate station appears with only a single machine. The pattern may be described by a diagram shown in Fig. 4.1.1.

FIG. 4.1.1

a) Model and Analysis

For a nested two-factor experiment with both factors at fixed levels, we write the model as

$$y_{ijk} = \mu + \alpha_i + \beta_{j(i)} + \epsilon_{k(ij)}$$
$$(i = 1, 2, \ldots, a; \quad j = 1, 2, \ldots, b; \quad k = 1, 2, \ldots, r)$$

The subscript $j(i)$ means the jth level of B within the ith level of A. It is convenient to regard replications as being nested within the combinations of the levels of A and B; hence we use the subscript $k(ij)$ for the error term. The model has no interaction term, since each level of B is not associated with every level of A. We assume that the $\epsilon_{k(ij)}$ are distributed independently $N(0, \sigma^2)$, and that α_i and $\beta_{j(i)}$ are fixed effects with conditions

$$\sum_i \alpha_i = 0, \qquad \sum_j \beta_{j(i)} = 0$$

Using the identity

$$y_{ijk} - y_{...} = (y_{i..} - y_{...}) + (y_{ij.} - y_{i..}) + (y_{ijk} - y_{ij.})$$

squaring both sides, and summing over i, j, and k, we partition the total sum of

TABLE 4.1.1

Source	SS	d.f.	MS	$E[MS]$
A	$\sum_i rb(y_{i..}-y_{...})^2$	$a-1$	$\dfrac{SS_A}{a-1}$	$\sigma^2+\dfrac{rb}{a-1}\sum_i \alpha_i^2$
B (within A)	$\sum_i\sum_j r(y_{ij.}-y_{i..})^2$	$a(b-1)$	$\dfrac{SS_B}{a(b-1)}$	$\sigma^2+\dfrac{r}{a(b-1)}\sum_i\sum_j \beta_{j(i)}^2$
Error	$\sum_i\sum_j\sum_k (y_{ijk}-y_{ij.})^2$	$ab(r-1)$	$\dfrac{SS_E}{ab(r-1)}$	σ^2
Total	$\sum_i\sum_j\sum_k (y_{ijk}-y_{...})^2$	$abr-1$		

squares into components which are shown in the analysis-of-variance table (Table 4.1.1). The cross-product terms all vanish. The hypotheses

$$H_A: \text{all } \alpha_i = 0, \qquad H_B: \text{all } \beta_{j(i)} = 0$$

can be tested by the ratios MS_A/MS_E and MS_B/MS_E, respectively. Under the null hypotheses, the ratios are distributed as $F((a-1),\ ab(r-1))$ and $F(a(b-1),\ ab(r-1))$.

For the computation of the sums of squares, we may use the following formulas:

$$SS_A = \sum_i \frac{(\sum_j \sum_k y_{ijk})^2}{rb} - \frac{(\sum_i \sum_j \sum_k y_{ijk})^2}{rab}$$

$$= rb \sum_i y_{i..}^2 - rab y_{...}^2$$

$$SS_B = \sum_i \sum_j \frac{(\sum_k y_{ijk})^2}{r} - \sum_i \frac{(\sum_j \sum_k y_{ijk})^2}{rb}$$

$$= r \sum_i \sum_j y_{ij.}^2 - rb \sum_i y_{i..}^2$$

$$SS_E = \sum_i \sum_j \sum_k y_{ijk}^2 - \sum_i \sum_j \frac{(\sum_k y_{ijk})^2}{r}$$

$$= \sum_i \sum_j \sum_k y_{ijk}^2 - r \sum_i \sum_j y_{ij.}^2$$

$$SS_T = \sum_i \sum_j \sum_k y_{ijk}^2 - \frac{(\sum_i \sum_j \sum_k y_{ijk})^2}{rab}$$

$$= \sum_i \sum_j \sum_k y_{ijk}^2 - rab y_{...}^2$$

TABLE 4.1.2

	Machine 1				Machine 2				Machine 3			
	Stations				Stations				Stations			
	1(1)	2(1)	3(1)	4(1)	1(2)	2(2)	3(2)	4(2)	1(3)	2(3)	3(3)	4(3)
	10.1	12.2	8.0	10.1	11.0	13.0	9.0	10.0	12.9	13.9	6.9	9.9
	11.1	8.2	10.0	11.1	14.0	11.0	10.0	9.0	9.9	12.9	8.9	6.9
	9.1	10.2	12.0	9.1	8.0	9.0	8.0	8.0	15.9	11.9	4.9	3.9
$y_{ij.}$	10.1	10.2	10.0	10.1	11.0	11.0	9.0	9.0	12.9	12.9	6.9	6.9
$y_{i..}$	10.1				10.0				9.9			

$$y_{...} = 10, \quad \sum_i \sum_j \sum_k y_{ijk}^2 = 3826.3$$

Note that the form for SS_B can be written as

$$\sum_i \left(\sum_j \frac{(\sum_k y_{ijk})^2}{r} - \frac{(\sum_j \sum_k y_{ijk})^2}{rb} \right)$$

which shows that SS_B can be obtained by first calculating the sum of squares between levels of B for each level of A and then pooling or summing over all levels of A.

b) Example

We shall now consider a numerical example. Suppose that the data of the two-factor nested experiment in Fig. 4.1.1 are shown in Table 4.1.2.

The α_i and $\beta_{j(i)}$ are estimated by

$$\hat{\alpha}_i = y_{i..} - y_{...}, \qquad \hat{\beta}_{j(i)} = y_{ij.} - y_{i..}$$

and we have

$$\hat{\alpha}_i = 0.1, 0, -0.1$$
$$\hat{\beta}_{j(1)} = 0, 0.1, -0.1, 0$$
$$\hat{\beta}_{j(2)} = 1, 1, -1, -1$$
$$\hat{\beta}_{j(3)} = 3, 3, -3, -3$$

Clearly,

$$\sum_i \hat{\alpha}_i = 0, \qquad \sum_j \hat{\beta}_{j(i)} = 0$$

The analysis-of-variance table is shown in Table 4.1.3. Assuming that machines and stations are fixed, we test the machine mean square and the station mean square against the error mean square, and find that the latter is significant.

TABLE 4.1.3

Source	SS	d.f.	MS
A (Machines)	0.240	2	0.120
B (Stations within machines)	120.060	9	13.340
Error	96.000	24	4.000
Total	216.300	35	

TABLE 4.1.4

Source	SS	d.f.	MS
A (Machines)	0.240	2	0.120
B (Stations)	65.620	3	21.873
AB	54.440	6	9.073
Error	96.000	24	4.000
Total	216.300	35	

To show the difference between a two-factor regular experiment and a two-factor nested experiment, let us calculate the analysis-of-variance table for the same data in Table 4.1.2, but assume that the machines and stations are not nested (see Section 1.5a). The results are given in Table 4.1.4. Note that the sum of SS_B and SS_{AB} in Table 4.1.4 is equal to the sum of squares of B within A in Table 4.1.3. The other sums of squares are the same in Table 4.1.3 and Table 4.1.4.

The sums of squares of B within A and error in the two-factor nested experiment can also be obtained by first calculating those for each level of A and then pooling over all levels of A. For A at the first level:

$$SS_B = 0.06, \quad \text{d.f.} = 3; \quad SS_E = 20.0, \quad \text{d.f.} = 8$$

for A at the second level:

$$SS_B = 12.0, \quad \text{d.f.} = 3; \quad SS_E = 30.0, \quad \text{d.f.} = 8$$

for A at the third level:

$$SS_B = 108.0, \quad \text{d.f.} = 3; \quad SS_E = 46.0, \quad \text{d.f.} = 8$$

Pooling them, we have

$$SS_{B \text{ within } A} = 120.06, \quad \text{d.f.} = 9$$
$$SS_E = 96.0, \quad \text{d.f.} = 24$$

The sum of squares of B for A at the third level is the largest. This indicates that repair or adjustment work is most needed on the stations of machine 3 in order to reduce variability on the particular characteristic of a product under investigation.

4.2 COMPLETELY NESTED EXPERIMENT

The nested situation may occur in experiments involving several factors. It is convenient to call a factor A *crossed* with a factor B if A is not nested within B. An experiment may be *completely crossed* or *completely nested* or a combination of nesting and crossing. The completely crossed experiments are the regular factorial experiments. A completely nested experiment is the case in which each factor is nested within the preceding factor. Consider the example in Section 4.1. If several manufacturing plants are included in the study and if machines are nested under the plants, then it is a completely nested three-factor experiment.

a) Model and Analysis

For a completely nested three-factor experiment, the model equation is

$$y_{ijkm} = \mu + \alpha_i + \beta_{j(i)} + \gamma_{k(ij)} + \epsilon_{m(ijk)}$$
$$(i = 1, 2, \ldots, a; \quad j = 1, 2, \ldots, b; \quad k = 1, 2, \ldots, c; \quad m = 1, 2, \ldots, r)$$

with the terms at the right corresponding to general mean, A, B within A, C within B, and error, respectively. The analysis-of-variance table (model I) is given in Table 4.2.1.

b) Special Remarks on Computation

The calculation of sums of squares for a completely nested experiment with several stages of nesting can be carried out by successive decomposition of the observed data into subsets and by repeated application of the operator calculus described in Chapter 2. For simplicity, consider the 3-factor experiment discussed above. First, introduce a fictitious factor to represent the r replications. Then apply the following sequences of operators to y_{ijkm}:

$$
\begin{array}{ll}
\Sigma_i\ \Sigma_j\ \Sigma_k\ \Sigma_m, & \Sigma_i\ \Sigma_j\ \Sigma_k\ D_m \\
\Sigma_i\ \Sigma_j\ D_k\ \Sigma_m, & \Sigma_i\ \Sigma_j\ D_k\ D_m \\
\Sigma_i\ D_j\ \Sigma_k\ \Sigma_m, & \Sigma_i\ D_j\ \Sigma_k\ D_m \\
\Sigma_i\ D_j\ D_k\ \Sigma_m, & \Sigma_i\ D_j\ D_k\ D_m \\
D_i\ \Sigma_j\ \Sigma_k\ \Sigma_m, & D_i\ \Sigma_j\ \Sigma_k\ D_m \\
D_i\ \Sigma_j\ D_k\ \Sigma_m, & D_i\ \Sigma_j\ D_k\ D_m \\
D_i\ D_j\ \Sigma_k\ \Sigma_m, & D_i\ D_j\ \Sigma_k\ D_m \\
D_i\ D_j\ D_k\ \Sigma_m, & D_i\ D_j\ D_k\ D_m
\end{array}
$$

and apply operator $(\ )^2$ to the deviates.

The sum of squares due to A is directly available from the above analysis. The error sum of squares is obtained by summing the main-effect sum of squares

TABLE 4.2.1

Source	SS	d.f.	MS	E[MS]
A	$rbc \sum_i y_{i...}^2 - rabc y_{....}^2$	$a-1$	MS_A	$\sigma^2 + \dfrac{rbc}{a-1} \sum_i \alpha_i^2$
B (within A)	$rc \sum_i \sum_j y_{ij..}^2 - rbc \sum_i y_{i...}^2$	$a(b-1)$	MS_B	$\sigma^2 + \dfrac{rc}{a(b-1)} \sum_i \sum_j \beta_{j(i)}^2$
C (within B)	$r \sum_i \sum_j \sum_k y_{ijk.}^2 - rc \sum_i \sum_j y_{ij..}^2$	$ab(c-1)$	MS_C	$\sigma^2 + \dfrac{r}{ab(c-1)} \sum_i \sum_j \sum_k \gamma_{k(ij)}^2$
Error	$\sum_i \sum_j \sum_k \sum_m y_{ijkm}^2 - r \sum_i \sum_j \sum_k y_{ijk.}^2$	$abc(r-1)$	MS_E	σ^2
Total	$\sum_i \sum_j \sum_k \sum_m y_{ijkm}^2 - rabc y_{....}^2$	$abcr-1$		

of the fictitious factor R and all sums of squares of those interactions involving the fictitious factor.

Next, decompose the data into a subsets according to levels of A, and apply

$$\Sigma_j \; \Sigma_k \; \Sigma_m, \qquad \Sigma_j \; \Sigma_k \; D_m$$
$$\Sigma_j \; D_k \; \Sigma_m, \qquad \Sigma_j \; D_k \; D_m$$
$$D_j \; \Sigma_k \; \Sigma_m, \qquad D_j \; \Sigma_k \; D_m$$
$$D_j \; D_k \; \Sigma_m, \qquad D_j \; D_k \; D_m$$

and operator $(\;\;)^2$ repeatedly to each of these a subsets. Summing all the main-effect sums of squares due to B from the analyses of subsets of data, we obtain the B main-effect sum of squares within A.

Finally, further decompose each of the b subsets of data into smaller subsets according to levels of B, and apply

$$\Sigma_k \; \Sigma_m, \qquad \Sigma_k \; D_m$$
$$D_k \; \Sigma_m, \qquad D_k \; D_m$$

and operator $(\;\;)^2$ repeatedly to each smaller subsets. Summing all sums of squares due to C obtained from these analyses, we have the main-effect sum of squares due to C within B.

It may be noted that in the analyses of subsets of data, one may use only $D_j \; \Sigma_k \; \Sigma_m$ to single out main effect B within each a, and $D_k \; \Sigma_m$ to single out main effect C within each b. However, the complete analysis of each subset of data often reveal useful additional information, and the increased amount of computational time on a large scale computer is very small.

In general, an experiment with n-stages of nesting in K-factors $(n < K)$ can be analyzed by decomposing the data n times successively and applying the operator calculus repeatedly in a manner as described above.

4.3 AN EXPERIMENT WITH BOTH NESTING AND CROSSING

Combined crossing and nesting situations in multifactor experiments may present great complexity, and their analyses under different model assumptions can be more efficiently handled by using a general procedure for determining expected mean squares, which will be described in Chapter 5. Here, we shall give a simple example and briefly discuss its model I analysis.

Suppose that in a study in industrial engineering we wish to test three different methods. For each method, we employ four operators. The experiment covers a period of three days, and four observations are obtained for each combination of method, operator, and day. Because of the nature of the experiment, the four operators employed under method 1 are really individuals different from the four operators under method 2 or method 3, and the four individuals under method 2 are different from those under method 3. The situation is described by a layout in Table 4.3.1. The operators are nested under methods.

TABLE 4.3.1

Methods	Operators	Days		
		1	2	3
1	1(1)	. . . .	. . . .	. . . .
	2(1)	. . . .	. . . .	. . . .
	3(1)	. . . .	. . . .	. . . .
	4(1)	. . . .	. . . .	. . . .
2	1(2)	. . . .	. . . .	. . . .
	2(2)	. . . .	. . . .	. . . .
	3(2)	. . . .	. . . .	. . . .
	4(2)	. . . .	. . . .	. . . .
3	1(3)	. . . .	. . . .	. . . .
	2(3)	. . . .	. . . .	. . . .
	3(3)	. . . .	. . . .	. . . .
	4(3)	. . . .	. . . .	. . . .

The days are crossed with the methods and the operators. The model is written as

$$y_{ijkm} = \mu + \alpha_i + \beta_{j(k)} + \gamma_k + \delta_{ij(k)} + \xi_{ik} + \epsilon_{m(ijk)}$$
$$(i = 1, 2, \ldots, a; \quad j = 1, 2, \ldots, b; \quad k = 1, 2, \ldots, c; \quad m = 1, 2, \ldots, r)$$

where μ is the general mean, α_i are the main effects due to A (days), $\beta_{j(k)}$ the effects due to B (operators) within C (methods), γ_k the effects due to C, $\delta_{ij(k)}$ the interactions of AB within C, and ξ_{ik} the AC interactions. The interactions BC and ABC cannot exist in the data; therefore they are not included in the model.

The side conditions on the model are

$$\sum_i \alpha_i = 0, \qquad \sum_k \gamma_k = 0$$

$$\sum_i \xi_{ik} = \sum_k \xi_{ik} = 0$$

$$\sum_j \beta_{j(k)} = 0 \quad \text{for each } k$$

and

$$\sum_i \delta_{ij(k)} = 0 \quad \text{for all } j(k), \qquad \sum_j \delta_{ij(k)} = 0 \quad \text{for all } k, i$$

Using the identity

$$
\begin{aligned}
y_{ijkm} - y_{....} = {}& (y_{i...} - y_{....}) + (y_{.jk.} - y_{..k.}) + (y_{..k.} - y_{....}) \\
& + (y_{ijk.} - y_{.jk.} - y_{i.k.} + y_{..k.}) \\
& + (y_{i.k.} - y_{i...} - y_{..k.} + y_{....}) + (y_{ijkm} - y_{ijk.})
\end{aligned}
$$

TABLE 4.3.2

Source	SS	d.f.	E[MS]
A	$rbc \sum_i (y_{i...} - y_{....})^2$	$a-1$	$\sigma^2 + \dfrac{rbc}{a-1}\sum_i \alpha_i^2$
B (within C)	$ra \sum_j \sum_k (y_{.jk.} - y_{..k.})^2$	$c(b-1)$	$\sigma^2 + \dfrac{ra}{c(b-1)}\sum_j \sum_k \beta_{j(k)}^2$
C	$rab \sum_k (y_{..k.} - y_{....})^2$	$c-1$	$\sigma^2 + \dfrac{rab}{c-1}\sum_k \gamma_k^2$
AB (within C)	$r \sum_i \sum_j \sum_k (y_{ijk.} - y_{.jk.} - y_{i.k.} + y_{..k.})^2$	$c(a-1)(b-1)$	$\sigma^2 + \dfrac{r}{c(a-1)(b-1)}\sum_i \sum_j \sum_k \delta_{ij(k)}^2$
AC	$rb \sum_i \sum_k (y_{i.k.} - y_{i...} - y_{..k.} + y_{....})^2$	$(a-1)(c-1)$	$\sigma^2 + \dfrac{rb}{(a-1)(c-1)}\sum_i \sum_k \xi_{ik}^2$
Error	$\sum_i \sum_j \sum_k \sum_m (y_{ijkm} - y_{ijk.})^2$	$abc(r-1)$	σ^2
Total	$\sum_i \sum_j \sum_k \sum_m (y_{ijkm} - y_{....})^2$	$abcr-1$	

and performing the operations of squaring and summing, we obtain the sums of squares in the analysis-of-variance table (Table 4.3.2), where the MS column is omitted.

The following formulas may be used for calculating the sums of squares:

$$SS_A = rbc \sum_i y_{i...}^2 - rabc y_{....}^2$$

$$SS_B = ra \sum_j \sum_k y_{.jk.}^2 - rab \sum_k y_{..k.}^2$$

$$SS_C = rab \sum_k y_{..k.}^2 - rabc y_{....}^2$$

$$SS_{AB} = r \sum_i \sum_j \sum_k y_{ijk.}^2 - ra \sum_j \sum_k y_{.jk.}^2 - rb \sum_i \sum_k y_{i.k.}^2 + rab \sum_k y_{..k.}^2$$

$$SS_{AC} = rb \sum_i \sum_k y_{i.k.}^2 - rbc \sum_i y_{i...}^2 - rab \sum_k y_{..k.}^2 + rabc y_{....}^2$$

$$SS_E = \sum_i \sum_j \sum_k \sum_m y_{ijkm}^2 - r \sum_i \sum_j \sum_k y_{ijk.}^2$$

$$SS_T = \sum_i \sum_j \sum_k \sum_m y_{ijkm}^2 - rabc y_{....}^2$$

Examining the forms for SS_B and SS_{AB}, we note that SS_B can be obtained by first calculating the sum of squares among levels of B for each level of C, then pooling over all levels of C; and SS_{AB} can be obtained by first computing the sum of squares among levels of A and B for each level of C, then pooling over all levels of C. Their degrees of freedom can be determined in a similar way.

REFERENCES

1. BROWNLEE, K. A., *Statistical Theory and Methodology in Science and Engineering*, 2nd Ed. Wiley, New York, 1965.
2. SCHEFFÉ, H., *The Analysis of Variance*. Wiley, New York, 1959.

5 FIXED, RANDOM, AND MIXED MODELS

5.1 INTRODUCTION

In the preceding chapters it has been assumed that the levels of the factors are set at fixed values. This is usually the case when one of the following experimental situations should occur.

1) A factor has a definite number of qualitatively distinguishable forms or categories, and we plan to study all of them.

2) Although a factor has an array of continuous, quantitative settings, we choose to study a suitable, definite subset in a limited region and to confine inferences to that subset.

However, as discussed in Section 1.5, sometimes it may be desirable for the experimenter to choose the levels at random from a large number of possible levels of a factor and consider the levels as a random sample from an infinite population. For example, a factor, such as operators or days, consists of a large population of distinct individuals or units, and we wish to estimate its contribution in general to the variability of the experiment. We include only a small random sample in the experiment.

Under different model assumptions (fixed, random, or mixed), the calculations of sums of squares, degrees of freedom, and mean squares remain the same. The difference lies in the derivation of expected mean squares and consequently in the testing of hypotheses.

5.2 MODELS FOR THE TWO-WAY ARRANGEMENT WITH r REPLICATIONS PER CELL

a) Two-Way Finite Population Model

We shall present the expected mean square, $E[MS]$, formulas under different model assumptions for the two-way arrangement by way of a general finite population model.

For a two-factor experiment, with factor A at a levels, B at b levels, and r replications per cell, the linear mathematical model is

$$y_{ijk} = \mu + \alpha_i + \beta_j + \gamma_{ij} + \epsilon_{ijk}$$
$$(i = 1, 2, \ldots, a; \quad j = 1, 2, \ldots, b; \quad k = 1, 2, \ldots, r) \qquad (5.2.1)$$

where y_{ijk} is the value of kth observation for the ith level of A and the jth level of B.

Underlying this model, we have several assumptions:

1) There is a constant general effect μ.
2) There is a population of main effects due to A of size A and variance σ_A^2. The α_i's are a random sample of size a from this population. Denote a potential level of A by I.
3) There is a population of main effects due to B of size B and variance σ_B^2. The β_j's are a random sample of size b from this population. Denote a potential level of B by J.
4) For each combination of a potential level of A with a potential level of B, there is a population of size R with variance σ_{IJ}^2. This combination determines a cell and interaction γ_{IJ}. The averages $\gamma_{I.}$ are independent of I and the averages $\gamma_{.J}$ are independent of J. The ϵ_{ijk}'s are a sample of size r from the (I, J)th population.
5) Sampling is at random in each cell and independent between cells. The sampling in assumptions (2) and (3) and in the cells takes place independently. The value of Kth element in the (I, J)th cell is denoted by Y_{IJK}.

The finite population model is flexible. If we take $a = A$ and $b = B$, then both factors are fixed and we have the fixed model or model I. If we take A and B both infinite, we have the random model or model II. If we choose $b = B$ and take A infinite, we obtain the mixed model or model III. The finite population model is also of interest in itself, since the assumption of infinite population is sometimes questionable.

For the finite population model, the sums of squares and mean squares are the same as those shown in Table 1.5.1. We define

$$\sigma_A^2 = \frac{1}{(A-1)} \sum_I (Y_{I..} - Y_{...})^2$$

$$\sigma_B^2 = \frac{1}{(B-1)} \sum_J (Y_{.J.} - Y_{...})^2$$

$$\sigma_{AB}^2 = \frac{1}{(A-1)(B-1)} \sum_I \sum_J (Y_{IJ.} - Y_{I..} - Y_{.J.} + Y_{...})^2$$

$$\sigma_E^2 = \frac{1}{AB(R-1)} \sum_I \sum_J \sum_K (Y_{IJK} - Y_{IJ.})^2$$

Under the assumptions stated above, it can be shown that the expected mean squares are those shown in Table 5.2.1. The derivation involves some stiff algebra and can be found in Cornfield and Tukey [3].

b) Fixed, Random, and Mixed Models (Two-Way)

When $a = A$, $b = B$, $R = \infty$, we obtain the formulas for the fixed model. When a and b are finite and A, B, and R are infinite, we get those for the random model. When $b = B$, a is finite, and A and R are infinite, then we have those for the mixed model. These formulas are shown in Table 5.2.2.

TABLE 5.2.1

Source	d.f.	$E[MS]$
A	$(a-1)$	$br\sigma_A^2 + r\left(1 - \dfrac{b}{B}\right)\sigma_{AB}^2 + \left(1 - \dfrac{r}{R}\right)\sigma_E^2$
B	$(b-1)$	$ar\sigma_B^2 + r\left(1 - \dfrac{a}{A}\right)\sigma_{AB}^2 + \left(1 - \dfrac{r}{R}\right)\sigma_E^2$
AB	$(a-1)(b-1)$	$r\sigma_{AB}^2 + \left(1 - \dfrac{r}{R}\right)\sigma_E^2$
Error	$ab(r-1)$	σ_E^2

In the fixed model, the hypotheses we usually wish to test are

$$H_A:\text{ all } \alpha_i = 0$$
$$H_B:\text{ all } \beta_j = 0$$
$$H_{AB}:\text{ all } \gamma_{ij} = 0$$

Since

$$\sigma_A^2 = \frac{\sum_i \alpha_i^2}{(a-1)}, \qquad \sigma_B^2 = \frac{\sum_j \beta_j^2}{(b-1)}$$

$$\sigma_{AB}^2 = \frac{\sum_i \sum_j \gamma_{ij}^2}{(a-1)(b-1)}$$

the hypotheses may be expressed as

$$H_A: \sigma_A^2 = 0$$
$$H_B: \sigma_B^2 = 0$$
$$H_{AB}: \sigma_{AB}^2 = 0$$

Note that the σ_A^2, σ_B^2, and σ_{AB}^2 do not denote the variances of any random variable, but merely represent functions of the parameters in the fixed model.

We shall introduce the additional assumption that the ϵ_{ijk}'s in the model are independently, normally distributed with zero mean and equal variance σ_E^2. The tests of significance have been discussed in Section 1.5.

TABLE 5.2.2

Source	E[MS]		
	Fixed	Random	Mixed
A	$br\sigma_A^2 + \sigma_E^2$	$br\sigma_A^2 + r\sigma_{AB}^2 + \sigma_E^2$	$br\sigma_A^2 + \sigma_E^2$
B	$ar\sigma_B^2 + \sigma_E^2$	$ar\sigma_B^2 + r\sigma_{AB}^2 + \sigma_E^2$	$ar\sigma_B^2 + r\sigma_{AB}^2 + \sigma_E^2$
AB	$r\sigma_{AB}^2 + \sigma_E^2$	$r\sigma_{AB}^2 + \sigma_E^2$	$r\sigma_{AB}^2 + \sigma_E^2$
Error	σ_E^2	σ_E^2	σ_E^2

In the random model, we shall assume that the α_i, β_j, γ_{ij}, and ϵ_{ijk} are independently and normally distributed with zero means and respective variances σ_A^2, σ_B^2, σ_{AB}^2, and σ_E^2. The hypotheses to be tested are

$$H_A: \sigma_A^2 = 0$$
$$H_B: \sigma_B^2 = 0$$
$$H_{AB}: \sigma_{AB}^2 = 0$$

The SS_A is distributed as $E[MS_A]\chi^2$ with $(a-1)$ d.f.; SS_B is distributed as $E[MS_B]\chi^2$ with $(b-1)$ d.f.; SS_{AB} is distributed as $E[MS_{AB}]\chi^2$ with $(a-1)(b-1)$ d.f.; and SS_E is distributed as $E[MS_E]\chi^2$ with $ab(r-1)$ d.f. Under H_A, SS_A is $(r\sigma_{AB}^2 + \sigma_E^2)\chi_{(a-1)}^2$, and SS_{AB} is $(r\sigma_{AB}^2 + \sigma_E^2)\chi_{(a-1)(b-1)}^2$; hence MS_A/MS_{AB} is $F((a-1), (a-1)(b-1))$. Similarly, to test H_B, the ratio MS_B/MS_{AB} is used. Inferences about σ_{AB}^2 may be made by using the ratio MS_{AB}/MS_E, which is $F((a-1)(b-1), ab(r-1))$.

The σ_A^2, σ_B^2, and σ_{AB}^2 are estimated by

$$\hat{\sigma}_A^2 = \frac{MS_A - MS_{AB}}{br}$$

$$\hat{\sigma}_B^2 = \frac{MS_B - MS_{AB}}{ar}$$

$$\hat{\sigma}_{AB}^2 = \frac{MS_{AB} - MS_E}{r}$$

To construct confidence intervals for these variance components, we may use a general approximation method. (See Bulmer [2] and Scheffé [5].)

Let MS_1 and MS_2 be two mean squares independently distributed with v_1 and v_2 d.f. and expected values $(\theta + \sigma^2)$ and σ^2, respectively, where θ and σ^2 are nonnegative. In other words, $v_1 MS_1$ is $(\theta + \sigma^2)\chi_{v_1}^2$, and $v_2 MS_2$ is $\sigma^2\chi_{v_2}^2$.

Then it can be shown that the upper confidence limit for θ, the difference between the expected values of the two mean squares, with approximate confidence coefficient $(1 - \alpha_1)$ is given by $MS_2 g_U(MS_1/MS_2)$, where

$$g_U\left(\frac{MS_1}{MS_2}\right) = F_{\alpha_1}\left(\frac{MS_1}{MS_2}\right) - 1 + \frac{MS_2}{F'_{\alpha_1}MS_1}\left(1 - \frac{F_{\alpha_1}}{F'_{\alpha_1}}\right)$$

for $(MS_1/MS_2) \geq (1/F'_{\alpha_1})$, and

$$g_U\left(\frac{MS_1}{MS_2}\right) = 0$$

for $(MS_1/MS_2) \leq (1/F'_{\alpha_1})$, where F_{α_1} has degrees of freedom ∞ and v_1, and F'_{α_1} has degrees of freedom v_2 and v_1. The lower confidence limit for θ with approximate confidence coefficient $(1 - \alpha_2)$ is given by $MS_2 g_L(MS_1/MS_2)$, where

$$g_L\left(\frac{MS_1}{MS_2}\right) = \frac{MS_1}{F_{\alpha_2}MS_2} - 1 - \frac{F'_{\alpha_2}MS_2}{MS_1}\left(\frac{F'_{\alpha_2}}{F_{\alpha_2}} - 1\right)$$

for $(MS_1/MS_2) \geq F'_{\alpha_2}$, and

$$g_L\left(\frac{MS_1}{MS_2}\right) = 0$$

for $(MS_1/MS_2) \leq F'_{\alpha_2}$, where F_{α_2} has d.f. v_1 and ∞ and F'_{α_2} has d.f. v_1 and v_2.

From the upper and lower confidence limits, we get a confidence interval between these limits with confidence coefficient $(1 - \alpha_1 - \alpha_2)$.

In the mixed model, with A random and B fixed, we assume that the α_i, γ_{ij}, and ϵ_{ijk} are independently and normally distributed with zero means and have respective variances σ_A^2, σ_{AB}^2, and σ_E^2. The σ_A^2 and σ_{AB}^2 are estimated by

$$\hat{\sigma}_A^2 = \frac{MS_A - MS_E}{br}$$

$$\hat{\sigma}_{AB}^2 = \frac{MS_{AB} - MS_E}{r}$$

The hypothesis $(H_A : \sigma_A^2 = 0)$ may be tested by the ratio MS_A/MS_E which has, under H_A, the F-distribution with $(a - 1)$ and $ab(r - 1)$ d.f.

The hypothesis $(H_{AB} : \sigma_{AB}^2 = 0)$ may be tested by the ratio MS_{AB}/MS_E which has, under H_{AB}, the F-distribution with $((a - 1)(b - 1))$ and $ab(r - 1)$ d.f.

The hypothesis $(H_B :$ all $\beta_j = 0)$ may be tested by the approximate F-test based on the ratio MS_B/MS_{AB} with $(b - 1)$ and $((a - 1)(b - 1))$ d.f.

5.3 EXPECTED MEAN SQUARES FOR THE THREE-WAY ARRANGEMENT WITH r REPLICATIONS PER CELL

a) Three-Way Finite Population Model

The finite population model for the replicated three-way arrangement is the natural generalization of the two-way model. The model equation may be written as

$$y_{ijkm} = \mu + \alpha_i + \beta_j + \gamma_k + \delta_{ij} + \zeta_{ik} + \eta_{jk} + \xi_{ijk} + \epsilon_{ijkm}$$
$$(i = 1, 2, \ldots, a; \quad j = 1, 2, \ldots, b; \quad k = 1, 2, \ldots, c; \quad m = 1, 2, \ldots, r)$$

with the terms corresponding to general mean, A, B, C, AB, AC, BC, ABC, and error, respectively. The variance components are defined in a way similar to those for the two-way. The expected mean values are given for the general finite population model in Table 5.3.1.

b) Fixed, Random, and Mixed Models (Three-Way)

The finite population model becomes the fixed model when $a = A$, $b = B$, $c = C$, and $R = \infty$. The usual assumptions include normality, statistical independence, and equal error variance. The seven mean squares are all tested against MS_E. The $E[MS]$ formulas are listed in Table 5.3.2.

When a, b, c are finite and A, B, C, R are infinite, we have the random model. The α_i, β_j, γ_k, δ_{ij}, ζ_{ik}, η_{jk}, ξ_{ijk}, ϵ_{ijkm} are assumed to be independently and nor-

TABLE 5.3.1

Source	d.f.	$E[MS]$
A	$a - 1$	$\left(1 - \dfrac{r}{R}\right)\sigma_E^2 + r\left(1 - \dfrac{b}{B}\right)\left(1 - \dfrac{c}{C}\right)\sigma_{ABC}^2$ $+ rb\left(1 - \dfrac{c}{C}\right)\sigma_{AC}^2 + rc\left(1 - \dfrac{b}{B}\right)\sigma_{AB}^2 + rbc\sigma_A^2$
B	$b - 1$	$\left(1 - \dfrac{r}{R}\right)\sigma_E^2 + r\left(1 - \dfrac{a}{A}\right)\left(1 - \dfrac{c}{C}\right)\sigma_{ABC}^2$ $+ ra\left(1 - \dfrac{c}{C}\right)\sigma_{BC}^2 + rc\left(1 - \dfrac{a}{A}\right)\sigma_{AB}^2 + rac\sigma_B^2$
C	$c - 1$	$\left(1 - \dfrac{r}{R}\right)\sigma_E^2 + r\left(1 - \dfrac{a}{A}\right)\left(1 - \dfrac{b}{B}\right)\sigma_{ABC}^2$ $+ ra\left(1 - \dfrac{b}{B}\right)\sigma_{BC}^2 + rb\left(1 - \dfrac{a}{A}\right)\sigma_{AC}^2 + rab\sigma_C^2$
AB	$(a - 1)(b - 1)$	$\left(1 - \dfrac{r}{R}\right)\sigma_E^2 + r\left(1 - \dfrac{c}{C}\right)\sigma_{ABC}^2 + rc\sigma_{AB}^2$
AC	$(a - 1)(c - 1)$	$\left(1 - \dfrac{r}{R}\right)\sigma_E^2 + r\left(1 - \dfrac{b}{B}\right)\sigma_{ABC}^2 + rb\sigma_{AC}^2$
BC	$(b - 1)(c - 1)$	$\left(1 - \dfrac{r}{R}\right)\sigma_E^2 + r\left(1 - \dfrac{a}{A}\right)\sigma_{ABC}^2 + ra\sigma_{BC}^2$
ABC	$(a - 1)(b - 1)(c - 1)$	$\left(1 - \dfrac{r}{R}\right)\sigma_E^2 + r\sigma_{ABC}^2$
Error	$abc(r - 1)$	σ_E^2

TABLE 5.3.2

Source	$E[MS]$ Fixed model	Random model
A	$\sigma_E^2 + rbc\sigma_A^2$	$\sigma_E^2 + r\sigma_{ABC}^2 + rb\sigma_{AC}^2 + rc\sigma_{AB}^2 + rbc\sigma_A^2$
B	$\sigma_E^2 + rac\sigma_B^2$	$\sigma_E^2 + r\sigma_{ABC}^2 + ra\sigma_{BC}^2 + rc\sigma_{AB}^2 + rac\sigma_B^2$
C	$\sigma_E^2 + rab\sigma_C^2$	$\sigma_E^2 + r\sigma_{ABC}^2 + ra\sigma_{BC}^2 + rb\sigma_{AC}^2 + rab\sigma_C^2$
AB	$\sigma_E^2 + rc\sigma_{AB}^2$	$\sigma_E^2 + r\sigma_{ABC}^2 + rc\sigma_{AB}^2$
AC	$\sigma_E^2 + rb\sigma_{AC}^2$	$\sigma_E^2 + r\sigma_{ABC}^2 + rb\sigma_{AC}^2$
BC	$\sigma_E^2 + ra\sigma_{BC}^2$	$\sigma_E^2 + r\sigma_{ABC}^2 + ra\sigma_{BC}^2$
ABC	$\sigma_E^2 + r\sigma_{ABC}^2$	$\sigma_E^2 + r\sigma_{ABC}^2$
Error	σ_E^2	σ_E^2

mally distributed with zero means and variances σ_A^2, σ_B^2, σ_C^2, σ_{AB}^2, σ_{AC}^2, σ_{BC}^2, σ_{ABC}^2, σ_E^2, respectively. The $E[MS]$ formulas are listed in Table 5.3.2.

The hypothesis

$$H_{ABC}: \sigma_{ABC}^2 = 0$$

is tested with the ratio MS_{ABC}/MS_E. The hypothesis

$$H_{AB}: \sigma_{AB}^2 = 0$$

is tested with MS_{AB}/MS_{ABC}, and similarly for

$$\sigma_{AC}^2 = 0 \quad \text{and} \quad \sigma_{BC}^2 = 0$$

If we are willing to assume that $\sigma_{AB}^2 = 0$, then an exact F-test of the hypothesis

$$H_A: \sigma_A^2 = 0$$

can be based on the ratio MS_A/MS_{AC}, and since SS_{AB} and SS_{ABC} have the same $E[MS]$, they can be pooled together. An alternative would be to assume $\sigma_{AC}^2 = 0$, test H_A with MS_A/MS_{AB}, and pool SS_{AC} and SS_{ABC}.

However, if we are not willing to assume

$$\sigma_{AB}^2 = 0 \quad \text{or} \quad \sigma_{AC}^2 = 0$$

then only an approximate F-test can be performed. In this case, we write

$$\theta = \sigma_E^2 + r\sigma_{ABC}^2 + cr\sigma_{AB}^2 + br\sigma_{AC}^2$$

so that

$$E[MS_A] = \theta + rbc\sigma_A^2$$

Then

$$\theta = E[MS_{AB}] + E[MS_{AC}] - E[MS_{ABC}]$$

and θ is estimated by

$$\hat{\theta} = MS_{AB} + MS_{AC} - MS_{ABC}$$

The MS_{AB}, MS_{AC}, MS_{ABC} are independently distributed as

$$E[MS_{AB}]\chi_{v_1}^2/((a-1)(b-1)),$$
$$E[MS_{AC}]\chi_{v_2}^2/((a-1)(c-1)),$$
$$E[MS_{ABC}]\chi_{v_3}^2/((a-1)(b-1)(c-1))$$

where v_1, v_2, v_3 are the respective degrees of freedom of the mean squares.

Now we shall approximate $\hat{\theta}$ by a random variable:

$$Z = \theta\chi_v^2/v$$

Since θ and Z have equal means, we shall determine v such that θ and Z also have equal variances. Recall that the mean of χ_v^2 is v, the variance is $2v$, and the variance of a random variable with a constant multiplier is equal to the square of the constant times the variance of the random variable. Therefore the condition of equal variances gives

$$\frac{2\theta^2}{v} = 2\left\{\frac{\{E[MS_{AB}]\}^2}{(a-1)(b-1)} + \frac{\{E[MS_{AC}]\}^2}{(a-1)(c-1)} + \frac{\{E[MS_{ABC}]\}^2}{(a-1)(b-1)(c-1)}\right\}$$

or

$$v = \frac{\theta^2}{\dfrac{\{E[MS_{AB}]\}^2}{(a-1)(b-1)} + \dfrac{\{E[MS_{AC}]\}^2}{(a-1)(c-1)} + \dfrac{\{E[MS_{ABC}]\}^2}{(a-1)(b-1)(c-1)}}$$

where v is estimated by

$$\hat{v} = \frac{\hat{\theta}^2}{\dfrac{(MS_{AB})^2}{(a-1)(b-1)} + \dfrac{(MS_{AC})^2}{(a-1)(c-1)} + \dfrac{(MS_{ABC})^2}{(a-1)(b-1)(c-1)}}$$

The approximate F-test for testing H_A is then based on the ratio $MS_A/\hat{\theta}$, which is distributed approximately as

$$\frac{rbc\sigma_A^2 + \theta}{\theta}\frac{v}{(a-1)}\frac{\chi^2_{(a-1)}}{\chi^2_v} = \frac{rbc\sigma_A^2 + \theta}{\theta} F_{(a-1),v}$$

where v is taken to be equal to $\hat{v}$.

In general, let us test $H_x: \sigma_x^2 = 0$, for any MS_x of the form $p\sigma_x^2 + \theta$. If there is no $E[MS]$ in the analysis-of-variance table equal to θ, we may consider a linear combination of several mean squares with expected value equal to θ, approximate θ by $\theta\chi_v^2/v$, and proceed as above.

From the 3-way finite population model we can derive two distinct mixed models:

1) when factor A is random and factors B and C are fixed, that is, A and R infinite, $b = B$, and $c = C$;

2) when factors A and B are random and factor C is fixed, that is, A, B, and R infinite, and $c = C$.

The ϵ_{ijkm} are independently distributed with zero means and equal variances σ_E^2, and all effects or interaction involving a random factor are random variables with zero means and respective variances.

The expected mean squares are listed in Table 5.3.3. Using the results from the table, we can perform the F-tests of significance of the hypothesis corresponding to each row above the error term of the table. The numerator mean square is that of a given row, and the denominator is the one that has the same $E[MS]$ under the null hypothesis. If no such row exists for the denominator, a linear combination of several mean squares is used to obtain an approximate F-test as described under the 3-way random model.

In the finite population model, in general, only approximate F-tests can be obtained. In practice, if the population sizes are not much larger than the number of selected levels, it may be reasonable to regard the factors as fixed.

TABLE 5.3.3

Source	$E[MS]$	
	A random; B and C fixed	A and B random; C fixed
A	$\sigma_E^2 + rbc\sigma_A^2$	$\sigma_E^2 + rc\sigma_{AB}^2 + rbc\sigma_A^2$
B	$\sigma_E^2 + rc\sigma_{AB}^2 + rac\sigma_B^2$	$\sigma_E^2 + rc\sigma_{AB}^2 + rac\sigma_B^2$
C	$\sigma_E^2 + rb\sigma_{AC}^2 + rab\sigma_C^2$	$\sigma_E^2 + r\sigma_{ABC}^2 + ra\sigma_{BC}^2 + rb\sigma_{AC}^2 + rab\sigma_C^2$
AB	$\sigma_E^2 + rc\sigma_{AB}^2$	$\sigma_E^2 + rc\sigma_{AB}^2$
AC	$\sigma_E^2 + rb\sigma_{AC}^2$	$\sigma_E^2 + r\sigma_{ABC}^2 + rb\sigma_{AC}^2$
BC	$\sigma_E^2 + r\sigma_{ABC}^2 + ra\sigma_{BC}^2$	$\sigma_E^2 + r\sigma_{ABC}^2 + ra\sigma_{BC}^2$
ABC	$\sigma_E^2 + r\sigma_{ABC}^2$	$\sigma_E^2 + r\sigma_{ABC}^2$
Error	σ_E^2	σ_E^2

5.4   GENERAL RULES FOR EXPECTED MEAN SQUARES

A general procedure is available for writing down $E[MS]$ formulas rapidly. The procedure begins with the model equation and covers regular factorial experiments as well as nested experiments.

Consider the example in Section 4.3, where the efficiency of several methods is studied. Imagine an additional factor D, say machines, is introduced. Within each method (factor C) and machine combination, the operators (factor B) are nested. Factor A (days) is crossed with C, D, and B. Several repeated measurements are made for each operator in each combination of machine, method, and day. The model equation is

$$y_{ijkmq} = \mu + \alpha_i + \beta_{j(km)} + \gamma_k + \delta_m + \kappa_{ij(km)} + \theta_{ik} + \eta_{im} + \xi_{km}$$
$$+ \lambda_{ikm} + \epsilon_{q(ijkm)}$$
$$(i = 1, 2, \ldots, a; \quad j = 1, 2, \ldots, b; \quad k = 1, 2, \ldots, c;$$
$$m = 1, 2, \ldots, d; \quad q = 1, 2, \ldots, r)$$

with the terms corresponding to general mean, A, B, C, D, AB, AC, AD, CD, ACD, and error, respectively. The terms corresponding to BD, BC, BCD, ABD, ABC, $ABCD$ are not included in the model, because they cannot exist in the experiment.

The general procedure for obtaining the $E[MS]$ formulas may be illustrated by reference to the above example. We construct a two-way table as in Table 5.4.1. The row headings are the terms in the model equation and their corresponding effects. The column headings are the indices used in the model with sample size and population size listed below in parentheses. The table can be rapidly filled in by the following rules:

1) For those columns whose indices are not present in the subscripts of the term defining a row being considered, enter the sample size.

TABLE 5.4.1

		i	j	k	m	q
		(a, A)	(b, B)	(c, C)	(d, D)	(r, R)
$\epsilon_{q(ijkm)}$	Error	1	1	1	1	$\left(1 - \dfrac{r}{R}\right)$
λ_{ikm}	ACD	$\left(1 - \dfrac{a}{A}\right)$	b	$\left(1 - \dfrac{c}{C}\right)$	$\left(1 - \dfrac{d}{D}\right)$	r
ξ_{km}	CD	a	b	$\left(1 - \dfrac{c}{C}\right)$	$\left(1 - \dfrac{d}{D}\right)$	r
η_{im}	AD	$\left(1 - \dfrac{a}{A}\right)$	b	c	$\left(1 - \dfrac{d}{D}\right)$	r
θ_{ik}	AC	$\left(1 - \dfrac{a}{A}\right)$	b	$\left(1 - \dfrac{c}{C}\right)$	d	r
$\kappa_{ij(km)}$	AB	$\left(1 - \dfrac{a}{A}\right)$	$\left(1 - \dfrac{b}{B}\right)$	1	1	r
δ_m	D	a	b	c	$\left(1 - \dfrac{d}{D}\right)$	r
γ_k	C	a	b	$\left(1 - \dfrac{c}{C}\right)$	d	r
$\beta_{j(km)}$	B	a	$\left(1 - \dfrac{b}{B}\right)$	1	1	r
α_i	A	$\left(1 - \dfrac{a}{A}\right)$	b	c	d	r

2) For those columns whose indices are present in the bracketed subscripts of the term defining a row being considered, enter 1.

3) For the remaining empty cells, enter

$$\left(1 - \frac{\text{sample size}}{\text{population size}}\right)$$

For any mean square, the expected value is a linear combination of the σ^2's corresponding to the rows whose headings have in their subscripts all the indices which also appear in the subscripts of the term corresponding to the mean square being considered. The coefficients of the σ^2's are formed from the corresponding rows by taking the product of the entries in all columns in which indices are not in the subscripts of the term whose corresponding $E[MS]$ is being calculated.

TABLE 5.4.2 87

Source	$E[MS]$
A	$\left(1 - \dfrac{r}{R}\right)\sigma_E^2 + br\left(1 - \dfrac{c}{C}\right)\left(1 - \dfrac{d}{D}\right)\sigma_{ACD}^2$ $+ bcr\left(1 - \dfrac{d}{D}\right)\sigma_{AD}^2$ $+ bdr\left(1 - \dfrac{c}{C}\right)\sigma_{AC}^2$ $+ r\left(1 - \dfrac{b}{B}\right)\sigma_{AB}^2 + bcdr\sigma_A^2$
B	$\left(1 - \dfrac{r}{R}\right)\sigma_E^2 + r\left(1 - \dfrac{a}{A}\right)\sigma_{AB}^2 + ar\sigma_B^2$
C	$\left(1 - \dfrac{r}{R}\right)\sigma_E^2 + br\left(1 - \dfrac{a}{A}\right)\left(1 - \dfrac{d}{D}\right)\sigma_{ACD}^2$ $+ abr\left(1 - \dfrac{d}{D}\right)\sigma_{CD}^2$ $+ bdr\left(1 - \dfrac{a}{A}\right)\sigma_{AC}^2$ $+ r\left(1 - \dfrac{a}{A}\right)\left(1 - \dfrac{b}{B}\right)\sigma_{AB}^2$ $+ abdr\sigma_C^2 + ar\left(1 - \dfrac{b}{B}\right)\sigma_B^2$
D	$\left(1 - \dfrac{r}{R}\right)\sigma_E^2 + br\left(1 - \dfrac{a}{A}\right)\left(1 - \dfrac{c}{C}\right)\sigma_{ACD}^2 + abr\left(1 - \dfrac{c}{C}\right)\sigma_{CD}^2$ $+ bcr\left(1 - \dfrac{a}{A}\right)\sigma_{AD}^2 + r\left(1 - \dfrac{a}{A}\right)\left(1 - \dfrac{b}{B}\right)\sigma_{AB}^2$ $+ abcr\sigma_D^2 + ar\left(1 - \dfrac{b}{B}\right)\sigma_B^2$
AB	$\left(1 - \dfrac{r}{R}\right)\sigma_E^2 + r\sigma_{AB}^2$
AC	$\left(1 - \dfrac{r}{R}\right)\sigma_E^2 + br\left(1 - \dfrac{d}{D}\right)\sigma_{ACD}^2 + bdr\sigma_{AC}^2 + r\left(1 - \dfrac{b}{B}\right)\sigma_{AB}^2$
AD	$\left(1 - \dfrac{r}{R}\right)\sigma_E^2 + br\left(1 - \dfrac{c}{C}\right)\sigma_{ACD}^2 + bcr\sigma_{AD}^2 + r\left(1 - \dfrac{b}{B}\right)\sigma_{AB}^2$
CD	$\left(1 - \dfrac{r}{R}\right)\sigma_E^2 + br\left(1 - \dfrac{a}{A}\right)\sigma_{ACD}^2 + abr\sigma_{CD}^2 + r\left(1 - \dfrac{a}{A}\right)\left(1 - \dfrac{b}{B}\right)\sigma_{AB}^2$ $+ ar\left(1 - \dfrac{b}{B}\right)\sigma_B^2$
ACD	$\left(1 - \dfrac{r}{R}\right)\sigma_E^2 + br\sigma_{ACD}^2 + r\left(1 - \dfrac{b}{B}\right)\sigma_{AB}^2$
Error	σ_E^2

For example, to calculate $E[MS_C]$ we need to form a linear combination of σ_E^2, σ_{ACD}^2, σ_{CD}^2, σ_{AC}^2, σ_{AB}^2, σ_B^2, σ_C^2. Their respective coefficients are

$$\left(1 - \frac{r}{R}\right), \quad br\left(1 - \frac{a}{A}\right)\left(1 - \frac{d}{D}\right), \quad abr\left(1 - \frac{d}{D}\right),$$

$$bdr\left(1 - \frac{a}{A}\right), \quad r\left(1 - \frac{a}{A}\right)\left(1 - \frac{b}{B}\right), \quad ar\left(1 - \frac{b}{B}\right), \quad abdr$$

The complete list of $E[MS]$ formulas for this example is shown in Table 5.4.2.

As before, the $E[MS]$ formulas for the finite population model can be reduced easily to those for any one of the three special models.

5.5 GENERAL RULES FOR CALCULATING SUM OF SQUARES

A formal procedure for calculating sum of squares and degrees of freedom will be described below. It is based on the model equation and applicable to crossing, nesting situations, or a combination of both in a multifactor experiment. It may be regarded as an alternative method to the operator calculus described in Chapter 2.

We will describe the rules by reference to the same example discussed in the preceding section for writing $E[MS]$ formulas. First, we state the formal rules as follows:

For the term in the model equation corresponding to any sum of squares being calculated, form a symbolic product from the subscripts of the term. For each of the bracketed subscripts (if any), use the subscript in the product; for each of the unbracketed subscripts, use the subscript minus 1 in the product, and expand the product.

For example, the term corresponding to the AB-interaction in our example is $\kappa_{ij(km)}$. The symbolic product is

$$(i - 1)(j - 1)km = ijkm - jkm - ikm + km$$

The quantity squared in the sum of squares consists of terms corresponding to each term in the expanded symbolic product. The terms are the symbols $\pm y$ with subscripts corresponding to each term in the product and additional dots making up the number of subscripts in the observation; however, when the term in the product is 1, then only dots are used. The sign of $\pm y$ is the same as that of the term in the symbolic product.

After this quantity is formed and squared, it is then summed over all the subscripts appearing in the term in the model equation, and finally it is multiplied by the limits of the subscripts which are not appearing in the term of the model equation. For example,

$$SS_{AB} = r \sum_i \sum_j \sum_k \sum_m \left(y_{ijkm.} - y_{.jkm.} - y_{i.km.} + y_{..km.}\right)^2$$

The computational form of SS may be obtained by a similar formalism. The terms in the symbolic product give the signs and subscripts of the symbols

$\pm y^2$ which may have additional make-up dots and are summed over the present subscripts and multiplied by the limits of the absent subscripts. For example,

$$SS_{AB} = r \sum_i \sum_j \sum_k \sum_m y^2_{ijkm.} - ar \sum_j \sum_k \sum_m y^2_{.jkm.} - br \sum_i \sum_k \sum_m y^2_{i.km.}$$
$$+ abr \sum_k \sum_m y^2_{..km.}$$

The degrees of freedom of each SS is also given by the symbolic product when the subscripts are substituted by their numerical limits. For example, the degrees of freedom for AB interaction is

$$(a - 1)(b - 1)cd$$

Based on these rules, the following list is obtained for the example which has, as we recall, the model equation:

$$y_{ijkmq} = \mu + \alpha_i + \beta_{j(km)} + \gamma_k + \delta_m + \kappa_{ij(km)} + \theta_{ik} + \eta_{im}$$
$$+ \xi_{km} + \lambda_{ikm} + \epsilon_{q(ijkm)}$$

α_i: $SS_A = bcdr \sum_i (y_{i....} - y_{.....})^2$

$$= bcdr \sum_i y^2_{i....} - abcdry^2_{.....}$$

     d.f. $= (a - 1)$

$\beta_{j(km)}$: $SS_B = ar \sum_j \sum_k \sum_m (y_{.jkm.} - y_{..km.})^2$

$$= ar \sum_j \sum_k \sum_m y^2_{.jkm.} - abr \sum_k \sum_m y^2_{..km.}$$

     d.f. $= cd(b - 1)$

γ_k: $SS_C = abdr \sum_k (y_{..k..} - y_{.....})^2$

$$= abdr \sum_k y^2_{..k..} - abcdry^2_{.....}$$

     d.f. $= (c - 1)$

δ_m: $SS_D = abcr \sum_m (y_{...m.} - y_{.....})^2$

$$= abcr \sum_m y^2_{...m.} - abcdry^2_{.....}$$

     d.f. $= (d - 1)$

$\kappa_{ij(km)}$: $SS_{AB} = r \sum_i \sum_j \sum_k \sum_m (y_{ijkm.} - y_{.jkm.} - y_{i.km.} + y_{..km.})^2$

$$= r \sum_i \sum_j \sum_k \sum_m y^2_{ijkm.} - ar \sum_j \sum_k \sum_m y^2_{.jkm.}$$

$$- br \sum_i \sum_k \sum_m y^2_{i.km.} + abr \sum_k \sum_m y^2_{..km.}$$

     d.f. $= (a - 1)(b - 1)cd$

$$\theta_{ik}: \quad SS_{AC} = bdr \sum_i \sum_k (y_{i.k..} - y_{i...} - y_{..k..} + y_{.....})^2$$

$$= bdr \sum_i \sum_k y_{i.k..}^2 - bcdr \sum_i y_{i....}^2 - abdr \sum_k y_{..k..}^2$$

$$+ abcdr y_{.....}^2$$

$$\text{d.f.} = (a-1)(c-1)$$

$$\eta_{im}: \quad SS_{AD} = bcr \sum_i \sum_m (y_{i..m.} - y_{i....} - y_{...m.} + y_{.....})^2$$

$$= bcr \sum_i \sum_m y_{i..m.}^2 - bcdr \sum_i y_{i....}^2 - abcr \sum_m y_{...m.}^2$$

$$+ abcdr y_{.....}^2$$

$$\text{d.f.} = (a-1)(d-1)$$

$$\xi_{km}: \quad SS_{CD} = abr \sum_k \sum_m (y_{..km.} - y_{..k..} - y_{...m.} + y_{.....})^2$$

$$= abr \sum_k \sum_m y_{..km.}^2 - abdr \sum_k y_{..k..}^2$$

$$- abcr \sum_m y_{...m.}^2 + abcdr y_{.....}^2$$

$$\text{d.f.} = (c-1)(d-1)$$

$$\lambda_{ikm}: SS_{ACD} = br \sum_i \sum_k \sum_m (y_{i.km.} - y_{i.k..} - y_{i..m.} - y_{..km.}$$

$$+ y_{i....} + y_{..k..} + y_{...m.} - y_{.....})^2$$

$$= br \sum_i \sum_k \sum_m y_{i.km.}^2 - bdr \sum_i \sum_k y_{i.k..}^2 - bcr \sum_i \sum_m y_{i..m.}^2$$

$$- abr \sum_k \sum_m y_{..km.}^2 + bcdr \sum_i y_{i....}^2 + abdr \sum_k y_{..k..}^2$$

$$+ abcr \sum_m y_{...m.}^2 - abcdr y_{.....}^2$$

$$\text{d.f.} = (a-1)(c-1)(d-1)$$

$$\epsilon_{q(ijkm)}: \quad SS_E = \sum_i \sum_j \sum_k \sum_m \sum_q (y_{ijkmq} - y_{ijkm.})^2$$

Finally, by definition, we have

$$\text{Total:} \quad SS_T = \sum_i \sum_j \sum_k \sum_m \sum_q (y_{ijkmq} - y_{.....})^2$$

$$= \sum_i \sum_j \sum_k \sum_m \sum_q y_{ijkmq}^2 - abcdr y_{.....}^2$$

$$\text{d.f.} = abcdr - 1$$

REFERENCES

1. WILK, M. B., and O. KEMPTHORNE, "Fixed, Mixed, and Random Models," *Amer. Stat. Assoc. Jour.*, **50,** 1144–1167 (1955).

2. BULMER, M. G., "Approximate Confidence Limits for Components of Variance," *Biometrika*, **44,** 159–167 (1957).

3. CORNFIELD, J., and J. W. TUKEY, "Average Values of Mean Squares in Factorials," *Annals of Math. Stat.*, **27,** 907–949 (1956).

4. "Components of Variance," a special issue of *Biometrics*, **7,** 1–112 (1951).

5. SCHEFFÉ, H., *The Analysis of Variance.* Wiley, New York, 1959.

6 RANDOMIZED-BLOCKS, LATIN-SQUARE, AND SPLIT-PLOT DESIGNS

6.1 INTRODUCTION

The simplest factorial design is the complete factorial with no restriction on randomization (complete randomization). This means that all experimental units are considered as the same and that no division or grouping among them exists. The treatment replications are assigned to the experimental units by one randomization procedure without any modification applied to any subset of experimental units.

If the experimental units are divided into a number of groups and a complete replication of all treatments is assigned to each group, we have a *randomized-blocks design*. Randomization is carried out separately in each group of experimental units which is usually called a *block*. The blocks may be so chosen as to coincide with the degrees of variability in experimental material. Thus, the experimental units in each block are more homogeneous. In other situations, the blocks may be identified with some source of environment variability, so that this will not affect the experimental error.

However, sometimes a two-way variation may exist in the experimental material or two kinds of systematic differences may be present in the environment. A device called *Latin squares* can then be used to produce a double grouping which eliminates variations in two directions from the experimental error. The randomization is carried out by selecting a particular square at random from Latin squares of a given size.

These designs and some other complex experiments suitable for different experimental situations are discussed in some detail in this chapter.

6.2 RANDOMIZED BLOCKS

To illustrate the layout of a randomized-blocks design, let us consider eight treatments (say t_1, t_2, ..., t_8, corresponding to eight levels of a factor) to be included in each of 3 blocks. Table 6.2.1 shows such an experimental layout. The treatments are randomly allotted within each block. The blocks, for example, may be periods of time in a day, or machines performing a certain operation in industrial experiments.

TABLE 6.2.1

Block I	t_2	t_1	t_5	t_6	t_4	t_3	t_8	t_7
Block II	t_5	t_3	t_4	t_7	t_6	t_1	t_2	t_8
Block III	t_7	t_6	t_8	t_1	t_2	t_4	t_3	t_5

a) Model and Analysis

The fixed model for a randomized-blocks design may be written as

$$y_{ij} = \mu + \alpha_i + \beta_j + \epsilon_{ij} \quad (i = 1, 2, \ldots, a; \quad j = 1, 2, \ldots, b) \quad (6.2.1)$$

where y_{ij} is the observation from the ith block and jth treatment, ϵ_{ij} are independently $N(0, \sigma^2)$, and α_i and β_j are fixed constants with the conditions

$$\sum_i \alpha_i = 0, \qquad \sum_j \beta_j = 0$$

Clearly, this is the same as a two-way arrangement with one observation per cell. The block and treatment effects are assumed to be additive. The analysis-of-variance table is the same as Table 1.5.2 where A becomes "blocks" and B denotes "treatments."

b) Efficiency of Blocking

The purpose of grouping the experimental units into blocks and restricting randomization within each block instead of having complete randomization is to reduce experimental error. To evaluate how much of this has been accomplished, we may compare the error variances in the two cases. Let σ_{cr}^2 denote the error variance for the completely randomized design, and let σ_{rb}^2 denote that for the randomized-blocks design. Then the ratio

$$E = \frac{\sigma_{cr}^2}{\sigma_{rb}^2}$$

measures the efficiency of the randomized-blocks design relative to the completely randomized design.

To derive the formula for estimating E, we assume that dummy treatments or uniformity trials were used. This means that all treatment effects are zero. If the experiment were conducted in complete randomization, the error variance would be

$$\sigma_{cr}^2 = \frac{SS_T}{ab - 1}$$

where SS_T is the total sum of squares. Now imagine that the experiment with dummy treatments were run in blocks. The total sum of squares SS_T must remain the same. However, the partition of SS_T gives two components: sum of squares due to blocks and sum of squares due to replications within blocks.

TABLE 6.2.2

Source	MS	d.f.	SS	E[MS]
Blocks	MS_{BL}	$a-1$	$(a-1)MS_{BL}$	
Within blocks	MS_{WB}	$a(b-1)$	$a(b-1)MS_{WB}$	σ_{rb}^2
Total		$ab-1$	$(a-1)MS_{BL} + a(b-1)MS_{WB}$	

The analysis of variance is shown in Table 6.2.2. The error variance for the completely randomized design is estimated by

$$\hat{\sigma}_{cr}^2 = \frac{(a-1)MS_{BL} + a(b-1)MS_{WB}}{(ab-1)}$$

The error variance with blocking is estimated by MS_{WB}. Hence the ratio E is estimated by

$$\hat{E} = \frac{\hat{\sigma}_{cr}^2}{\hat{\sigma}_{rb}^2} = \frac{(a-1)MS_{BL} + a(b-1)MS_{WB}}{(ab-1)MS_{WB}}$$

Actually the efficiency of the randomized-blocks design is slightly smaller than $\hat{E}$, since there is a loss, due to blocking, of $(a-1)$ degrees of freedom from the $(ab-1)$ degrees of freedom for error in the completely randomized design. Following the discussions in Section 0.2, we have the relative efficiency adjusted as

$$\frac{(a(b-1)+1)(ab-1+3)}{(ab-1+1)(a(b-1)+3)} \hat{E}$$

c) When Blocks are Chosen at Random

In a randomized-blocks experiment, the blocks may be chosen randomly from a population of blocks, but the treatments are fixed; then we have a mixed model. The model equation is

$$y_{ij} = \mu + \alpha_i + \beta_j + \epsilon_{ij} \quad (i = 1, 2, \ldots, a; \quad j = 1, 2, \ldots, b)$$

where ϵ_{ij} are independently $N(0, \sigma_E^2)$, α_i are independently $N(0, \sigma_A^2)$, and β_j are fixed constants such that

$$\sum_j \beta_j = 0$$

The $E[MS]$ forms are shown in Table 6.2.3. When the treatments are also random, we have a random model. Then, the assumption on β_j should be changed so that β_j are independently $N(0, \sigma_B^2)$. The $E[MS]$ for treatments becomes $\sigma_E^2 + a\sigma_B^2$.

TABLE 6.2.3

Source	$E[MS]$
A (blocks)	$\sigma_E^2 + b\sigma_A^2$
B (treatments)	$\sigma_E^2 + \dfrac{a}{b-1}\sum_j \beta_j^2$
Error	σ_E^2

TABLE 6.2.4

Treatment	t_1	t_2	t_3	t_4	t_5	t_6	t_7	t_8	Total	Mean
Block I	53.4	31.2	23.2	16.2	50.2	22.0	26.0	33.8	256.0	32.0
Block II	47.4	25.2	17.2	10.2	50.2	22.0	26.0	33.8	232.0	29.0
Block III	43.2	33.6	19.6	15.6	43.6	22.0	20.0	34.4	232.0	29.0
Total	144.0	90.0	60.0	42.0	144.0	66.0	72.0	102.0	720.0	
Mean	48.0	30.0	20.0	14.0	48.0	22.0	24.0	34.0		30.0

TABLE 6.2.5

Treatment	$\hat{\epsilon}_{ij}$								$\hat{\alpha}_i$
	t_1	t_2	t_3	t_4	t_5	t_6	t_7	t_8	
Block I	3.4	−0.8	1.2	0.2	0.2	−2.0	0	−2.2	2
Block II	0.4	−3.8	−1.8	−2.8	3.2	1.0	3.0	0.8	−1
Block III	−3.8	4.6	0.6	2.6	−3.4	1.0	−3.0	1.4	−1
$\hat{\beta}_j$	18	0	−10	−16	18	−8	−6	4	

TABLE 6.2.6

Source	SS	d.f.	MS
Blocks	48.00	2	24.00
Treatments	3360.00	7	480.00
Error	135.36	14	9.67
Total	3543.36	23	

d) Example

The data for the layout in Table 6.2.1 are given in Table 6.2.4. The estimates of α_i, β_j, and ϵ_{ij} are given in Table 6.2.5. Note that the $\hat{\epsilon}_{ij}$ add up to zero for each block and for each treatment. The analysis-of-variance table is shown in Table 6.2.6. The treatment differences are very significant.

6.3 LATIN SQUARE

The randomized-blocks design discussed in the preceding section may be considered as a one-dimensional blocking method to control heterogeneity of the experimental units. A more complex method, called Latin squares, can be used for two-dimensional blocking. Latin squares were first used extensively in agricultural experiments where soil conditions often vary rowwise as well as columnwise in a field. However, this method was soon found to be useful in other scientific and industrial experiments.

Let us consider, for example, that homogeneous batches of material (each adequate for four runs) are available and that four presumably equivalent sets of equipment are to be used for testing the effects of four catalysts. The layout in Table 6.3.1 provides a Latin-square design in which each catalyst is run once on each set of equipment and once on each batch of material. The catalysts are denoted by A, B, C, and D. The sets of equipment may be referred to as rows, the batches as columns, and the catalysts as treatments. We note that in a Latin square, the numbers of rows, columns, and treatments must be the same. This requirement somewhat restricts the usefulness of Latin-square designs.

TABLE 6.3.1

Equipment	Batch			
	1	2	3	4
1	A	B	C	D
2	B	A	D	C
3	C	D	A	B
4	D	C	B	A

a) Examples and Randomization

Table 6.3.2 gives examples of Latin squares of sizes from 3×3 to 8×8. Higher-order squares can be constructed by the same method used to write down the 7×7 and 8×8 squares that is, each row of letters consists of the preceding row of letters shifted one place to the left. Latin squares with first row and first column in the standard order as those shown in Table 6.3.2 are called standard squares. Table 6.3.3 lists the numbers of standard squares for sizes 3×3 to 7×7.

From each standard square, additional squares may be generated. Table 6.3.4 gives the numbers of Latin squares, all different, for sizes 3×3 to 7×7. This

TABLE 6.3.2

3×3	4×4				5×5	6×6	7×7	8×8
	(a)	(b)	(c)	(d)				
ABC	ABCD	ABCD	ABCD	ABCD	ABCDE	ABCDEF	ABCDEFG	ABCDEFGH
BCA	BADC	BCDA	BDAC	BADC	BAECD	BCFADE	BCDEFGA	BCDEFGHA
CAB	CDBA	CDAB	CADB	CDAB	CDAEB	CFBEAD	CDEFGAB	CDEFGHAB
	DCAB	DABC	DCBA	DCBA	DEBAC	DEABFC	DEFGABC	DEFGHABC
					ECDBA	EADFCB	EFGABCD	EFGHABCD
						FDECBA	FGABCDE	FGHABCDE
							GABCDEF	GHABCDEF
								HABCDEFG

TABLE 6.3.3

Size	3 × 3	4 × 4	5 × 5	6 × 6	7 × 7
No. of standard squares	1	4	56	9408	16,942,080

TABLE 6.3.4

Size	3 × 3	4 × 4	5 × 5	6 × 6	7 × 7
No. of Latin squares	12	576	161,280	812,851,200	61,479,419,904,000

indicates that when the size of a Latin square is large, the random selection of a Latin square becomes a difficult problem. For practical purposes, the following procedure for randomly selecting a Latin square of a particular size is suitable.

1) For the 3 × 3 square, randomize the rows and columns of the square shown here.

2) For the 4 × 4 square, randomly select one of the four squares shown, and randomize the rows and columns.

3) For larger squares, randomize rows and columns independently, and assign treatments randomly to the letters.

b) Model and Analysis

Latin squares are often used to study the effects of three factors, and the factors corresponding to rows and columns are of interest in themselves, but not introduced for the main purpose of reducing experimental error. Consider, for example, the first Latin square of size 4 × 4 in Table 6.3.2. Associating the levels 0, 1, 2, 3 with the 4 rows, columns, and letters, we obtain the factorial level combinations:

$$000, \quad 011, \quad 022, \quad 033$$
$$101, \quad 110, \quad 123, \quad 132$$
$$202, \quad 213, \quad 221, \quad 230$$
$$303, \quad 312, \quad 320, \quad 331$$

Thus there are only 4^2 combinations to be used in the experiment instead of the 4^3 possible combinations in a complete factorial design. However, this reduction is paid for by the assumption of additivity, or the absence of interactions among the factors.

An important property of the Latin-square design is that of orthogonality. For any two of the factors:

I (rows),   II (columns),   III (letters)

the levels of one factor occur once with each of the levels of the other factor.

TABLE 6.3.5

Source	SS	d.f.	MS	E[MS]
Factor I (rows)	$SS_I = n \sum_i (y_{i..} - y_{...})^2$	$n - 1$	$\dfrac{SS_I}{n-1}$	$\sigma^2 + \dfrac{n}{n-1} \sum_i \alpha_i^2$
Factor II (columns)	$SS_{II} = n \sum_j (y_{.j.} - y_{...})^2$	$n - 1$	$\dfrac{SS_{II}}{n-1}$	$\sigma^2 + \dfrac{n}{n-1} \sum_j \beta_j^2$
Factor III (letters)	$SS_{III} = n \sum_k (y_{..k} - y_{...})^2$	$n - 1$	$\dfrac{SS_{III}}{n-1}$	$\sigma^2 + \dfrac{n}{n-1} \sum_k \gamma_k^2$
Error	$SS_E = \displaystyle\sum_{(i,j,k)\epsilon L} (y_{ijk} - y_{i..} - y_{.j.} - y_{..k} + 2y_{...})^2$	$(n-1)(n-2)$	$\dfrac{SS_E}{(n-1)(n-2)}$	σ^2
Total	$SS_T = \displaystyle\sum_{(i,j,k)\epsilon L} (y_{ijk} - y_{...})^2$	$n^2 - 1$		

The three factors are said to be mutually orthogonal. This property ensures that the three main effects can be estimated independently.

Let y_{ijk} denote the observed value corresponding to the ith level of factor I, jth level of factor II, and kth level of factor III. Note that (i, j, k) take on only the n^2 values specified by the particular Latin square of size $n \times n$, which is selected randomly for the experiment. The model equation is

$$y_{ijk} = \mu + \alpha_i + \beta_j + \gamma_k + \epsilon_{ijk} \tag{6.3.1}$$

where α_i, β_j, and γ_k are the main effects, ϵ_{ijk} are independently $N(0, \sigma^2)$, and

$$\sum_i \alpha_i = \sum_j \beta_j = \sum_k \gamma_k = 0$$

Equation (6.3.1) implies the additivity assumption.

Denote the set of n^2 values of (i, j, k) by L. Using the identity

$$\sum_{(i,j,k)\epsilon L} (y_{ijk} - y_{...})^2 = \sum_{(i,j,k)\epsilon L} [(y_{i..} - y_{...}) + (y_{.j.} - y_{...}) + (y_{..k} - y_{...})$$
$$+ (y_{ijk} - y_{i..} - y_{.j.} - y_{..k} + 2y_{...})]^2$$

we partition the total sum of squares into components as shown in Table 6.3.5, which is the analysis-of-variance table for a $n \times n$ Latin square. The $E[MS]$ column given here is for model I analysis. For model II and model III, this column should be changed. The computations can be easily performed by using the following formulas:

$$SS_{\text{I}} = \frac{\sum_i T_{i..}^2}{n} - \frac{T_{...}^2}{n^2}$$

$$SS_{\text{II}} = \frac{\sum_j T_{.j.}^2}{n} - \frac{T_{...}^2}{n^2}$$

$$SS_{\text{III}} = \frac{\sum_k T_{..k}^2}{n} - \frac{T_{...}^2}{n^2}$$

$$SS_T = \sum_{(i,j,k)\epsilon L} y_{ijk}^2 - \frac{T_{...}^2}{n^2}$$

$$SS_E = SS_T - SS_{\text{I}} - SS_{\text{II}} - SS_{\text{III}}$$

where $T_{i..}$, $T_{.j.}$, $T_{..k}$ are totals corresponding to rows, columns, and letters, and $T_{...}$ is the sum of all the n^2 observations.

The hypotheses (H_{I}: all $\alpha_i = 0$), (H_{II}: all $\beta_j = 0$), and (H_{III}: all $\gamma_k = 0$) are tested by the ratios

$$MS_{\text{I}}/MS_E, \quad MS_{\text{II}}/MS_E, \quad MS_{\text{III}}/MS_E$$

respectively. Each ratio will be distributed as $F((n - 1), (n - 1)(n - 2))$ under the corresponding null hypothesis. If real interactions are present, they will inflate MS_E and make the tests less sensitive.

TABLE 6.3.7

	A	B	C	D	$T_{i..}$
	34	31	15	28	108
	B	A	D	C	
	28	37	17	10	92
	C	D	A	B	
	12	21	33	26	92
	D	C	B	A	
	26	23	23	36	108
$T_{.j.}$	100	112	88	100	400
$T_{..k}$	140	108	60	92	400

TABLE 6.3.8

	$\hat{\epsilon}_{ijk}$: $y_{ijk} - y_{i..} - y_{.j.} - y_{..k} + 2y_{...}$				$\hat{\alpha}_i$: $y_{i..} - y_{...}$
	A	B	C	D	
	−3	−1	1	3	2
	B	A	D	C	
	3	1	−1	−3	−2
	C	D	A	B	
	−1	−3	3	1	−2
	D	C	B	A	
	1	3	−3	−1	2
$\hat{\beta}_j$: $y_{.j.} - y_{...}$	0	3	−3	0	0
$\hat{\gamma}_k$: $y_{..k} - y_{...}$	10	2	−10	2	0

TABLE 6.3.9

Source	SS	d.f.	MS
Rows	64.0	3	21.3
Columns	72.0	3	24.0
Letters	832.0	3	277.3
Error	80.0	6	13.3
Total	1048.0	15	

TABLE 6.3.10

Block			
1	2	3	4
34	37	33	36
28	31	23	26
12	23	15	10
26	21	17	28

c) Efficiency

When a Latin square is used for two-dimensional blocking, its efficiency of row grouping (ignoring the loss of degrees of freedom) as compared with a randomized-blocks design with the columns as blocks is estimated by

$$E_1 = \frac{MS_\mathrm{I} + (n - 1)MS_E}{nMS_E} \qquad (6.3.2)$$

Similarly, the efficiency for column grouping is estimated by replacing MS_I in (6.3.2) by MS_II. The efficiency of a Latin square as compared with complete randomization (ignoring the loss of degrees of freedom) is estimated by

$$E_2 = \frac{MS_\mathrm{I} + MS_\mathrm{II} + (n - 1)MS_E}{(n + 1)MS_E}$$

d) Numerical Example

Now we shall consider a numerical example. Table 6.3.7 shows the data for the Latin square in Table 6.3.1. The estimates of α_i, β_j, γ_k, and ϵ_{ijk} are shown in Table 6.3.8. Note that the $\hat{\epsilon}_{ijk}$ add up to zero for each row, each column, and each letter.

Using the computational formulas in terms of totals for sums of squares, we obtain the analysis-of-variance table in Table 6.3.9. The results can also be verified by using the values in Table 6.3.8 and the closed forms of sums of squares in Table 6.3.5. The F-ratio $277.3/13.3 = 20.8$ indicates that the effect due to letters (catalysts) is highly significant.

To compare some aspects of the analysis of a Latin square with that of randomized blocks, let us regard the same data in Table 6.3.7 as data from a randomized blocks-design and perform the analysis accordingly. The rearranged data are shown in Table 6.3.10 with blocks corresponding to columns in Table 6.3.7. Following the computing formulas for sums of squares in Section 1.6(b), we get the analysis-of-variance table in Table 6.3.11. Note that the block sum of squares and degrees of freedom are the same as the column values of the corresponding Latin-square analysis. The quantities related to letters (treatments) also remain unchanged, but the sums of squares and degrees of freedom of rows and error in the Latin-square analysis have been combined to form those for the error term in the randomized blocks. The gain of the additional row

TABLE 6.3.11

Source	SS	d.f.	MS
Blocks	72.0	3	24.0
Treatments	832.0	3	277.3
Error	144.0	9	16.0
Total	1048.0	15	

blocking in the Latin square may be measured by formula (6.3.2), that is,

$$E_1 = \frac{21.3 + (4 - 1)13.3}{4(13.3)} = 1.1504$$

Considering the loss of degrees of freedom, we may adjust E_1 by the factor (see Section 0.2)

$$\frac{(6 + 1)(9 + 3)}{(9 + 1)(6 + 3)} = 0.93$$

Thus $(0.93)(1.15) = 1.07$. This may be interpreted to mean that the Latin-square design is 107 percent as efficient as randomized blocks.

6.4 GRAECO-LATIN SQUARE

In the example we discussed in the preceding section, if four operators are considered as an additional classification and if each is required to measure once for each catalyst, once for each batch of material, and once on each set of equipment, a Graeco-Latin square can be constructed to satisfy these requirements. Let α, β, γ, and δ denote the operators; then Table 6.4.1 shows such a square. In such an arrangement, the effects of equipment, batch, and operator are equalized for all catalysts.

The construction of Graeco-Latin squares attracted the attention of mathematicians long before statisticians used them in planning experiments. Leonhard Euler (1707–1783) studied Graeco-Latin squares extensively; hence they are also called *Euler squares*. Euler proposed the well-known problem of 36 officers. The problem was to arrange 36 officers of 6 ranks and from 6 regiments in a square of size 6×6. Each row and each column of this square must contain one officer of each rank and one officer from each regiment. Euler's problem reduces to the construction of a Graeco-Latin square of size 6×6 or of order 6. In 1782, Euler conjectured that there exist no Graeco-Latin squares of order $n = 2$ (mod 4). In 1900, Tarry [1] verified the validity of Euler's conjecture for $n = 6$ by a systematic enumeration.

Euler's conjecture was proved only recently to be false for $n > 6$. From 1959 to 1962, a series of papers were published by Bose, Shrikhande, and Parker [2], [3], [4], [8], culminating in the following theorem:

Let $n > 6$ and $n \equiv 2$ (mod 4). Then there exists a Graeco-Latin square of order n.

Of course, the existence of a Graeco-Latin square of order $n \not\equiv 2$ (mod 4) was established much earlier. Graeco-Latin squares of order 10 and 22 were constructed by Parker, Bose, and Shrikhande recently.

A Graeco-Latin square is equivalent to a pair of *orthogonal Latin squares*. Two Latin squares of the same size are orthogonal to each other if, when they are superimposed, every letter of one square appears once and only once with every letter of the other. For Latin squares of order $n \geqq 3$, the set of t orthog-

TABLE 6.4.1

Equipment	Batch			
	1	2	3	4
1	A_α	B_β	C_γ	D_δ
2	B_δ	A_γ	D_β	C_α
3	C_β	D_α	A_δ	B_γ
4	D_γ	C_δ	B_α	A_β

onal Latin squares is called *complete* if

$$t = n - 1.$$

In any event, t cannot be greater than $n - 1$. For certain values of n, more definite results are available. In other cases, the question of how many orthogonal Latin squares exist remains to be settled. The following result can be proved by utilizing the theory of Galois fields:

Let $n = p^\eta$, where p is a prime and η is a positive integer. Then for $n \geq 3$ there exists a complete set of $n - 1$ orthogonal Latin squares of order n.

But, for example, for $n = 10$, no one yet has constructed a set of 3 orthogonal Latin squares of order 10.

a) Examples of Graeco-Latin Squares

Table 6.4.2 gives several examples of Graeco-Latin squares, where numerical subscripts are used instead of Greek letters. To select an arrangement for actual use, the rows and columns of a square should be arranged independently at random, and the Latin letters and the subscripts should be assigned to their respective classifications randomly.

b) Model and Analysis

Graeco-Latin squares are used for triple blocking to reduce experimental error as well as for studying 4 factors simultaneously when they are of interest themselves. However, the design is not often used in practical experiments due to its requirement of a square formation and the assumption of no interactions among the factors.

The model for a Graeco-Latin square experiment is

$$y_{ijkm} = \mu + \alpha_i + \beta_j + \gamma_k + \delta_m + \epsilon_{ijkm} \tag{6.4.1}$$

where ϵ_{ijkm} are independently $N(0, \sigma^2)$; α_i, β_j, γ_k, and δ_m are main effects of factors I (rows), II (columns), III (Latin letters), and IV (Greek letters or subscripts); and

$$\sum_i \alpha_i = \sum_j \beta_j = \sum_k \gamma_k = \sum_m \delta_m = 0$$

TABLE 6.4.2

3×3			4×4				5×5					7×7						
A_1	B_3	C_2	A_1	B_3	C_4	D_2	A_1	B_3	C_5	D_2	E_4	A_1	B_5	C_2	D_6	E_3	F_7	G_4
B_2	C_1	A_3	B_2	A_4	D_3	C_1	B_2	C_4	D_1	E_3	A_5	B_2	C_6	D_3	E_7	F_4	G_1	A_5
C_3	A_2	B_1	C_3	D_1	A_2	B_4	C_3	D_5	E_2	A_4	B_1	C_3	D_7	E_4	F_1	G_5	A_2	B_6
			D_4	C_2	B_1	A_3	D_4	E_1	A_3	B_5	C_2	D_4	E_1	F_5	G_2	A_6	B_3	C_7
							E_5	A_2	B_4	C_1	D_3	E_5	F_2	G_6	A_3	B_7	C_4	D_1
												F_6	G_3	A_7	B_4	C_1	D_5	E_2
												G_7	A_4	B_1	C_5	D_2	E_6	F_3

8×8								9×9								
A_1	B_5	C_2	D_3	E_7	F_4	G_8	H_6	A_1	B_3	C_2	D_7	E_9	F_8	G_4	H_6	I_5
B_2	A_8	G_1	F_7	H_3	D_6	C_5	E_4	B_2	C_1	A_3	E_8	F_7	D_9	H_5	I_4	G_6
C_3	G_4	A_7	E_1	D_2	H_5	B_6	F_8	C_3	A_2	B_1	F_9	D_8	E_7	I_6	G_5	H_4
D_4	F_3	E_6	A_5	C_8	B_1	H_7	G_2	D_4	E_6	F_5	G_1	H_3	I_2	A_7	B_9	C_8
E_5	H_1	D_8	C_4	A_6	G_3	F_2	B_7	E_5	F_4	D_6	H_2	I_1	G_3	B_8	C_7	A_9
F_6	D_7	H_4	B_8	G_5	A_2	E_3	C_1	F_6	D_5	E_4	I_3	G_2	H_1	C_9	A_8	B_7
G_7	C_6	B_3	H_2	F_1	E_8	A_4	D_5	G_7	H_9	I_8	A_4	B_6	C_5	D_1	E_3	F_2
H_8	E_2	F_5	G_6	B_4	C_7	D_1	A_3	H_8	I_7	G_9	B_5	C_4	A_6	E_2	F_1	D_3
								I_9	G_8	H_7	C_6	A_5	B_4	F_3	D_2	E_1

				10×10					
A_1	E_8	B_9	H_7	C_{10}	J_4	I_6	D_5	G_2	F_3
I_7	B_2	F_8	C_9	H_1	D_{10}	J_5	E_6	A_3	G_4
J_6	I_1	C_3	G_8	D_9	H_2	E_{10}	F_7	B_4	A_5
F_{10}	J_7	I_2	D_4	A_8	E_9	H_3	G_1	C_5	B_6
H_4	G_{10}	J_1	I_3	E_5	B_8	F_9	A_2	D_6	C_7
G_9	H_5	A_{10}	J_2	I_4	F_6	C_8	B_3	E_7	D_1
D_8	A_9	H_6	B_{10}	J_3	I_5	G_7	C_4	F_1	E_2
B_5	C_6	D_7	E_1	F_2	G_3	A_4	H_8	I_9	J_{10}
C_2	D_3	E_4	F_5	G_6	A_7	B_1	I_{10}	J_8	H_9
E_3	F_4	G_5	A_6	B_7	$\cdot C_1$	D_2	J_9	H_{10}	I_8

We note that (i, j, k, m) take on only the set (denoted by G) of n^2 values specified by the square of n by n. The model equation (6.4.1) implies the assumption of no interactions. The analysis-of-variance table is given in Table 6.4.3, where computational forms for the sums of squares are shown, and the $T_{i...}$, $T_{.j..}$, $T_{..k.}$, and $T_{...m}$ are totals corresponding to rows, columns, Latin letters, and Greek letters, and $T_{....}$ is the sum of all the n^2 observations. The $E[MS]$ column given in Table 6.4.3 is for model I analysis. For model II and model III, the $E[MS]$ column should be changed.

c) Hypersquares

The concept of using a pair of orthogonal Latin squares to form a Graeco-Latin square can be extended to the construction of hypersquares. For a square of

TABLE 6.4.3

Source	SS	d.f.	MS	E[MS]
Factor I (rows)	$SS_I = \dfrac{\sum_i T^2_{i\cdots}}{n} - \dfrac{T^2_{\cdots\cdots}}{n^2}$	$n-1$	$\dfrac{SS_I}{n-1}$	$\sigma^2 + \dfrac{n}{n-1}\displaystyle\sum_i \alpha_i^2$
Factor II (columns)	$SS_{II} = \dfrac{\sum_j T^2_{\cdot j\cdots}}{n} - \dfrac{T^2_{\cdots\cdots}}{n^2}$	$n-1$	$\dfrac{SS_{II}}{n-1}$	$\sigma^2 + \dfrac{n}{n-1}\displaystyle\sum_j \beta_j^2$
Factor III (Latin letters)	$SS_{III} = \dfrac{\sum_k T^2_{\cdot\cdot k\cdot}}{n} - \dfrac{T^2_{\cdots\cdots}}{n^2}$	$n-1$	$\dfrac{SS_{III}}{n-1}$	$\sigma^2 + \dfrac{n}{n-1}\displaystyle\sum_k \gamma_k^2$
Factor IV (Greek letters)	$SS_{IV} = \dfrac{\sum_m T^2_{\cdots m}}{n} - \dfrac{T^2_{\cdots\cdots}}{n^2}$	$n-1$	$\dfrac{SS_{IV}}{n-1}$	$\sigma^2 + \dfrac{n}{n-1}\displaystyle\sum_m \delta_m^2$
Error	$SS_E = SS_T - SS_I - SS_{II} - SS_{III} - SS_{IV}$	$(n-1)(n-3)$	$\dfrac{SS_E}{(n-1)(n-3)}$	σ^2
Total	$SS_T = \displaystyle\sum_{(i,j,k,m)\in G} y^2_{ijkm} - \dfrac{T^2_{\cdots\cdots}}{n^2}$	$n^2 - 1$		

TABLE 6.4.4

4×4				5×5				
A_{1_1}	B_{2_2}	C_{3_3}	D_{4_4}	$A_{1_{1_1}}$	$B_{2_{2_2}}$	$C_{3_{3_3}}$	$D_{4_{4_4}}$	$E_{5_{5_5}}$
B_{3_4}	A_{4_3}	D_{1_2}	C_{2_1}	$B_{3_{4_5}}$	$C_{4_{5_1}}$	$D_{5_{1_2}}$	$E_{1_{2_3}}$	$A_{2_{3_4}}$
C_{4_2}	D_{3_1}	A_{2_4}	B_{1_3}	$C_{5_{2_4}}$	$D_{1_{3_5}}$	$E_{2_{4_1}}$	$A_{3_{5_2}}$	$B_{4_{1_3}}$
D_{2_3}	C_{1_4}	B_{4_1}	A_{3_2}	$D_{2_{5_3}}$	$E_{3_{1_4}}$	$A_{4_{2_5}}$	$B_{5_{3_1}}$	$C_{1_{4_2}}$
				$E_{4_{3_2}}$	$A_{5_{4_3}}$	$B_{1_{5_4}}$	$C_{2_{1_5}}$	$D_{3_{2_1}}$

size 3×3, the pair of Latin squares which form a Graeco-Latin square for studying 4 factors is complete, and no additional factors can be introduced. For a square of size $n \times n$ and $n > 3$, a hypersquare can be constructed by superimposing 3 or up to $(n-1)$ orthogonal Latin squares if a complete set of $(n-1)$ orthogonal Latin squares is available. The maximum number of factors which can be handled in a $n \times n$ square is $(n+1)$, and the assumption of no interactions is always necessary.

For example, Table 6.4.4 gives a 4×4 hypersquare for studying 5 factors, and a 5×5 hypersquare for studying 6 factors. Consider a hypersquare of size $n \times n$. If $(n+1)$ factors are considered, since each sum of squares corresponding to a factor takes $(n-1)$ degrees of freedom, and $(n+1)(n-1) = n^2 - 1$, it will not be possible to compute the error sum of squares. In order to perform the tests of significance in such a case, a separate estimate of the error variance must be obtained. The 3×3 Graeco-Latin square also has the same weakness.

6.5 SPLIT-PLOT DESIGN

The split-plot design can be easily described by a simple example in agricultural experimentation where the terms whole plots (large areas of land) and subplots (small areas of land) are frequently used. Suppose that in a variety and fertilizer experiment on oats, 3 varieties of oats (factor B) and 4 quantitative levels of fertilizer (factor C) are used. It is inconvenient to use small plots for the varieties. Instead of completely randomizing the combinations of variety and fertilizer, we randomly assign levels of factor B to the whole plots within block I (replication I), and then randomly assign levels of factor C to the subplots within each whole plot. This procedure is repeated for the other blocks. If 3 blocks are used, a split-plot design may be laid out as in Table 6.5.1.

This type of arrangement is also of practical utility in other scientific or industrial experiments when the technical nature of an experiment necessitates the use of large experimental units for some factors and small experimental units for some other factors. We note that in the design in Table 6.5.1, the differences from one whole plot to another cannot be separated from the variety differences. In other words, the main effects of variety are confounded with the whole plots. Thus in a split-plot design, it is desirable to assign the levels of a factor which may not be of primary importance to the whole plots.

TABLE 6.5.1

Block I			Block II			Block III		
B_2	B_1	B_3	B_1	B_3	B_2	B_3	B_1	B_2
C_3	C_4	C_1	C_3	C_2	C_4	C_2	C_4	C_1
C_2	C_3	C_3	C_2	C_4	C_3	C_1	C_1	C_3
C_1	C_1	C_2	C_1	C_3	C_2	C_3	C_3	C_4
C_4	C_2	C_4	C_4	C_1	C_1	C_4	C_2	C_2

a) Model and Analysis

The model for the split-plot experiment described above is

$$y_{ijk} = \mu + \alpha_i + \beta_j + \epsilon_{ij} + \gamma_k + \delta_{ik} + \zeta_{jk} + \epsilon'_{ijk} \qquad (6.5.1)$$
$$(i = 1, 2, \ldots, a; \quad j = 1, 2, \ldots, b; \quad k = 1, 2, \ldots, c)$$

where μ is the general mean; α_i, β_j, ϵ_{ij} represent the whole plot and correspond to factor A (blocks), factor B (variety), and whole plot error; and γ_k, δ_{ik}, ζ_{jk}, ϵ'_{ijk} represent the subplot and correspond to factor C (fertilizer), AC, BC, and subplot error. We note that ϵ_{ij} is the AB interaction and ϵ'_{ijk} is the ABC interaction.

Usually the blocks are considered as random, and factors B and C are fixed. The degrees of freedom and $E[MS]$ values for analysis of variance are shown in Table 6.5.2. The $E[MS]$ column can be obtained by the general procedure in Section 5.4, and, indeed, it is the same as the left portion of Table 5.3.3, with $r = 1$ (hence σ_E^2 not retrievable). Assuming $\sigma_{AB}^2 = 0$, we can test A and B main effects against whole plot error. Assuming $\sigma_{ABC}^2 = 0$, we can test AC and

TABLE 6.5.2

Source	d.f.	$E[MS]$
A	$(a-1)$	$\sigma_E^2 + bc\sigma_A^2$
B	$(b-1)$	$\sigma_E^2 + c\sigma_{AB}^2 + ac\sigma_B^2$
Whole plot error (AB)	$(a-1)(b-1)$	$\sigma_E^2 + c\sigma_{AB}^2$
C	$(c-1)$	$\sigma_E^2 + b\sigma_{AC}^2 + ab\sigma_C^2$
AC	$(a-1)(c-1)$	$\sigma_E^2 + b\sigma_{AC}^2$
BC	$(b-1)(c-1)$	$\sigma_E^2 + \sigma_{ABC}^2 + a\sigma_{BC}^2$
Subplot error (ABC)	$(a-1)(b-1)(c-1)$	$\sigma_E^2 + \sigma_{ABC}^2$

TABLE 6.5.3

| | Block I | | | Block II | | | Block III | | |
	B_1	B_2	B_3	B_1	B_2	B_3	B_1	B_2	B_3
C_1	6	8	6	7	6	9	5	9	10
C_2	9	8	7	6	10	13	7	8	10
C_3	10	9	11	11	9	13	12	9	12
C_4	12	13	10	9	10	12	11	10	12

BC interactions against subplot error. The C main effect can be tested against AC interaction. Sometimes, the AC interaction is also considered to be negligible and not included in the model. Then it is pooled with ABC as the subplot error, and C main effect as well as BC interaction are tested against this subplot error.

The computation of sums of squares follows the methods in Chapter 2 or Chapter 5. Clearly, the analysis of split-plot experiments gives no additional difficulty if it is treated as a special type of completely crossed experiment. The important thing is to recognize the whole plot factors and subplot factors and to derive the appropriate error terms.

The concept of a split-plot design may be extended by further subdividing the subplots into sub-subplots, to which levels of another factor may be assigned at random. The arrangement may be called a *split-split-plot design*. The analysis follows the same general procedure as above. There will be one additional error term for the sub-subplot.

b) Example

The data of the split-plot experiment shown in Table 6.5.1 are listed in Table 6.5.3. Using the computing formulas in Section 2.1(b) to calculate the sums of squares, we get the results in Table 6.5.4, where the AC term has been pooled

TABLE 6.5.4

Source	SS	d.f.	MS
A (blocks)	2.00	2	1.00
B (varieties)	18.67	2	9.33
Whole plot error (AB)	24.33	4	6.08
C (fertilizers)	80.75	3	26.92
BC	15.33	6	2.55
Subplot error ($AC + ABC$)	31.67	18	1.76
Total	172.75	35	

with ABC to form the subplot error. It is immediately clear that the effect of fertilizer is highly significant, but the effect of variety does not show significance. Note that the whole plot error variance (6.08) is larger than the subplot error variance (1.76). This is usually true in a split-plot experiment, because the subplots within a whole plot are generally more homogeneous than the whole plots themselves. Therefore, in a split-plot design, if possible, the levels of a more important factor should be assigned to the subplots so that they may be compared with more precision.

If, instead of assigning varieties to whole plots, we randomly assign the twelve variety-and-fertilizer combinations in each block, the experiment would be performed in randomized blocks and would have only one error term. Obviously, the sum of the two sums of squares of error in Table 6.5.4 is the error sum of squares for the corresponding randomized-blocks experiment. This gives an error mean square of 2.54 with 22 degrees of freedom, which increases the precision of variety comparisons. Thus, if the two factors—variety and fertilizer— are of equal importance, complete randomization in each block (if there is no practical difficulty) will be the better approach.

6.6 MISSING VALUE TECHNIQUE

It happens occasionally that in a planned experiment one or more observations may be missing because of accident or practical difficulty. Consequently, the standard form of analysis for a balanced design, which was originally planned, will not be completely appropriate. However, a special technique may be used to estimate a missing value. The estimated value is used in the place of the missing observation, and some adjustment is made on the standard analysis.

a) Missing Value in Randomized Blocks

Suppose that there is one missing value in the ith block on the jth treatment of a randomized blocks design. Let $T'_{..}$, $T'_{i.}$, and $T'_{.j}$ be the grand total and block and treatment totals with one value missing. We wish to estimate the missing value, denoted by x, such that the cell with x will have minimum contribution to the error sum of squares. This is carried out by calculating the error sum of squares involving x and minimizing it with regard to x. The model equation remains the same as (6.2.1). From Section 1.6(b), we get

$$SS_E = \sum_i \sum_j y_{ij}^2 - \frac{1}{b} \sum_i \left(\sum_j y_{ij} \right)^2 - \frac{1}{a} \sum_j \left(\sum_i y_{ij} \right)^2 + \frac{1}{ab} \left(\sum_i \sum_j y_{ij} \right)^2$$

which can be written as

$$SS_E = x^2 - \frac{1}{b}(T'_{i.} + x)^2 - \frac{1}{a}(T'_{.j} + x)^2 + \frac{1}{ab}(T'_{..} + x)^2 + R \qquad (6.6.1)$$

where R represents terms not involving x. To find the value of x which makes SS_E a minimum, we differentiate (6.6.1) with respect to x and equate to zero, that is,

$$\frac{d(SS_E)}{dx} = 2x - \frac{2}{b} (T'_{i.} + x) - \frac{2}{a} (T'_{.j} + x) + \frac{2}{ab} (T'_{..} + x) = 0$$

Solving for x, we get

$$x = \frac{aT'_{i.} + bT'_{.j} - T'_{..}}{(a-1)(b-1)} \tag{6.6.2}$$

The estimated value is used to substitute for the missing observation, and the standard analysis is carried out as usual except that the degrees of freedom for the total and the error is reduced by one. However, this procedure introduces an upward bias into the treatment mean square so that the significance of treatment differences tends to be exaggerated slightly. It can be shown that the adjustment for bias in the treatment sum of squares is given by the expression

$$\frac{[T'_{i.} - (b-1)x]^2}{b(b-1)}$$

which is subtracted from the sums of squares of the treatments and the total.

The variance of the difference between the mean of the treatment with a missing observation and the mean of any other treatment is larger than the usual $2\sigma^2/a$. It may be shown that the variance is

$$\sigma^2 \left[\frac{2}{a} + \frac{b}{a(a-1)(b-1)} \right]$$

If several values are missing, an iteration procedure may be used to estimate them. Reasonable values may be inserted for the missing values except for the valve approximated by formula (6.6.2). With this approximation, formula (6.6.2) is then used for computing another missing value. This continues for the other missing values to complete one iteration. Several iterations may be required to reach stability. The standard analysis of variance may then be computed with the final values inserted, and for each missing value, one degree of freedom is reduced for the total and error sums of squares. Methods for obtaining the variances between treatment means are given in Yates [5] and Taylor [6].

b) Missing Value Formulas for Some Other Designs

In an $n \times n$ Latin square, a missing value, x, in the ith row, jth column, on the kth treatment may be estimated by

$$x = \frac{n(T'_{i..} + T'_{.j.} + T'_{..k}) - 2T'_{...}}{(n-1)(n-2)}$$

where $T'_{i..}$, $T'_{.j.}$, $T'_{..k}$, and $T'_{...}$ are the row, column, treatment totals, and grand total with one value missing. One degree of freedom is subtracted from the error. The adjustment for bias in the treatment sum of squares is

$$\frac{[T'_{...} - T'_{i..} - T'_{.j.} - (n - 1)T'_{..k}]^2}{(n - 1)^2(n - 2)^2}$$

The variance of the difference between the treatment mean with missing value and any other treatment mean is

$$\sigma^2 \left[\frac{2}{n} + \frac{1}{(n - 1)(n - 2)} \right]$$

In a split-plot design as shown in Table 6.5.1, with model equation (6.5.1), a missing value for a subplot in the ith block, jth whole plot, which receives the $B_j C_k$ treatment combination, is estimated by

$$x = \frac{aT'_{ij.} + cT'_{.jk} - T'_{.j.}}{(a - 1)(c - 1)}$$

where $T'_{ij.}$, $T'_{.jk}$, $T'_{.j.}$ are the totals with one value missing. The degrees of freedom for the subplot error is reduced by one. A small upward bias is introduced into the whole plot error sum of squares and treatment sum of squares. Methods for adjusting the biases may be found in Anderson [7].

REFERENCES

1. TARRY, G., "Le problème de 36 officieurs," *Compte Rendu de l'Association Française pour l'Avancement de Science Naturel*, **1**, 122–123 (1900); **2**, 170–203 (1901).

2. BOSE, R. C., and S. S. SHRIKHANDE, "On the Falsity of Euler's Conjecture about the Nonexistence of Two Orthogonal Latin Squares of Order $4t + 2$," *Proc. Nat. Acad. Sci. U.S.A.*, **45**, 734–737 (1959).

3. BOSE, R. C., and S. S. SHRIKHANDE, "On the Construction of Sets of Mutually Orthogonal Latin Squares and the Falsity of a Conjecture of Euler," *Trans. Amer. Math. Soc.*, **95**, 191–209 (1960).

4. BOSE, R. C., S. S. SHRIKHANDE, and E. T. PARKER, "Further Results on the Construction of Mutually Orthogonal Latin Squares and Falsity of Euler's Conjecture," *Canad. J. Math*, **12**, 189–203 (1960).

5. YATES, F., "The Analysis of Replicated Experiments when the Field Results are Incomplete," *Emp. J. Exp. Agr.*, **1**, 129–142 (1933).

6. TAYLOR, J., "Errors of Treatment Comparisons when Observations are Missing," *Nature*, **162**, 262–263 (1948).

7. ANDERSON, R. L., "Missing-Plot Techniques," *Biom. Bull.*, **2**, 41–47 (1946).

8. PARKER, E. T., "Orthogonal Latin Squares," *Proc. Nat. Acad. Sci. U.S.A.*, **45**, 859–862 (1959).

7 FRACTIONAL FACTORIAL DESIGNS AND CONFOUNDING

7.1 INTRODUCTION

Factorial designs have been widely used for carrying out experiments involving many different controllable factors so that the effect of several factors on the response or dependent variable can be evaluated jointly and efficiently. However, in a complete factorial design the required number of measurements is often beyond the resources of the investigator, or it is not feasible to carry out, or it gives more precision in the estimates of the main effects than necessary, or estimates of higher-order interaction effects are of less interest. For example, in a 2^8 complete factorial design, each main effect is an average over 128 combinations of the other factors. Perhaps $\frac{1}{2}$ or $\frac{1}{4}$ or $\frac{1}{8}$ of these combinations would be sufficient.

In a 2^K factorial design, the 2^K combinations provide independent minimum variance estimates of the general mean and of the $2^K - 1$ effects:

K
$\qquad$ main effects

$\dfrac{K(K-1)}{2}$
$\qquad$ 2-factor interaction effects

$\dfrac{K(K-1)(K-2)}{2 \cdot 3}$
$\qquad$ 3-factor interaction effects

$\vdots$

$\dfrac{K(K-1)(K-2)\cdots(K-h+1)}{h!}$
$\qquad$ h-factor interaction effects

and a single K-factor interaction effect. When K is large, the wealth of such estimates surely becomes a burden for interpretation. The interaction effects above second order (3-factor) are difficult to explain.

In many practical situations, a certain degree of continuity and regularity can be expected in regard to the manner in which the response varies, and the higher-order interaction effects involving three or more factors are often negligible. Thus a design requiring only a definite fraction of a complete factorial may be used to estimate the main effects and 2-factor interaction effects in such a way that these are confused only with higher-order interactions.

In screening situations where the number of variables which may have some influence on the response is large but only a subset of variables might be important, then a fractional factorial design which may be regarded as a complete factorial for a smaller number of factors is very useful.

7.2 FACTORIAL DESIGNS WITH FACTORS AT TWO LEVELS (THE 2^K SYSTEMS)

a) Special Notations and Definitions

For the 2^K series of factorial designs, some special notations and definitions may be employed to facilitate our discussion. For convenience, consider a 2^3 design as an example. The 8 combinations comprising the design are shown in the following:

$$1$$
$$a$$
$$b$$
$$ab$$
$$c$$
$$ac$$
$$bc$$
$$abc$$

The "1" represents the treatment with all factors at the low levels. In each of the remaining treatment combinations, the high level of any factor is denoted by the corresponding letter and the low level is implied by absence of the corresponding letter.

We shall now introduce special definitions of main effects and interactions in the 2^K systems. These definitions are convenient conventions, and each of them will produce twice the value of an effect given by the definition in Chapter 1. However, the sums of squares will be the same as before.

The effect of changing A when the other two factors are at the low levels is

$$a - 1$$

Similarly, the effect of changing A when B is at the high level and C at the low level is

$$ab - b$$

The effect of changing A when B is low and C is high is

$$ac - c$$

Finally, the effect of changing A when B and C are both at the high level is

$$abc - bc$$

The *main effect of A* for the whole experiment is defined to be the mean of these four, namely

$$\tfrac{1}{4}(a + ab + ac + abc - 1 - b - c - bc)$$

When C is at the low level, the interaction AB is defined to be one-half the difference between the effects of A at the two levels of B, that is,

$$\tfrac{1}{2}[(ab - b) - (a - 1)]$$

Similarly, when C is at the high level, the interaction AB is defined to be

$$\tfrac{1}{2}[(abc - bc) - (ac - c)]$$

Hence the AB *interaction* for the whole experiment (over both levels of C) is the average of these two:

$$AB = \tfrac{1}{4}(ab + 1 + abc + c - b - a - bc - ac)$$

The ABC *interaction* is defined to be one-half the difference between AB interactions for the two different levels of C:

$$ABC = \tfrac{1}{4}[(abc - bc) - (ac - c) - (ab - b) + (a - 1)]$$
$$= \tfrac{1}{4}(abc - bc - ac + c - ab + b + a - 1)$$

Thus, if AB is the same for both levels of C, ABC is zero.

Other main effects and interactions can be defined similarly, and the process can be extended to a general 2^K experiment. There is a *formal mathematical expression for representing interactions* in a general 2^K experiment. It is written as

$$\frac{1}{2^{K-1}}(a \pm 1)(b \pm 1)(c \pm 1)\cdots$$

with "+" for absence and "−" for presence of the corresponding letter in the interaction under consideration. This symbolic form is expanded by using ordinary algebra.

Another systematic way of forming main effects and interactions is useful. In the 2^3 design, denote the low levels by minus signs and the high levels by plus signs in any treatment combination. An effect matrix can be generated easily from this representation by signs as shown in Table 7.2.1.

TABLE 7.2.1

Treatment combination	Representation by signs			Effect matrix							
	A	B	C	Mean	A	B	AB	C	AC	BC	ABC
1	−	−	−	+	−	−	+	−	+	+	−
a	+	−	−	+	+	−	−	−	−	+	+
b	−	+	−	+	−	+	−	−	+	−	+
ab	+	+	−	+	+	+	+	−	−	−	−
c	−	−	+	+	−	−	+	+	−	−	+
ac	+	−	+	+	+	−	−	+	+	−	−
bc	−	+	+	+	−	+	−	+	−	+	−
abc	+	+	+	+	+	+	+	+	+	+	+

An interaction effect column is obtained by multiplying the columns of those factors appearing in the interaction. To compute any effect, we simply associate the particular effect column with the treatments and multiply the algebraic sum by $(\frac{1}{2})^{K-1}$. For example,

$$ABC = \tfrac{1}{4}(-1 + a + b - ab + c - ac - bc + abc)$$

The method can be extended to a general 2^K system.

Note that the effect matrix in Table 7.2.1 has several important properties: (1) The product of any two columns yields another column included in the matrix. (2) The square of any column is equal to the mean column. (3) If any column is multiplied by the mean column, it remains unchanged. (4) Except for the mean column, the number of plus and minus signs are equal in each column. (5) The sum of products of signs of any two columns (pairwise) is zero. Properties (1) through (3) lead to group theoretic considerations to be discussed in Section 7.4. Properties (4) and (5) are implied by the orthogonality of the effects.

Note also that the products of the effects are formed modulo 2. For example,

$$A \times AB = A^2B = B, \qquad AB \times ABC = A^2B^2C = C$$

That is, the exponent can be only zero or one. If it is greater than one, we reduce it by multiples of 2 until it becomes zero or one.

b) Yates' Method

Yates [10] developed a simple scheme for computing the effects for a 2^K factorial experiment. The scheme is described symbolically in Table 7.2.2 for a 2^3 experiment. In Table 7.2.2, the order of the treatment combinations must be maintained. For actual computation, the symbols of treatment combinations are replaced by corresponding total responses. The first half of column (1) is obtained by adding the responses in adjacent pairs. The second half of column (1) is obtained by subtracting the responses in pairs, always subtracting the first from the second (of the pair). Column (2) is obtained from column (1) in the same manner. This process is carried out K times for a 2^K experiment. Clearly, column (3) does give the proper expressions for the effects of a 2^3 experiment. To get the sums of squares for a 2^K experiment with r replications, the values in column (K) are squared and divided by $r2^K$. Note that the first sum of squares, $(\text{Total})^2/r2^K$, is the correction term given in Section 2.1(a). Following the concepts and notations in Section 3.1, we may consider the $(2^K - 1)$ effects in a 2^K experiment as a set of orthogonal contrasts, each with a single degree of freedom, and for an effect $\hat{\psi}$, we have

$$SS_{\hat{\psi}} = \frac{(\sum_i c_i T_i)^2}{r\sum_i c_i^2}$$

where T_i are the total responses, and c_i are either $+1$ or -1. Therefore the divisor for each sum of squares is $r2^K$.

TABLE 7.2.2

Treatment combination	(1)	(2)	(3)
1	$1 + a$	$1 + a + b + ab$	$1 + a + b + ab + c + ac + bc + abc =$ Total
a	$b + ab$	$c + ac + bc + abc$	$a - 1 + ab - b + ac - c + abc - bc = 4A$
b	$c + ac$	$a - 1 + ab - b$	$b + ab - 1 - a + bc + abc - c - ac = 4B$
ab	$bc + abc$	$ac - c + abc - bc$	$ab - b - a + 1 + abc - bc - ac + c = 4AB$
c	$a - 1$	$b + ab - 1 - a$	$c + ac + bc + abc - 1 - a - b - ab = 4C$
ac	$ab - b$	$bc + abc - c - ac$	$ac - c + abc - bc - a + 1 - ab + b = 4AC$
bc	$ac - c$	$ab - b - a + 1$	$bc + abc - c - ac - b - ab + 1 + a = 4BC$
abc	$abc - bc$	$abc - bc - ac + c$	$abc - bc - ac + c - ab + b + a - 1 = 4ABC$

TABLE 7.2.3

Treatment	Total	(1)	(2)	(3)	Effect (3)/12	SS (3)²/24
1	144	234	336	720		21600
a	90	102	384	−120	−10	600
b	60	210	−72	−168	−14	1176
ab	42	174	−48	144	12	864
c	144	−54	−132	48	4	96
ac	66	−18	−36	24	2	24
bc	72	−78	36	96	8	384
abc	102	30	108	72	6	216

To fix ideas, let us use the above procedure on a numerical example. A set of data is provided in Table 6.2.4 where the treatments $t_1, t_2, \ldots, t_8$ will be identified as the 8 treatment combinations of a 2^3 factorial and correspond to 1, a, b, ab, c, ac, bc, abc, respectively. The treatment totals (from Table 6.2.4), steps of taking sums and differences in pairs, average effects, and sums of squares are all shown in Table 7.2.3. The seven sums of squares (from the second to the last in the SS column) add up exactly to the total treatment sum of squares, 3360, with 7 degrees of freedom, which was shown in Table 6.2.6. The error sum of squares with 14 degrees of freedom and the blocks sum of squares with 2 degrees of freedom remain to be 135.36 and 48, as given in Table 6.2.6.

7.3 FRACTIONAL FACTORIAL DESIGNS WITH FACTORS AT TWO LEVELS
a) Basic Concepts

The basic concepts of fractional factorial designs with factors at two levels may be explained by a simple example. In a 2^3 design, a total of 8 degrees of freedom are available for estimating the general mean and the effects. Each effect is estimated by one degree of freedom. If one-half of the treatment combinations are selected for the experiment, obviously some loss of information or precision cannot be avoided. It is reasonable to consider sacrificing the information on the highest-order interaction ABC. The 8 terms for estimating ABC can be grouped into two sets, one with positive signs and another with negative signs:

$$+a, \quad +b, \quad +c, \quad +abc$$
$$-1, \quad -ab, \quad -ac, \quad -bc$$

Suppose that we take the treatments with positive signs and estimate the effects from them. An effect matrix is generated in Table 7.3.1, from which it is seen immediately that the estimates of A, B, and C are mutually independent. The ABC interaction is the same as the general mean; hence its information is lost. Furthermore, the estimates of the following pairs of effects are also identical; therefore they are confounded (or confused) with one another, that is,

$$A = BC$$
$$B = AC$$
$$AB = C \tag{7.3.1}$$

TABLE 7.3.1

Treatment combination	Effect matrix							
	Mean	A	B	AB	C	AC	BC	ABC
a	$+$	$+$	$-$	$-$	$-$	$-$	$+$	$+$
b	$+$	$-$	$+$	$-$	$-$	$+$	$-$	$+$
c	$+$	$-$	$-$	$+$	$+$	$-$	$-$	$+$
abc	$+$	$+$	$+$	$+$	$+$	$+$	$+$	$+$

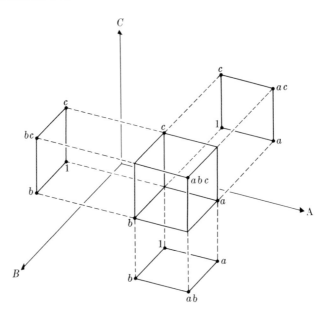

FIG. 7.3.1

The two effects such as A and BC represented by the same function of available responses are conventionally called *aliases*. The ABC interaction is called the *defining contrast*. The price for reducing half of the number of measurements is that each main effect estimation is entangled with a two-factor interaction and the information on ABC interaction is lost. The aliases system which describes the entangling situation should be carefully checked by the experimenter before he adopts a fractional factorial design.

The $\frac{1}{2}$-replicate of a 2^3 factorial supplies a complete factorial in any one of three possible pairs of factors. This becomes apparent if we observe that the four treatment combinations provide a complete factorial in two factors after any one factor is ignored. This can be seen even more simply by considering the alias pairs in (7.3.1). If any one of the factors is dropped, one member of each pair will vanish; thus the resulting design is shown to be a complete factorial. This basic structure is also clearly revealed by a geometric consideration. In Fig. 7.3.1, the $\frac{1}{2}$-replicate of a 2^3 factorial is represented by dotted vertices of a cube, and each projection of it into a two dimensional space produces a square representing a complete factorial.

Suppose that we choose the treatment combinations 1, ab, ac, and bc instead of a, b, c, and abc for the $\frac{1}{2}$-replicate of a 2^3 factorial. Then the effects in an alias pair will have opposite signs. For example,

$$A: ab + ac - 1 - bc$$
$$BC: bc + 1 - ab - ac$$

so

$$A = -BC$$

The sums of squares due to A and BC, of course, are the same.

We have used a $\frac{1}{2}$-replicate of a 2^3 factorial to illustrate the basic properties of fractional factorial designs. However, in practice it is generally not advisable to conduct a $\frac{1}{2}$-replicate of a 2^3 experiment, since each main effect is confounded with a 2-factor interaction. When the number of factors increases, we will be in a better position to avoid confounding a main effect with a 2-factor interaction, or confounding a 2-factor interaction with another 2-factor interaction.

b) Examples

A $\frac{1}{2}$-replicate of a 2^4 factorial can be constructed by using defining contrast $ABCD$. The two $\frac{1}{2}$-replicates are shown in Table 7.3.2. Now each main effect has a 3-factor interaction as its alias. However, each 2-factor interaction has another 2-factor interaction as its alias. The alias of any effect can be found by multiplying (modulo 2) the given effect with the defining contrast. For example, for defining contrast $ABCD$, the alias of A is

$$A \times ABCD = A^2BCD = BCD$$

and the alias of AB is

$$AB \times ABCD = A^2B^2CD = CD$$

TABLE 7.3.2

$\frac{1}{2}$-replicate (1)	$\frac{1}{2}$-replicate (2)
1	a
ab	b
bd	c
ad	d
bc	abc
ac	acd
cd	abd
$abcd$	bcd

In Table 7.3.2, the $\frac{1}{2}$-replicate (1) contains the treatment combination "1," and is called the *principal block*. Note that all treatment combinations in the principal block have an even number (including zero) of letters in common with the defining contrast $ABCD$, and the other $\frac{1}{2}$-replicate can be generated by multiplying every treatment combination in the principal block with any treatment combination which is not in the principal block and replacing the square of any letter with 1. This fact also leads to more theoretical generalizations in the next section.

TABLE 7.3.3

1	ae	cd	$abce$
ab	bc	ce	$abde$
ac	bd	de	$acde$
ad	be	$abcd$	$bcde$

Following the same principles as discussed above, we can easily write down a $\frac{1}{2}$-replicate of a 2^5 factorial by using $ABCDE$ as the defining contrast. The principal block is given in Table 7.3.3. Now if we assume that the 3-factor interactions are zero, then we can use the available 15 degrees of freedom to estimate the main effects and 2-factor interactions separately. However, unless we can assume some of the 2-factor interactions to be zero, an error sum of squares cannot be formed from the experiment.

TABLE 7.3.4

1	be	abcd	acef
ab	bf	abce	adef
ac	cd	abcf	bcde
ad	ce	abde	bcdf
ae	cf	abdf	bcef
af	de	abef	bdef
bc	df	acde	cdef
bd	ef	acdf	abcdef

TABLE 7.3.5

1	bef
abcdef	acd
cdef	bcd
ab	aef
abdf	ade
ce	bcf
abce	acf
df	bde

The principal block of a $\frac{1}{2}$-replicate of a 2^6 factorial, with $ABCDEF$ as the defining contrast, is shown in Table 7.3.4. Each main effect has a 5-factor interaction as alias, and each 2-factor interaction has a 4-factor interaction as alias. The twenty 3-factor interactions form ten alias pairs among themselves. Assuming that the 4-factor and 5-factor interactions are negligible, we can estimate all main effects and 2-factor interactions separately. If the 3-factor interactions can be also neglected, the ten degrees of freedom for the ten alias pairs may be used to estimate the error mean square.

Suppose that we want to use only a $\frac{1}{4}$-replicate of a 2^6 factorial instead of a $\frac{1}{2}$-replicate. Since another interaction effect must be used as a defining contrast to divide the 32 combinations in Table 7.3.4 into two halves and since its information is lost, naturally one may wish to try a 5-factor interaction, say $BCDEF$. Selecting the 16 combinations from Table 7.3.4, which have an even number of letters in common with $BCDEF$, we get

$$1, \quad bc, \quad bd, \quad be, \quad bf, \quad cd, \quad ce, \quad cf,$$
$$de, \quad df, \quad ef, \quad bcde, \quad bcdf, \quad bcef, \quad bdef, \quad cdef$$

It is immediately seen that a is missing from all 16 combinations (that is, factor A will be tested at the higher level throughout the experiment), so we have unintentionally constructed a design from which the main effect A cannot be estimated. In other words, A becomes also a defining contrast. Note that A is the *generalized interaction* of $ABCDEF$ and $BCDEF$, that is,

$$ABCDEF \times BCDEF = AB^2C^2D^2E^2F^2 = A$$

This shows that in order to construct a $\frac{1}{4}$-replicate of a 2^K factorial, we can choose any two effects as defining contrasts, and their generalized interaction is also a defining contrast.

With this fact in mind, we soon find, by trial and error, that we cannot avoid confounding 2-factor interactions with some other 2-factor interactions in a $\frac{1}{4}$-replicate of a 2^6 factorial and that the best way is to choose two 4-factor interactions which have two letters in common, such as $ABCE$ and $ABDF$, as defining contrasts. Table 7.3.5 gives the principal block of such a design. Note that each of the 16 combinations has an even number of letters in common with $ABCE$ and $ABDF$. To get a second $\frac{1}{4}$-replicate, multiply all treatment com-

TABLE 7.3.6

Effect		Aliases	
A	BCE	BDF	$ACDEF$
B	ACE	ADF	$BCDEF$
C	ABE	$ABCDF$	DEF
D	$ABCDE$	ABF	CEF
E	ABC	$ABDEF$	CDF
F	$ABCEF$	ABD	CDE
AB	CE	DF	$ABCDEF$
AC	BE	$BCDF$	$ADEF$
AD	$BCDE$	BF	$ACEF$
AE	BC	$BDEF$	$ACDF$
AF	$BCEF$	BD	$ACDE$
CD	$ABDE$	$ABCF$	EF
CF	$ABEF$	$ABCD$	DE
ACF	BEF	BCD	ADE
ACD	BDE	BCF	AEF

binations in the first quarter by any combination which does not appear in the first quarter with the convention that the square of any letter is replaced by 1. To generate a third $\frac{1}{4}$-replicate, multiply the combinations in the first quarter by any combination which is not contained in either the first quarter or the second quarter. Any one of the four quarters may be used in practice. However, the principal block is conventionally used with convenience in theoretical formulations, which will be treated in the next section.

Each effect in a $\frac{1}{4}$-replicate of a 2^K factorial has 3 aliases and can be found by multiplying (modulo 2) the given effect with the defining contrasts. For example, the aliases of A in the above design are

$$A \times ABCE = A^2BCE = BCE$$
$$A \times ABDF = A^2BDF = BDF$$
$$A \times CDEF = ACDEF$$

The complete alias system of the above design is listed in Table 7.3.6. Clearly, if 3-factor and 5-factor interactions can be ignored, the design gives valid estimates of the main effects. There are two sets of aliases involving only 3-factor interactions. The error mean square may be formed from these two sets or from a combination of these two sets with some or all of the alias sets involving 2-factor interactions, provided that additional assumptions can be made on the 2-factor interactions.

7.4 FINITE GROUPS AND FRACTIONAL FACTORIAL DESIGNS WITH FACTORS AT TWO LEVELS

The principles of fractional replication for the 2^K system can be easily explained in terms of some basic concepts in *group theory*. The concept of a *group* is perhaps the simplest one in abstract algebra. A group G is a nonempty set of elements a, b, c, $\ldots$, for which a *binary operation* $*$ is defined so that the following axioms are satisfied:

1) If a and b are in G, there exists one and only one c in G such that $a * b = c$.

2) $(a * b) * c = a * (b * c)$ for all a, b, c in G.

3) There exists an *identity element* e in G such that $a * e = a = e * a$ for every a in G.

4) To each a in G there corresponds a unique *inverse* a^{-1} such that

$$a^{-1} * a = a * a^{-1} = e.$$

The simplicity of these axioms is deceptive, because they really impose a great deal of structure on the set G. A group G is said to be *finite* if the number of elements in G is finite, and the number of elements is called the *order* of G. A group G is called *commutative* (or *abelian*) if

$$a * b = b * a$$

for all a and b in G.

A nonempty subset S of a group G is a *subgroup* if S is itself a group with respect to the binary operation of G. Two groups G and G' are said to be *isomorphic* if there exists a *one-to-one mapping* $a \rightarrow a'$ of G onto G' such that $(a * b)' = a' * b'$, and the mapping is called an *isomorphism* of G onto G'. This definition implies that we arrive at the same result if we first perform the group operation on two elements in G and then take the image in G' or if we first take the images in G' and then carry out the group operation on these images. Isomorphism does not simply mean that there is some close resemblance between the two groups. It means that the two systems have exactly the same structure.

In a 2^K system, if we define a multiplication operation as in ordinary algebra and impose the additional condition that

$$a^2 = b^2 = c^2 = \cdots = 1$$

the product of any two treatment combinations is also a treatment combination in the system; for example,

$$(ab)(c) = abc$$
$$(ab)(ab) = 1$$

There are 2^K treatment combinations, and they form a *finite Abelian group of order* 2^K with 1 as the identity.

The general mean, main effects, and interactions estimated by 2^K degrees of freedom may be represented by elements A, B, C, $\ldots$, AB, AC, $\ldots$ of a group subject to the condition that

$$A^2 = B^2 = C^2 = \cdots = I$$

The identity element I corresponds to the general mean. The *effect group* and *treatment combination group* are isomorphic.

The concept of a subgroup is useful in the study of fractional factorial designs. Consider for an example the 2^6 system, a subset consisting of the following elements may be chosen as a $\frac{1}{4}$-replicate (see the procedure discussed in Section 7.3):

$$1, \quad abcdef, \quad cdef, \quad ab, \quad abdf, \quad ce, \quad abce, \quad df$$
$$bef, \quad acd, \quad bcd, \quad aef, \quad ade, \quad bcf, \quad acf, \quad bde$$

It can be easily verified that they satisfy the definition of a subgroup. In constructing this design, the interactions $ABCE$, $ABDF$, $CDEF$ have been chosen to be confounded with the general mean. We write

$$I = ABCE = ABDF = CDEF$$

which is called the *fundamental identity* (or defining contrasts). The effects in this identity form a subgroup of the effect group, and sometimes it is called the *alias subgroup*. The aliases of any effect may be written down directly by multiplying the given effect by elements of the alias subgroup, for example,

$$A = BCE = BDF = ACDEF$$

as discussed earlier.

A certain relationship between subgroups is important. Two elements of either the treatment or the effect group are said to be orthogonal when the number of letters they have in common is even. This convenient definition is extended to cover orthogonality of an element of one subgroup and an element of another. Thus, for example, $abcdef$ is orthogonal to $ABCE$, $ABDF$, and $CDEF$.

If we select a subgroup, S, of order 2^P, of the effect group in a 2^K system, then we may find elements of another subgroup, T, of the treatment group, which are orthogonal to every element of S. The subgroup, T, of order 2^{K-P} is called the *complete orthogonal subgroup*. The crucial part of the construction of a 2^{-P} fractional factorial design in a 2^K system is the selection of a suitable subgroup S as the alias subgroup. The determination of the complete orthogonal subgroup of treatment combinations of order 2^{K-P} follows easily, and it is generally used as the first 2^{-P} fractional replicate. As noted earlier, this fraction is called the principal block. To obtain another fractional replicate, multiply all treatment combinations in the principal block by any combination of letters which does not appear in the principal block with the usual rule that the square of any letter is replaced by 1. However, this generated fractional replicate is not a subgroup, since it does not contain the identity element "1."

7.5 THE ANALYSIS OF FRACTIONAL FACTORIAL DESIGNS WITH FACTORS AT TWO LEVELS

The analysis of fractional factorial experiments with factors at two levels can be carried out by generating an effect matrix consisting of plus and minus signs as described in Section 7.2.

A more convenient method is based on the fact that a 2^{-P} replicate of a 2^K factorial experiment contains a complete replication of a 2^{K-P} factorial design of $K - P$ factors if P factors are ignored. The analysis of variance of a 2^{-P} replicate of a 2^K factorial experiment can be reduced to that of a complete factorial by selecting a subset of the factors for which the experiment is a complete replicate. With a $\frac{1}{2}$-replicate, one factor will be ignored temporarily; with a $\frac{1}{4}$-replicate, two factors; with a $\frac{1}{8}$-replicate, three factors; etc. After the effects and sums of squares are computed, we introduce the other factors by using the alias system. Identifying the factors to be temporarily ignored can be accomplished easily by sorting the factorial level combinations into a certain order. A numerical example will clarify the procedure.

TABLE 7.5.1

Observation	Treatment combination	
1.52	1	000000
2.03	ab	110000
0.58	acd	101100
1.03	bcd	011100
1.57	ce	001010
2.03	$abce$	111010
0.52	ade	100110
1.02	bde	010110
3.53	acf	101001
4.09	bcf	011001
2.53	df	000101
3.01	$abdf$	110101
3.55	aef	100011
4.00	bef	010011
2.59	$cdef$	001111
3.03	$abcdef$	111111

The data of a $\frac{1}{4}$-replicate of a 2^6 experiment are given in Table 7.5.1. The design has defining contrasts $ABCE$, $ABDF$, $CDEF$, and has been discussed in Sections 7.3 and 7.4. The treatment combinations are also represented by combinations of 0's and 1's which may be used as an aid for sorting the data mechanically into the order shown in Table 7.5.1. The analysis is carried out in Table 7.5.2 by using Yates' method (described in Section 7.2) for 4 factors. In the treatment combination column, a and c are enclosed in parentheses to indicate that the factors A and C are ignored temporarily. The process of taking sums and differences in pairs is followed through in columns (1) to (4). Dividing the quantities in column (4) by 8 (that is, 2^{4-1}) gives the effects. Squaring the quantities in column (4) and dividing by 16 (that is, 2^4) yields the sums of squares. To identify the effects and sums of squares, we use the alias system from Table 7.3.6. For easy reference, the system is shown here again. Note

TABLE 7.5.2

Treatment combination	Observation	(1)	(2)	(3)	(4)	Effect (4)/8	SS (4)²/16	Alias system
1	1.52	3.55	5.16	10.30	36.63		83.859802	$I = ABCE = ABDF = CDEF$
(a)b	2.03	1.61	5.14	26.33	3.85	0.4812	0.926406	$B = ACE = ADF = BCDEF$
(a)(c)d	0.58	3.60	13.16	1.92	-8.01	-1.0012	4.010006	$D = ABCDE = ABF = CEF$
b(c)d	1.03	1.54	13.17	1.93	-0.11	-0.0137	0.000756	$BD = AF = BCEF = ACDE$
(c)e	1.57	7.62	0.96	-4.00	-0.01	-0.0012	0.000006	$E = ABC = ABDEF = CDE$
(a)b(c)e	2.03	5.54	0.96	-4.01	-0.15	-0.0187	0.001406	$BE = AC = BCDF = ADEF$
(a)de	0.52	7.55	1.04	-0.02	0.03	0.0037	0.000056	$DE = CF = ABEF = ABCD$
bde	1.02	5.62	0.89	-0.09	0.17	0.0212	0.001806	$BDE = ACD = BCF = AEF$
(a)(c)f	3.53	0.51	-1.94	-0.02	16.03	2.0037	16.060056	$F = ABCEF = ABD = CDE$
b(c)f	4.09	0.45	-2.06	0.01	0.01	0.0012	0.000006	$BF = AD = BCDE = ACEF$
df	2.53	0.46	-2.08	0.00	-0.01	-0.0012	0.000006	$DF = AB = CE = ABCDEF$
(a)bdf	3.01	0.50	-1.93	-0.15	-0.07	-0.0087	0.000306	$BDF = A = BCE = ACDEF$
(a)ef	3.55	0.56	-0.06	-0.12	0.03	0.0037	0.000056	$EF = CD = ABDE = ABCF$
bef	4.00	0.48	0.04	0.15	-0.15	-0.0187	0.001406	$BEF = ACF = BCD = ADE$
(c)def	2.59	0.45	-0.08	0.10	0.27	0.0337	0.004556	$DEF = C = ABE = ABCDF$
(a)b(c)def	3.03	0.44	-0.01	0.07	-0.03	-0.0037	0.000056	$BDEF = AE = BC = ACDF$

that although we ignored factors A and C in the computations, the effects involving A, or C, or both are now identified.

A quick inspection on the sums of squares (with one degree of freedom each) reveals that factors B, D, and F stand out. Formal F-tests, using the two alias sets involving only 3-factor interactions (if we assume 3-factor interactions to be negligible) or using these combined with the seven alias sets involving 2-factor interactions (if we can also assume 2-factor interactions to be negligible) as the error term, will show that the main effects due to B, D, and F are highly significant.

7.6 FACTORIAL DESIGNS WITH FACTORS AT 3 LEVELS (THE 3^K SYSTEMS)

a) Special Notations and Properties

For the purpose of studying the fractionization of a 3^K factorial design, we need to discuss some special combinatorial properties of the 3^K systems. Consider a 3^2 arrangement as an example. The levels (i, j) of factors A and B are denoted by 0, 1, and 2. There are 9 treatment combinations which form a 3×3 square:

		B	
	(00)	(01)	(02)
A	(10)	(11)	(12)
	(20)	(21)	(22)

The AB interaction sum of squares which has 4 degrees of freedom can be partitioned into 4 components with a single degree of freedom each by the methods described in Chapter 3. However, there is another way of dividing the AB sum of squares into 2 components with 2 degrees of freedom each, and it will be useful for constructing fractional factorial designs with factors at 3 levels. This additional method of partitioning makes use of the basic properties of a 3×3 Graeco-Latin square.

Suppose that we superimpose a 3×3 Graeco-Latin square on the 9 treatment combinations of a 3^2 factorial as shown in Table 7.6.1.

The comparisons among rows:

$$(A)_{i=0} = (00) + (01) + (02)$$
$$(A)_{i=1} = (10) + (11) + (12)$$
$$(A)_{i=2} = (20) + (21) + (22)$$

give the main effect of A. The comparisons among columns:

$$(B)_{j=0} = (00) + (10) + (20)$$
$$(B)_{j=1} = (01) + (11) + (21)$$
$$(B)_{j=2} = (02) + (12) + (22)$$

give the main effect of B.

TABLE 7.6.1

		B		
		0	1	2
A	0	X_α (00)	Y_γ (01)	Z_β (02)
	1	Y_β (10)	Z_α (11)	X_γ (12)
	2	Z_γ (20)	X_β (21)	Y_α (22)

Consider the grouping of treatment combinations according to Latin letters:

$$(AB)_{i+j=0} = (00) + (12) + (21)$$
$$(AB)_{i+j=1} = (10) + (01) + (22)$$
$$(AB)_{i+j=2} = (02) + (11) + (20)$$

For the first set of 3 treatment combinations, $i + j = 0$, 3, and 3, that is, 0 modulo 3; for the second set, $i + j = 1$ modulo 3; and for the third set, $i + j = 2$ modulo 3. The comparisons among these three sets give 2 degrees of freedom. Similarly, the grouping of treatment combinations according to Greek letters yields

$$(AB^2)_{i+2j=0} = (00) + (11) + (22)$$
$$(AB^2)_{i+2j=1} = (10) + (02) + (21)$$
$$(AB^2)_{i+2j=2} = (01) + (20) + (12)$$

where $i + 2j = 0$, 1, and 2 (modulo 3), respectively, for the first, second, and third set of treatment combinations. The comparisons among these three sets again give 2 degrees of freedom.

The sums of squares may be computed in the following way: for A,

$$\frac{(A)^2_{i=0} + (A)^2_{i=1} + (A)^2_{i=2}}{3} - \frac{[(A)_{i=0} + (A)_{i=1} + (A)_{i=2}]^2}{9}$$

similarly for B;
for AB,

$$\frac{(AB)^2_{i+j=0} + (AB)^2_{i+j=1} + (AB)^2_{i+j=2}}{3}$$

$$- \frac{[(AB)_{i+j=0} + (AB)_{i+j=1} + (AB)_{i+j=2}]^2}{9}$$

similarly for AB^2.

It is a convenient convention to use the symbol AB for the component, with 2 degrees of freedom, corresponding to $i + j = 0$, 1, and 2, and to use AB^2 for

TABLE 7.6.2

		B		
		0	1	2
	0	25	28	22
A	1	21	21	15
	2	20	14	14

TABLE 7.6.3

Source	SS	d.f.
A	126	2
B	42	2
AB	24	4

TABLE 7.6.4

Source	SS	d.f.
Rows	126	2
Columns	42	2
Latin letters	18	2
Greek letters	6	2

the component, with 2 degrees of freedom, corresponding to $i + 2j = 0, 1,$ and 2. We observe that the treatment combinations specified by the equations

$$2i + 2j = 0, 1, 2 \text{ (modulo 3)}$$

for A^2B^2 are identical to those for AB; and the treatment combinations specified by

$$2i + j = 0, 1, 2 \text{ (modulo 3)}$$

for A^2B are the same as those for AB^2. In using symbols to represent components with pairs of degrees of freedom, we adopt the rule that the first letter of a symbol must be unity.

b) A 3^2 Factorial Design and a 3 × 3 Graeco-Latin Square

In a Graeco-Latin square, the comparisons among the Latin letter totals and the comparisons among the Greek letter totals are mutually orthogonal, and both are orthogonal to rows and columns. Their sums of squares must add up to the AB interaction sum of squares with 4 degrees of freedom. For example, consider the data of a 3^2 experiment in Table 7.6.2. The sums of squares calculated from a two-way analysis are shown in Table 7.6.3. Following the analysis of a Graeco-Latin square on the same data, we get the results in Table 7.6.4. Note that $18 + 6 = 24 =$ sum of squares of AB with 4 degrees of freedom.

c) Extensions

The above process may be extended to the general 3^K system. In the general case, we have $(3^K - 1)/2$ symbols, each with 2 degrees of freedom. For example, for 3 factors A, B, and C with levels (i, j, k), we have the results in Table 7.6.5, where the left side of each set of equations specifying the treatment

TABLE 7.6.5

Main effect or component of interaction	d.f.	Left side of equations specifying the treatments
A	2	i
B	2	j
AB	2	$i + j$
AB^2	2	$i + 2j$
C	2	k
AC	2	$i + k$
AC^2	2	$i + 2k$
BC	2	$j + k$
BC^2	2	$j + 2k$
ABC	2	$i + j + k$
ABC^2	2	$i + j + 2k$
AB^2C	2	$i + 2j + k$
AB^2C^2	2	$i + 2j + 2k$

combinations is shown; the corresponding right side has, of course, values 0, 1, 2 (modulo 3). The partitioning of an interaction into components of 2 degrees of freedom by this process is simply a convenient mathematical device to extract orthogonal components of an interaction. These components have no concrete physical interpretation. Testing each of these separately for significance is generally not meaningful.

The sums of squares are obtained as before. For example, for ABC^2, we have

$$\frac{(ABC^2)^2_{i+j+2k=0} + (ABC^2)^2_{i+j+2k=1} + (ABC^2)^2_{i+j+2k=2}}{9} - \frac{(\text{Grand total})^2}{27}$$

Note that for each subtotal such as $(ABC^2)_{i+j+2k=0}$, 9 responses are available; and for the grand total, 27 responses are available. The particular way of grouping treatment combinations simplifies the calculations.

The combinatorial properties of the 3^K systems (and indeed also of the 2^K systems) can be generalized to the general ρ^K system with ρ as a prime number. Denote the treatment combination by $(j_1, j_2, \ldots, j_K)$. The j_i's are the factorial levels having values from 0 to $(\rho - 1)$. All numbers are reduced modulo ρ. The $(\rho^K - 1)$ degrees of freedom may be partitioned into $(\rho^K - 1)/(\rho - 1)$ sets of $(\rho - 1)$ degrees of freedom. Each set of $(\rho - 1)$ degrees of freedom is given by the comparisons among the ρ sets of ρ^{K-1} treatment combinations specified by the following equations:

$$\left.\begin{aligned}
\alpha_1 j_1 + \alpha_2 j_2 + \cdots + \alpha_K j_K &= 0, \\
\alpha_1 j_1 + \alpha_2 j_2 + \cdots + \alpha_K j_K &= 1, \\
&\vdots \\
\alpha_1 j_1 + \alpha_2 j_2 + \cdots + \alpha_K j_K &= \rho - 1
\end{aligned}\right\} \quad (\text{modulo } \rho)$$

The α_i's must be positive integers between 0 and $(\rho - 1)$, and not all zero. For uniqueness, the convention is that the first α_i which is not zero equals unity.

The symbol $A^{\alpha_1}B^{\alpha_2}C^{\alpha_3} \ldots$ corresponding to the equation with left-hand side

$$\alpha_1 j_1 + \alpha_2 j_2 + \cdots + \alpha_K j_K$$

denotes a set of $(\rho - 1)$ degrees of freedom, and the first letter always appears with an exponent of unity.

7.7 FRACTIONAL FACTORIAL DESIGNS WITH FACTORS AT THREE LEVELS

a) Basic Concepts

The basic ideas of constructing a fractional replicate of a 3^K arrangement can be illustrated by a simple example. Consider a 3^3 factorial with 26 degrees of freedom which can be partitioned into 13 sets of 2 degrees of freedom. To obtain a $\frac{1}{3}$-replicate, it is natural to select as the defining contrast one of the four components of ABC:

$$\begin{aligned}
&1) \quad ABC \\
&2) \quad ABC^2 \\
&3) \quad AB^2C \\
&4) \quad AB^2C^2
\end{aligned}$$

For example, if we choose AB^2C^2, with the treatment combinations specified by

$$\left.\begin{aligned}
i + 2j + 2k &= 0, \\
i + 2j + 2k &= 1, \\
i + 2j + 2k &= 2,
\end{aligned}\right\} \quad \text{(modulo 3)}$$

a $\frac{1}{3}$-replicate determined by

$$i + 2j + 2k = 0 \quad \text{(modulo 3)}$$

is called the principal block which contains the treatment combination (0 0 0). The other two $\frac{1}{3}$-replicates determined by

$$i + 2j + 2k = 1 \quad \text{(modulo 3)} \qquad \text{or} \qquad i + 2j + 2k = 2 \quad \text{(modulo 3)}$$

are equally valid. These three $\frac{1}{3}$-replicates are all shown in Table 7.7.1. Note that the other two $\frac{1}{3}$-replicates can be generated by finding just one treatment in each of them and adding (modulo 3) that treatment to every treatment of the principal block. Since any one of the four components of ABC may be selected, there are a total of twelve $\frac{1}{3}$-replicates. The information on the chosen component of ABC is completely lost. From the four components we can write four sets of defining contrasts:

$$\begin{aligned}
&1) \quad I = ABC = A^2B^2C^2 \\
&2) \quad I = ABC^2 = A^2B^2C \\
&3) \quad I = AB^2C = A^2BC^2 \\
&4) \quad I = AB^2C^2 = A^2BC
\end{aligned}$$

TABLE 7.7.1

Replicate (1)			Replicate (2)			Replicate (3)		
0	0	0	1	0	0	2	0	0
1	0	1	2	0	1	0	0	1
2	0	2	0	0	2	1	0	2
0	1	2	1	1	2	2	1	2
1	1	0	2	1	0	0	1	0
2	1	1	0	1	1	1	1	1
0	2	1	1	2	1	2	2	1
1	2	2	2	2	2	0	2	2
2	2	0	0	2	0	1	2	0

TABLE 7.7.2

		B		
		0	1	2
	0	$0(C)$	$2(C)$	$1(C)$
A	1	$1(C)$	$0(C)$	$2(C)$
	2	$2(C)$	$1(C)$	$0(C)$

The defining contrasts are used to obtain the aliases system. The aliases of an effect or interaction are obtained by multiplying the effect or interaction with each term in the defining contrasts. For example, if we have

$$I = AB^2C^2 = A^2BC$$

then

$$A = BC = ABC$$
$$B = AC^2 = ABC^2$$
$$C = AB^2 = AB^2C$$
$$AB = AC = BC^2$$

where all exponents are reduced modulo 3 and the leading letter of every symbol has an exponent of unity. This design can be used only if we can assume that all interactions are negligible and be content with 2 degrees of freedom for error.

The 9 treatment combinations of a $\frac{1}{3}$-replicate in Table 7.7.1 may be written down in a form as shown in Table 7.7.2, where replicate (1) is used and the levels of factor C are denoted by $0(C)$, $1(C)$, and $2(C)$. It is immediately seen that this is a Latin square. Note that there are twelve 3×3 Latin squares; any one of them will provide a $\frac{1}{3}$-replicate of a 3^3 factorial.

b) Examples

Now consider 4 factors A, B, C, and D, each at 3 levels with treatment combinations (i, j, k, m). To construct a $\frac{1}{3}$-replicate, we may choose to confound $ABCD$, which gives the equations

$$\left. \begin{array}{l} i + j + k + m = 0, \\ i + j + k + m = 1, \\ i + j + k + m = 2, \end{array} \right\} \quad \text{(modulo 3)}$$

The first equation determines the principal block shown in Table 7.7.3. As in the preceding example, the other two $\frac{1}{3}$-replicates can be generated from the

TABLE 7.7.3

0000	0102	0201
1212	1011	1110
2121	2220	2022
0021	0120	0222
1200	1002	1101
2112	2211	2010
0012	0111	0210
1221	1020	1122
2100	2202	2001

TABLE 7.7.4

0000
1021
2012
0122
1110
2101
0211
1202
2220

TABLE 7.7.5

Effect	A	B	C	D
Aliases	AB^2C^2	AB^2C	ABC^2	$ABCD$
	BC	AC	AB	$ABCD^2$
	ACD^2	ABC^2D	AD	AC^2D^2
	CD^2	AB^2C^2D	ACD	AC^2
	ABD	AD^2	AB^2CD^2	AB^2
	BD	ABD^2	$AB^2C^2D^2$	AB^2D
	ABC^2D^2	BCD	BD^2	BC^2
	AB^2CD	CD	BCD^2	BC^2D

principal block, and the aliases of any effect can be obtained by using the defining contrasts.

To construct a $\frac{1}{9}$-replicate of a 3^4 factorial, we need to choose two interaction components as defining contrasts. Suppose that these are ABC and AC^2D. The generated interaction components:

$$ABC \times AC^2D = A^2BC^3D = A^2BD = (A^2BD)^2 = A^4B^2D^2 = AB^2D^2$$
$$ABC \times (AC^2D)^2 = A^3BC^5D^2 = BC^2D^2$$

also become defining contrasts. The interaction components ABC and AC^2D give 9 simultaneous equations:

$$i + j + k = 0, 1, 2 \quad \text{(modulo 3)}$$
$$i + 2k + m = 0, 1, 2 \quad \text{(modulo 3)}$$

Each of the 9 pairs: $(0, 0)$, $(0, 1)$, $(0, 2)$, $(1, 0)$, $(1, 1)$, $(1, 2)$, $(2, 0)$, $(2, 1)$, and $(2, 2)$, produces a pair of equations which will determine a $\frac{1}{9}$-replicate. The principal block shown in Table 7.7.4 is provided by the pair of equations

$$i + j + k = 0 \quad \text{(modulo 3)}$$
$$i + 2k + m = 0 \quad \text{(modulo 3)}$$

TABLE 7.7.6

000000	000121	000212
112122	112210	112001
221211	221002	221120
102211	102002	100110
211000	211121	212202
020122	020210	021021
001202	202200	202021
110021	011022	011110
222110	120111	120202
201210	201001	201122
010002	010120	010211
122121	122212	122000
100201	100022	001020
212020	212111	110112
021112	021200	222201
202112	200220	200011
011201	012012	012100
120020	121101	121222
102120	001111	200102
211212	110200	012221
020001	222022	121010
101100	101221	101012
210222	210010	210101
022011	022102	022220
002010	002101	002222
111102	111220	111011
220221	220012	220100

To find the aliases of an effect, we simply multiply it by the defining contrasts ABC, AC^2D, AB^2D^2, BC^2D^2, and their squares. Table 7.7.5 lists the alias sets. The main effects take up the total 8 degrees of freedom available in the experiment. The design has little practical use. It can be easily verified that the arrangement in Table 7.7.4 is also a 3×3 Graeco-Latin square.

As another example, consider a $\frac{1}{9}$-replicate of a 3^6 factorial design. Designate the factors by A, B, C, D, E, and F, and treatment combinations by $(i_1, i_2, i_3, i_4, i_5, i_6)$. Suppose that we use $ACDE$ and BC^2DE^2F as defining contrasts. Then the 81 treatment combinations which satisfy the two simultaneous equations

$$i_1 + i_3 + i_4 + i_5 = 0 \quad \text{(modulo 3)}$$
$$i_2 + 2i_3 + i_4 + 2i_5 + i_6 = 0 \quad \text{(modulo 3)}$$

provide a $\frac{1}{9}$-replicate (the principal block), and they are shown in Table 7.7.6. To determine the aliases of any effect, multiply that particular effect by $ACDE$, BC^2DE^2F, ABD^2F, $AB^2C^2E^2F^2$, and their squares. For example, the aliases of main effect A are

$$A = AC^2D^2E^2 = ABC^2DE^2F = AB^2DF^2 = ABCEF = CDE$$
$$= AB^2CD^2EF^2 = BD^2F = BCEF$$

7.8 FINITE GROUPS AND FRACTIONAL FACTORIAL DESIGNS WITH FACTORS AT THREE LEVELS

The group theoretic formulation for fractional factorial designs of the 3^K systems is very similar to that for the 2^K systems. Let $a^{\alpha_1}, b^{\alpha_2}, c^{\alpha_3}, \ldots$ denote the treatment combinations where the α_i's are levels of the factors having values 0, 1, and 2. Again, if we define a multiplication operation as in ordinary algebra but with an additional condition that

$$a^3 = b^3 = c^3 = \cdots = 1$$

the product of any two treatment combinations is again a treatment combination in the system. The treatment combinations form a *finite abelian group with the order* 3^K. The main effects and interactions represented by symbols $A, B, AB, \ldots$ subject to the condition that

$$A^3 = B^3 = C^3 = \cdots = I$$

is also a group isomorphic to the treatment group.

Effect subgroups of order 3 may be formed such that each corresponds to two degrees of freedom. For example, with $K = 3$, we have the following subgroups:

$$I = A = A^2$$

corresponding to two degrees of freedom for main effect A;

$$I = B = B^2$$

for main effect B;

$$I = AB = A^2B^2$$

for the AB component of interaction between A and B;

$$I = AB^2 = A^2B$$

for AB^2 component of interaction between A and B; and

$$I = C = C^2$$
$$I = AC = A^2C^2, \qquad I = AC^2 = A^2C$$
$$I = BC = B^2C^2, \qquad I = BC^2 = B^2C$$
$$I = ABC = A^2B^2C^2, \qquad I = ABC^2 = A^2B^2C$$
$$I = AB^2C = A^2BC^2, \qquad I = AB^2C^2 = A^2BC$$

for main effect C and components of the remaining interactions.

The concept of orthogonality introduced for the 2^K systems will be extended. Two treatment combinations, $a^{\alpha_1}, b^{\alpha_2}, c^{\alpha_3}, \ldots$ and $a^{\beta_1}, b^{\beta_2}, c^{\beta_3}, \ldots,$ are *orthogonal* if

$$\alpha_1\beta_1 + \alpha_2\beta_2 + \alpha_3\beta_3 + \cdots = 0 \quad (\text{modulo } 3)$$

This condition also holds for a treatment combination $a^{\alpha_1}, b^{\alpha_2}, c^{\alpha_3}, \ldots$ and an effect or interaction $A^{\beta_1}, B^{\beta_2}, C^{\beta_3} \ldots$.

If a subgroup S of order 3^P in one group is selected, elements in a second group orthogonal to elements in S form a subgroup of order 3^{K-P} called the *complete orthogonal subgroup.*

Now suppose any subgroup of order 3^P in the *effect group* is taken as an *alias subgroup* (i.e., defining contrasts or fundamental identity) with all its elements equated to the identity, then a 3^{-P} replicate is simply the *complete orthogonal subgroup* consisting of 3^{K-P} treatment combinations.

Each effect has $3^P - 1$ aliases. The aliases system may be determined by multiplying any given symbol representing an effect with elements of the alias subgroup.

For example, for $K = 3$, if the subgroup

$$I = AB^2C^2 = A^2BC$$

is chosen as the alias subgroup, the complete orthogonal subgroup of 3^2 treatment combinations which may be used as a $\frac{1}{3}$-replicate is

$$1, \quad ab, \quad a^2b^2, \quad ac, \quad a^2bc, \quad b^2c, \quad a^2c^2, \quad bc^2, \quad ab^2c^2$$

The group theoretic structure of the 3^K systems can be generalized to the ρ^K system, where ρ is any prime number. The ρ^K treatment combinations form a finite group with elements $a, b, ab, \ldots$ and

$$a^\rho = b^\rho = c^\rho = \cdots = 1$$

and a similar condition holds for the corresponding effect group. The orthogonality requirement is defined to be

$$\alpha_1\beta_1 + \alpha_2\beta_2 + \alpha_3\beta_3 + \cdots = 0 \quad (\text{modulo } \rho)$$

where α_i and β_j are exponents of the symbols denoting elements in the subgroups.

7.9 THE ANALYSIS OF FRACTIONAL FACTORIAL DESIGNS WITH FACTORS AT THREE LEVELS

The computation of sums of squares in a fractional factorial design with factors at 3 levels follows the procedure stated in Section 7.6. We shall describe the computational method by a numerical example. Suppose that the data for a $\frac{1}{3}$-replicate of a 3^4 factorial experiment are those given in Table 7.9.1. The design has defining contrast $ABCD$ and has been shown in Table 7.7.3. We shall need the one-way and two-way totals, which are shown in Tables 7.9.2, 7.9.3, 7.9.4, and 7.9.5.

TABLE 7.9.1

			A								
			0			1			2		
			B			B			B		
			0	1	2	0	1	2	0	1	2
D	0	C 0	9.85					22.00		12.65	
		C 1			16.00		13.75		12.35		
		C 2		16.65		11.40					11.80
	1	C 0			18.90		15.95		9.30		
		C 1		19.70		9.60					16.70
		C 2	12.20					16.65		15.35	
	2	C 0		13.80		8.95					17.15
		C 1	10.85					15.85		12.60	
		C 2			17.25		14.50		9.20		

TABLE 7.9.2

	0	1	2
A	93.70	134.95	152.30
B	135.20	128.65	117.10
C	128.55	127.40	125.00
D	126.45	134.35	120.15

TABLE 7.9.3

		B			C			D		
		0	1	2	0	1	2	0	1	2
A	0	32.90	29.95	30.85	28.10	32.80	32.80	33.60	31.10	29.00
	1	50.15	44.20	40.60	42.40	46.05	46.50	43.05	51.00	40.90
	2	52.15	54.50	45.65	58.05	48.55	45.70	49.80	52.25	50.25

TABLE 7.9.4

		C			D		
		0	1	2	0	1	2
B	0	42.55	46.55	46.10	42.50	50.80	41.90
	1	46.90	39.20	42.55	47.15	42.20	39.30
	2	39.10	41.65	36.35	36.80	41.35	38.95

TABLE 7.9.5

		D		
		0	1	2
C	0	44.50	44.15	39.90
	1	42.10	46.00	39.30
	2	39.85	44.20	40.95

The sums of squares of the main effects are calculated in the usual way, for example,

$$SS_A = \frac{(93.7)^2 + (134.95)^2 + (152.3)^2}{9} - \frac{(93.7 + 134.95 + 152.3)^2}{27}$$

$$= \frac{50186.4825}{9} - \frac{(380.95)^2}{27}$$

$$= 201.3524$$

To compute the sums of squares of the 2-factor interaction components, we first form sums from the two-way totals. For example, consider the AB component; the equations

$$\left.\begin{array}{l} i + j = 0, \\ i + j = 1, \\ i + j = 2, \end{array}\right\} \quad \text{(modulo 3)}$$

may be used to form three sums. From Table 7.9.3, we get 32.9, 54.5, and 40.6. Since they correspond to levels $(0, 0)$, $(2, 1)$, and $(1, 2)$ satisfying the first equation above, we form

$$32.9 + 54.5 + 40.6 = 128$$

Similarly, the second and third equation give

$$50.15 + 29.95 + 45.65 = 125.75$$

and

$$52.15 + 44.2 + 30.85 = 127.2$$

It follows that

$$SS_{AB} = \frac{(128)^2 + (125.75)^2 + (127.2)^2}{9} - \frac{(380.95)^2}{27} = 0.2893$$

Similarly, for the AB^2 component, the equations

$$\left.\begin{array}{l} i + 2j = 0, \\ i + 2j = 1, \\ i + 2j = 2, \end{array}\right\} \quad \text{(modulo 3)}$$

TABLE 7.9.6

Source	SS	d.f.
A	201.3524	2
B	18.6632	2
C	0.7293	2
D	11.2500	2
AB	0.2889	2
AB^2	12.0888	2
AC	16.6697	2
AC^2	18.7549	2
AD	1.6290	2
AD^2	10.6601	2
BC^2	15.4636	2
BD^2	2.5324	2
CD^2	3.7927	2
Total	313.8750	26

determine

$$32.9 + 44.2 + 45.65 = 122.75$$
$$50.15 + 54.50 + 30.85 = 135.50$$
$$52.15 + 29.95 + 40.60 = 122.70$$

and

$$SS_{AB^2} = \frac{(122.75)^2 + (135.50)^2 + (122.70)^2}{9} - \frac{(380.95)^2}{27} = 12.0888$$

The results are shown in Table 7.9.6. Note that each of the following pairs of 2-factor interaction components are alias pairs.

$$AB = CD; \qquad AC = BD; \qquad AD = BC$$

In order to make formal significance tests, we have to assume some or all 2-factor interactions negligible to form an error term.

The sums of squares may also be obtained from the estimates of the main effects or interaction components. For example, since the general mean is 14.1092, the main effects of A are estimated as

$$\frac{93.7}{9} - 14.1092 = -3.6981$$

$$\frac{134.95}{9} - 14.1092 = 0.8852$$

$$\frac{152.30}{9} - 14.1092 = 2.8130$$

Hence, of course

$$SS_A = 9[(3.6981)^2 + (0.8852)^2 + (2.8130)^2] = 201.352$$

The estimates of the AB interaction component, for example, are

$$\frac{128}{9} - 14.1092 = 0.1129$$

$$\frac{125.75}{9} - 14.1092 = -0.1370$$

$$\frac{127.2}{9} - 14.1092 = 0.0241$$

Thus

$$SS_{AB} = 9[(0.1129)^2 + (0.1370)^2 + (0.0241)^2] = 0.289$$

7.10   SOME OTHER FRACTIONAL FACTORIAL DESIGNS

Fractional factorial designs for factors at 2 and 4 levels, or all at 4 levels, can be constructed from fractional replicates of the 2^K factorial designs. This is carried out by dividing a 4-level factor, say U, into two "dummy" factors, say A and B, at 2 levels each. Denote the 4 levels of U by u_0, u_1, u_2, and u_3. We wish to associate these 4 levels, one-to-one, with the 4 factorial level combinations of A and B. The arrangement in Table 7.10.1 is suitable. Now the main effect of A is determined by

$$U' = u_3 + u_2 - u_1 - u_0$$

The main effect of B is determined by

$$U'' = u_3 - u_2 - u_1 + u_0$$

The AB interaction is determined by

$$U''' = u_3 - u_2 + u_1 - u_0$$

TABLE 7.10.1

		A	
		0	1
B	0	u_1	u_2
	1	u_0	u_3

These three comparisons are mutually orthogonal and have a single degree of freedom each. They provide a partitioning of the 3 degrees of freedom for the main effect of U into 3 orthogonal single degree-of-freedom components.

To construct the required design, we shall start on factors A and B in a 2^{-P} replicate of a 2^K factorial, and only need to make the transformations implied in Table 7.10.1, that is,

$$ab = u_3, \quad a = u_2, \quad 1 = u_1, \quad b = u_0$$

With another factor, say V, at 4 levels, another pair of factors, say C and D, at 2 levels each will be used, and similar transformations are made.

The defining contrasts and alias system for the newly constructed design can be obtained from those of the 2^{-P} replicate of a 2^K factorial by using transformations such as

$$A = U', \quad B = U'', \quad AB = U'''$$

For example, if a $\frac{1}{2}$-replicate of a 2^6 factorial is made into a $\frac{1}{2}$-replicate of a $2^2 \times 4^2$ factorial, a defining contrast for the original plan, $ABCDEF$, becomes

$U'''V'''EF$. An alias pair in the original plan, for example,

$$AB = CDEF$$

becomes

$$U''' = V'''EF$$

and

$$ABE = CDF$$

becomes

$$U'''E = V'''F$$

This means that a 2-factor interaction originally confounded with a 4-factor interaction becomes a main effect component confounded with a 3-factor interaction component, and a pair of 3-factor interactions confounded together becomes a pair of 2-factor interaction components confounded together. The alias system should be checked before a design is put into practice.

The analysis of a fractional replicate of a $2^N \times 4^M$ or 4^M factorial may be carried out by performing the formal computations according to the original plan of a fractional factorial with factors at 2 levels and subsequently by identifying the computed sums of squares with the aid of such transformations as

$$A = U', \quad B = U'', \quad AB = U'''$$

Fractional factorial designs with factors at two and three levels are not often used; however, they can be found in Connor and Young [6].

When factors are at a certain combination of mixed levels (i.e., the number of levels is not the same for every factor) and when all interactions are negligible, some designs which permit uncorrelated estimation of all main effects have been developed [7, 8]. These designs are called orthogonal main effect plans from which some additional designs which permit uncorrelated estimation of all main effects and some specific number of 2-factor interactions can be constructed for factors at the same number of levels or at certain mixed levels [9].

7.11 CONFOUNDING IN FACTORIAL EXPERIMENTS

In many situations, it may not be possible to perform a complete factorial experiment in one block such as one day or one homogeneous batch of experimental material, etc. Enlarging the block size may result in a large experimental error variance. Confounding is a device for increasing precision by arranging a complete factorial experiment in a number of blocks with fewer units per block than there are treatments in the entire experiment. The resulting blocks are called *incomplete blocks*. The basic idea of confounding, similar to that of fractional replication, is that information about certain treatment comparisons, such as higher-order interactions, may be sacrificed, and allowed to be mixed up with or confounded with the block differences. In the following discussions, we will continue to use some of the concepts and notations developed for fractional factorial designs.

a) Confounding in the 2^K Systems

Consider a 2^3 factorial experiment. If the 8 treatment combinations are to be divided into two incomplete blocks, any factorial effect can be confounded with blocks. Generally, we would confound the 3-factor interaction ABC, since it is likely the least important one. Using the notations in Section 7.2, we can divide the 8 treatment combinations into two sets determined by the formal expression

$$(a - 1)(b - 1)(c - 1)$$

The terms with a positive sign (a, b, c, abc) go into one block, and those with a negative sign $(-ab, -ac, -bc, -1)$ go into the other block. By so doing, the difference between the two blocks also represent ABC interaction, and it is said that ABC is confounded with blocks.

This arrangement produces no disturbance to the other factorial effects. The other effects are orthogonal to block effects and are composed entirely of within-block comparisons. For example, consider the main effect A which has terms

$$(a + abc - b - c) + (ab + ac - bc - 1)$$

The first four terms come from the first block. Since two of them have positive signs and the other two have negative signs, any effect due to the block is cancelled out. The same fact holds true for the remaining four terms which correspond to the second block. Therefore, the main effect A is independent of the block differences, and it is calculated in the same manner as in complete blocks. Similarly, we can verify that all the other effects are orthogonal to block effects. This simple result, of course, is really due to the property that ABC is orthogonal to every one of the other six effects.

With several replications for a confounded factorial experiment, the same interaction may be confounded in all replications. Then they are said to be *completely confounded* with blocks. An example is given in Table 7.11.1, where a 2^3 factorial is arranged in blocks of 4 units with ABC confounded in all three replications. The four treatment combinations in each block have been arranged in random order. The sums of squares are calculated in the usual way. The blocks sum of squares with 5 degrees of freedom consists of 3 parts: replications, blocks (or ABC), and replications and blocks interaction, with 2, 1,

TABLE 7.11.1

Block	Rep. I		Rep. II		Rep. III	
	1	2	3	4	5	6
	b	ab	c	bc	a	ac
	a	bc	a	1	c	bc
	c	1	b	ac	abc	1
	abc	ac	abc	ab	b	ab

TABLE 7.11.2

Treatment	Rep. I	Rep. II	Rep. III
	Block 1	Block 3	Block 5
a	31.2	25.2	33.6
b	23.2	17.2	19.6
c	50.2	50.2	43.6
abc	33.8	33.8	34.4
	Block 2	Block 4	Block 6
1	53.4	47.4	43.2
ab	16.2	10.2	15.6
ac	22.0	22.0	22.0
bc	26.0	26.0	20.0

and 2 degrees of freedom, respectively. The error sum of squares may be obtained by subtraction, or by adding the interaction sums of squares between replications and A, B, C, AB, AC, BC, and has 12 degrees of freedom.

Now let us consider a numerical example. The data for the layout in Table 7.11.1 are shown in Table 7.11.2.

The analysis-of-variance table is shown in Table 7.11.3. The computations seem to be quite straightforward if we regard "replication" as a fictitious factor and perform the formal analysis of variance of a 4-way arrangement. Testing the factorial effects against the error term, we find that B and AB are significant

TABLE 7.11.3

Source	SS	d.f.	MS
Replication	48.00	2	24.00
Block (or ABC)	216.00	1	216.00
Rep. $\times$ Block	7.68	2	3.84
A	600.00	1	600.00
B	1176.00	1	1176.00
AB	864.00	1	864.00
C	96.00	1	96.00
AC	24.00	1	24.00
BC	384.00	1	384.00
Error	127.68	12	10.64
Rep. $\times$ A	69.12	2	
Rep. $\times$ B	1.92	2	
Rep. $\times$ AB	7.68	2	
Rep. $\times$ C	48.00	2	
Rep. $\times$ AC	.48	2	
Rep. $\times$ BC	.48	2	

at the 5 percent level. The replication effect and block effect may be tested against the replication and block interaction. However, due to the small number of degrees of freedom here, these tests will not be powerful.

The set of data we used here is the same as that in Table 6.2.4, except that the replications here were called randomized complete blocks; in each replication incomplete blocks are formed, and treatments are identified as those of a 2^3 factorial. The new error term and replication $\times$ block interaction add up to the previous error term. The treatment sum of squares is now divided into 7 parts, and one of them (ABC interaction) is confounded with incomplete block differences. The subdivision of the treatment sum of squares was also shown in Table 7.2.3.

The procedure for constructing a fractional replicate of a 2^K factorial can be used to select the blocks in a confounded 2^K experiment. As before, the block which contains the treatment combination "1" is called the principal block. The principal block is made up by all those treatments which have an even or zero number of letters in common with the confounding interaction. To get the other block, choose any treatment combination which is not in the principal block, and multiply (modulo 2) it by every treatment in the principal block.

Sometimes we may wish to divide an experiment into more than two incomplete blocks. For example, if a 2^5 factorial is to be divided into 4 blocks of 2^3, we need to confound two factorial effects with blocks. One might select $ABCDE$ and $BCDE$. However, it turns out to be that the generalized interaction of these two, that is

$$ABCDE \times BCDE = AB^2C^2D^2E^2 = A$$

is also confounded with blocks (we recall that the same situation was encountered in selecting defining contrasts for constructing a 2^{-P} replicate of a 2^K factorial). Trying two 4-factor interactions, we find that a 2-factor interaction is also confounded. In order to avoid confounding any main effects or any 2-factor interactions, a better choice will be two 3-factor interactions such as ABC and ADE. Their generalized interaction is a 4-factor interaction, for example

$$ABC \times ADE = BCDE$$

The treatment combinations in the principal block must have an even or zero number of letters in common with two of the three confounding interactions (it follows that they will also have an even or zero number of letters in common with the third). The other blocks can be generated from the principal block by the rule described above. Note that the treatment combination which is used to generate a new block must be neither in the principal block nor in any block already formed. The 4 blocks are shown in Table 7.11.4.

In general, if a complete replicate of a 2^K factorial is to be divided into 2^P incomplete blocks of 2^{K-P} units each, any P factorial effects may be selected to be confounded with blocks, provided that none of these is a generalized interaction of any subset of the others. Additional $2^P - P - 1$ effects are also

TABLE 7.11.4

Block	1	2	3	4
	1	ab	a	b
	bc	ac	abc	c
	abd	d	bd	ad
	acd	bcd	be	abcd
	abe	e	ce	ae
	ace	bce	ade	abce
	de	abde	abcde	bde
	bcde	acde	cd	cde

confounded. These are the generalized interactions formed from the first chosen set of P effects. The analysis follows the same procedure for a 2^K factorial design, and the block sum of squares is computed by adding the sums of squares of the interactions which are confounded with blocks.

b) Partial Confounding

With several replications for a confounded factorial experiment, it is not necessary to confound the same interaction(s) in each replication. We may wish to spread the confounding among several factorial effects, and arrange the treatment combinations differently in each replication so that a different effect is confounded from one replication to another. Consider the plan in Table 7.11.5 for a confounded 2^3 experiment in blocks of 4 units and in 4 replications. The ABC interaction is confounded in replication I. However, in replication II, AC is confounded; in replication III, BC is confounded; and in replication IV, AB is confounded. The main effects A, B, and C are entirely free from all block effects, and their sums of squares are calculated as usual. The ABC interaction and its sum of squares is computed from replications II, III, and IV; similarly, AC is computed from I, III, and IV; BC from I, II, and IV; and AB from I, II, and III.

TABLE 7.11.5

	Rep. I		Rep. II		Rep. III		Rep. IV	
Block	1	2	3	4	5	6	7	8
	1	a	1	a	1	b	1	a
	ab	b	b	c	a	c	c	b
	ac	c	ac	ab	bc	ab	ab	ac
	bc	abc	abc	bc	abc	ac	abc	bc
Confounding	ABC		AC		BC		AB	

These four interactions are said to be *partially confounded* with blocks. The estimate of each of these interactions is obtained from three of the four replications. The ratio $\frac{3}{4}$ gives the amount of information available on a confounded interaction relative to that available on an unconfounded effect, and it may be called the *relative information* on the confounded interaction.

The sum of squares for blocks consists of two parts: replications, and blocks within replication with 3 and 4 degrees of freedom. The error sum of squares may be obtained by pooling interactions between replication and all effects, and has 17 degrees of freedom, because replication by A, B, and C gives 3 degrees of freedom each, and replication by each of the partially confounded interaction gives only 2 degrees of freedom.

c) Confounding in the 3^K System

To construct confounded 3^K factorial designs, we use a more general scheme which can be extended to any ρ^K system when ρ is a prime. The basic ideas are analogous to those stated in Sections 7.6, 7.7, and 7.8 for fractional factorial designs.

Consider a 3^3 factorial, and denote the treatment combinations by (i, j, k). The four components of ABC interaction are ABC, ABC^2, AB^2C, and AB^2C^2. If we wish to divide the experiment into 3 blocks of 9 treatment combinations each, we may choose to confound AB^2C^2. Then, the first of 3 blocks contains treatment combinations determined by

$$i + 2j + 2k = 0 \quad \text{(modulo 3)}$$

This block which includes the treatment combination $(0\,0\,0)$ is called, as before, the principal block. The second block has those treatment combinations determined by

$$i + 2j + 2k = 1 \quad \text{(modulo 3)}$$

and the third block has those determined by

$$i + 2j + 2k = 2 \quad \text{(modulo 3)}$$

These blocks have been listed in Table 7.7.1, where they correspond to three $\frac{1}{3}$-replicates of a 3^3 factorial.

If the 3^3 factorial is to be divided into 9 blocks of 3 treatment combinations each, 8 degrees of freedom must be confounded with blocks. One scheme is to confound AB^2C^2 and AB, and the generated interaction components:

$$AB \times AB^2C^2 = A^2C^2 = AC$$
$$AB \times (AB^2C^2)^2 = B^2C = BC^2$$

The 9 pairs of equations of the following form

$$i + 2j + 2k = m_1$$
$$i + j = m_2$$

TABLE 7.11.6

Block	1	2	3	4	5	6	7	8	9
	000	101	110	002	100	020	001	010	200
	122	220	202	121	222	112	120	102	022
	211	012	021	210	011	201	212	221	111

with (m_1, m_2) taking values, modulo 3, of $(0, 0)$, $(0, 1)$, $(0, 2)$, $(1, 0)$, $(1, 1)$, $(1, 2)$, $(2, 0)$, $(2, 1)$, $(2, 2)$ give 9 sets of treatment combinations, forming 9 incomplete blocks, as shown in Table 7.11.6. After the principal block (block 1) is written down, the other blocks can be generated by finding only one treatment combination in each block and adding (modulo 3) it to every treatment combination in the principal block.

The analysis of a confounded 3^K factorial experiment follows the method described in Section 7.6. The sum of squares for blocks is identical with the total of sums of squares of the interaction components confounded in the design.

d) Block Confounding in Fractional Factorial Designs

Fractional replication and confounding in blocks may be used together. This is useful, especially when the total number of treatment combinations in a fractionally replicated experiment is still large.

Consider a $\frac{1}{4}$-replicate of a 2^6 factorial. Suppose that we choose as the defining contrasts $ABCE$, $ABDF$, and their generalized interaction $CDEF$. A $\frac{1}{4}$-replicate (the principal block) has been given in Table 7.3.5. If we wish to divide the 16 treatment combinations into 2 blocks of 8 units, we must confound an interaction with blocks. Examining the alias system in Table 7.3.6, we find that there are two sets of aliases involving only 3-factor interactions. Using ACD as the confounding interaction, we obtain the 2 blocks in Table 7.11.7. The new principal block consists of treatment combinations (in the $\frac{1}{4}$-replicate) which have an even or zero number of letters in common with ACD. Note that the aliases of ACD are also confounded with blocks.

If we wish to divide the $\frac{1}{4}$-replicate into 4 blocks of 4 units, another interaction, not an alias of the preceding confounded interaction, will be used. We may choose to confound ACF (and its aliases). The product of ACD and ACF, that is DF (and its aliases), will be also confounded. The 4 blocks, shown in Table 7.11.8, are generated by (1) writing down the new principal block which has treatment combinations with even or zero number of letters in common with ACD and ACF, (2) finding a treatment combination not in the new principal block and multiplying (modulo 2) it with every one in the principal block to form a second block, and (3) selecting a treatment combination not in the preceding blocks for repeating the above process to get the remaining blocks.

TABLE 7.11.7

Block 1	Block 2
1	abcdef
cdef	ab
abdf	ce
abce	df
bef	acd
bcd	aef
ade	bcf
acf	bde

TABLE 7.11.8

Block 1	Block 2	Block 3	Block 4
1	bef	abcdef	acd
cdef	bcd	ab	aef
abdf	ade	ce	bcf
abce	acf	df	bde

The procedure described in the above example can be easily generalized for dividing a 2^{-P} replicate of a 2^K experiment into 2^b blocks of 2^{K-P-b} units by confounding $2^b - 1$ interactions (and their respective aliases) with blocks.

In the 3^K systems, in order to divide the 3^{K-P} treatment combinations of a 3^{-P} replicate into 3^b blocks of 3^{K-P-b} units each, we must confound $(3^b - 1)/2$ interaction components and their aliases with the blocks. We shall illustrate the procedure by an example.

Consider the $\frac{1}{3}$-replicate of a 3^4 factorial in Table 7.7.3. Suppose that we wish to divide the 27 treatment combinations into 3 blocks of 9 units. Keeping in mind that the defining contrast for this $\frac{1}{3}$-replicate is $ABCD$, and that the aliases of a block-confounded interaction component will be also confounded, we may choose to confound AB. The equations which serve as a basis for placing the 27 treatments into 3 blocks are

$$\left.\begin{array}{l} i + j = 0, \\ i + j = 1, \\ i + j = 2, \end{array}\right\} \quad \text{(modulo 3)}$$

The first equation determines the new principal block. Each one of the other blocks can be generated by finding only one treatment first, and then adding

TABLE 7.11.9

Block 1	Block 2	Block 3
0000	0102	0201
1212	1011	1110
2121	2220	2022
0021	0120	0222
1200	1002	1101
2112	2211	2010
0012	0111	0210
1221	1020	1122
2100	2202	2001

(modulo 3) it to every treatment in the principal block. These 3 blocks are shown in Table 7.11.9.

If we wish to divide the 27 treatments into 9 blocks instead of 3 blocks, four interaction components (and their aliases) must be confounded with blocks. We need to choose only two components, the interaction components generated from them will be also confounded with blocks. Suppose that we choose AB and AC^2. Then

$$AB \times AC^2 = A^2BC^2 = AB^2C$$

and

$$AB \times (AC^2)^2 = A^3BC^4 = BC$$

are also confounded. The components AB and AC^2 give 9 pairs of equations of the form

$$i + j = n_1$$
$$i + 2k = n_2$$

where (n_1, n_2) takes values, modulo 3, of $(0, 0)$, $(0, 1)$, $(0, 2)$, $(1, 0)$, $(1, 1)$, $(1, 2)$, $(2, 0)$, $(2, 1)$, $(2, 2)$. Each pair of equations will determine a block. The 9 blocks are shown in Table 7.11.10. After the new principal block (block 1) is formed, the other blocks can be easily generated (as in the confounding of a complete 3^K factorial) by finding just one treatment in each block and adding (modulo 3) it to every treatment in the principal block.

TABLE 7.11.10

Block	1	2	3	4	5	6	7	8	9
	0000	0021	0012	0102	0120	0111	0201	0222	0210
	1212	1200	1221	1011	1002	1020	1110	1101	1122
	2121	2112	2100	2220	2211	2202	2022	2010	2001

REFERENCES

1. Finney, D. J., "The Fractional Replication of Factorial Arrangements," *Annals of Eugenics*, **12**, 291–301 (1945).

2. Kempthorne, O., "A Simple Approach to Confounding and Fractional Replication in Factorial Experiments," *Biometrika*, **34**, 255–272 (1947).

3. Addelman, S., "Techniques for Constructing Fractional Replicate Plans," *Amer. Stat. Assoc. J.*, **58**, 45–71 (1963).

4. Statistical Engineering Laboratory of National Bureau of Standards, "Fractional Factorial Experiment Designs for Factors at Two Levels," National Bureau of Standards, Applied Math Series 48, 1957.

5. Connor, W. S., and M. Zelen, "Fractional Factorial Experiment Designs for Factors at Three Levels," National Bureau of Standards, Applied Math Series 54, 1959.

6. Connor, W. S., and S. Young, "Fractional Factorial Designs for Experiments With Factors at Two and Three Levels, National Bureau of Standards, Applied Math Series 58, 1961.

7. Addelman, S., "Orthogonal Main-Effect Plans for Asymmetrical Factorial Experiments," *Technometrics*, **4**, 21–46 (1962).

8. Addelman, S., and O. Kempthorne, "Orthogonal Main-Effect Plans," ARL 79, U. S. Air Force, 1961.

9. Addelman, S., "Symmetrical and Asymmetrical Fractional Factorial Plans," *Technometrics*, **4**, 47–58 (1962).

10. Yates, F., "The Design and Analysis of Factorial Experiments," Imperial Bureau of Soil Science, England, 1937.

11. Bose, R. C., and K. Kishen, "On the Problem of Confounding in General Symmetrical Factorial Designs," *Sankhya*, **5**, 21–26 (1940).

12. Bose, R. C., "Mathematical Theory of the Symmetrical Factorial Design," *Sankhya*, **8**, 107–166 (1947).

13. Li, J. C. R., "Design and Statistical Analysis of some Confounded Factorial Experiments," *Iowa Agr. Exp. Sta. Res. Bull.*, **333** (1944).

14. Binet, F. E., *et al.*, "Analysis of Confounded Factorial Experiments in Single Replications," *North Carolina Agr. Exp. Sta. Tech. Bull.*, **113** (1955).

15. Kitagawa, T., and M. Mitome, *Tables for the Design of Factorial Experiments*, Baifukan, Tokyo, 1953.

8 RESPONSE SURFACE DESIGNS

8.1 RESPONSE SURFACES

In many experimental situations, the experimenter is concerned with explaining certain aspects of a functional relationship

$$Y = \phi(x_1, x_2, \ldots, x_K)$$

between a response Y and the levels $x_1, x_2, \ldots, x_K$ of K quantitative variables or factors. The function ϕ is called the *response surface* or *response function*.

With two factors, x_1 and x_2, several common types of surfaces are sketched graphically in Fig. 8.1.1.

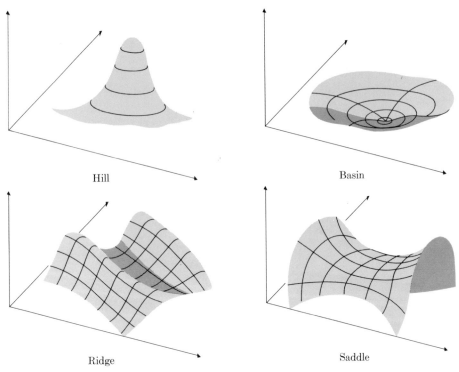

Hill

Basin

Ridge

Saddle

FIG. 8.1.1

The occurrence of ridge systems may be often due to a certain dependence among factors. "Natural" variables, such as temperature, pressure, etc., are often regarded as factors because they can be easily measured. But a combination of some of these factors may form a fundamental variable which describes the response surface more efficiently. A number of different conditions of several natural variables may be all equivalent to the optimum condition of a fundamental variable. For example, if

$$Z = x_1 x_2$$
$$Y = \phi(Z)$$

the relationship between Y and Z is represented in Fig. 8.1.2. If the experiment is carried out by varying x_1 and x_2, the response surface being explored would be a ridge system as shown in Fig. 8.1.3.

Other types of factor dependence such as

$$Z = a + bx_1 + cx_2$$
$$Z = ax_1^b x_2^c$$
$$Z = ax_1^b e^{-c/x_2}$$
$$Z = a + bx_1 - cx_2$$
$$Z = ax_1^b / x_2^c$$
$$Z = ax_1^b e^{-cx_2}$$

all produce ridge systems. Of course, the discovery of a certain type of factor dependence together with the experimenter's theoretical knowledge may result in a better understanding of the fundamental mechanism of the system, and a better mathematical model or structure equation may consequently be derived. For example, if he finds a response surface such as that in Fig. 8.1.3 from experimenting the factors x_1 and x_2, he may be led to consider a fundamental variable of the type

$$Z = x_1 x_2$$

If this turns out to be reasonable from his expert viewpoint, a term of this type would be included in the mathematical model.

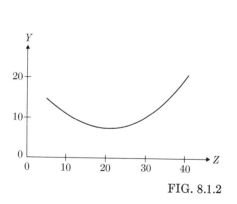

FIG. 8.1.2

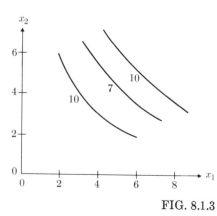

FIG. 8.1.3

8.2 LEAST SQUARES AND QUADRATIC SURFACES

a) Least Squares

In the space of the factors, within a limited region of immediate interest to the experimenter we shall assume that the response function ϕ can be represented by a polynomial model of degree c:

$$y_u = b_0 + b_1 x_{1u} + \cdots + b_K x_{Ku} + b_{11} x_{1u}^2 + \cdots + b_{KK} x_{Ku}^2$$
$$+ b_{12} x_{1u} x_{2u} + \cdots + b_{K-1,K} x_{K-1,u} x_{Ku} + b_{111} x_{1u}^3 + \cdots + e_u$$

$$(8.2.1)$$

The y_u are the observed responses, the x's are the quantitative factors considered to be fixed and measured without error, the b's are unknown coefficients to be determined, and e_u are random errors independent of the x's and with mean zero and variance σ^2.

Suppose that an experimental design is selected to study the response surface, and the uth experimental point is denoted by the $(1 \times K)$ row vector

$$(x_{1u}, x_{2u}, \ldots, x_{Ku})$$

These vectors form the *design matrix*

$$\mathbf{D} = \begin{bmatrix} x_{11} & x_{21} & \cdots & x_{K1} \\ x_{12} & x_{22} & \cdots & x_{K2} \\ \vdots & \vdots & & \vdots \\ x_{1N} & x_{2N} & \cdots & x_{KN} \end{bmatrix}$$

Here N must be greater than or equal to L, the number of coefficients in the polynomial model to be fitted. Enlarging $\mathbf{D}$ by adding a column vector of all one's to the left and by affixing to the right, column vectors formed by the appropriate products of columns of $\mathbf{D}$ according to the model (8.2.1), we form the matrix

$$\mathbf{X} = \begin{bmatrix} 1 & x_{11} & x_{21} & \cdots & x_{K1} & \cdots \\ 1 & x_{12} & x_{22} & \cdots & x_{K2} & \cdots \\ \vdots & & & & \vdots & \\ 1 & x_{1N} & x_{2N} & \cdots & x_{KN} & \cdots \end{bmatrix}$$

Furthermore, let $\mathbf{Y}$ be a column vector of observations:

$$\mathbf{Y} = \begin{bmatrix} y_1 \\ y_2 \\ \vdots \\ y_N \end{bmatrix}$$

let $\mathbf{B}$ be the column vector of the coefficients:

$$\mathbf{B} = \begin{bmatrix} b_0 \\ b_1 \\ \vdots \\ b_L \end{bmatrix}$$

and let $\mathbf{E}$ be the column vector of errors:

$$\mathbf{E} = \begin{bmatrix} e_1 \\ e_2 \\ \vdots \\ e_N \end{bmatrix}$$

Then the model takes the following matrix form:

$$\mathbf{Y} = \mathbf{XB} + \mathbf{E}$$

If the $(L \times 1)$ vector of the minimum variance unbiased estimates of the coefficients is denoted by $\hat{\mathbf{B}}$ it can be shown that

$$\hat{\mathbf{B}} = (\mathbf{X'X})^{-1}\mathbf{X'Y}$$

These are the least squares estimates of the coefficients. The variances and covariances of the estimates are the elements of the matrix

$$(\mathbf{X'X})^{-1}\sigma^2$$

and an unbiased estimate of $(N - L)\sigma^2$ is provided by the quantity

$$\mathbf{Y'Y} - \hat{\mathbf{B}}'\mathbf{X'X}\hat{\mathbf{B}}$$

For K factors a design which allows in the polynomial model all coefficients of terms up to order c to be determined is called a *K-dimensional cth order design*. Since in most experimental situations, approximations by polynomial of degree 2 are adequate, and useful response surface designs are constructed for second-order approximations, we shall review some results on *quadratic surfaces*.

b) Quadratic Surface

For simplicity, consider the case of three factors. The general form of the quadratic surface is fitted as

$$\hat{y} = \hat{b}_0 + \hat{b}_1 x_1 + \hat{b}_2 x_2 + \hat{b}_3 x_3 + \hat{b}_{11} x_1^2 + \hat{b}_{22} x_2^2 + \hat{b}_{33} x_3^2$$
$$+ \hat{b}_{12} x_1 x_2 + \hat{b}_{13} x_1 x_3 + \hat{b}_{23} x_2 x_3$$

The analysis of this surface can be simplified by reducing the fitted second-degree equation to a canonical form. Taking partial deviatives and setting them equal to zero, we have

$$\frac{\partial \hat{y}}{\partial x_1} = \hat{b}_1 + 2\hat{b}_{11} x_1 + \hat{b}_{12} x_2 + \hat{b}_{13} x_3 = 0$$

$$\frac{\partial \hat{y}}{\partial x_2} = \hat{b}_2 + \hat{b}_{12} x_1 + 2\hat{b}_{22} x_2 + \hat{b}_{23} x_3 = 0$$

$$\frac{\partial \hat{y}}{\partial x_3} = \hat{b}_3 + \hat{b}_{13} x_1 + \hat{b}_{23} x_2 + 2\hat{b}_{33} x_3 = 0$$

The solutions of these equations, x_{1S}, x_{2S}, x_{3S}, give the factorial combination at which $\hat{y}$ is a local maximum or minimum, or a local stationary value. The value of $\hat{y}$ at this point is given by the form

$$\hat{y}_S = \hat{b}_0 + \tfrac{1}{2}(\hat{b}_1 x_{1S} + \hat{b}_2 x_{2S} + \hat{b}_3 x_{3S})$$

If the origin of the x-coordinates is transferred to (x_{1S}, x_{2S}, x_{3S}) by

$$x_1' = x_1 - x_{1S}, \qquad x_2' = x_2 - x_{2S}, \qquad x_3' = x_3 - x_{3S}$$

then the linear terms will disappear, and we have

$$f = \hat{y} - \hat{y}_S = \hat{b}_{11}{x_1'}^2 + \hat{b}_{22}{x_2'}^2 + \hat{b}_{33}{x_3'}^2 + \hat{b}_{12}x_1'x_2' + \hat{b}_{13}x_1'x_3' + \hat{b}_{23}x_2'x_3'$$

Furthermore, the cross-product terms can be eliminated by rotating the principal axes. The above form, f, with coefficients in the real field, is known as a *quadratic form* which has a *real symmetric matrix*:

$$\hat{B} = \begin{bmatrix} \hat{b}_{11} & \tfrac{1}{2}\hat{b}_{12} & \tfrac{1}{2}\hat{b}_{13} \\ \tfrac{1}{2}\hat{b}_{21} & \hat{b}_{22} & \tfrac{1}{2}\hat{b}_{23} \\ \tfrac{1}{2}\hat{b}_{31} & \tfrac{1}{2}\hat{b}_{32} & \hat{b}_{33} \end{bmatrix}$$

where $\hat{b}_{21} = \hat{b}_{12}$ and $\hat{b}_{31} = \hat{b}_{13}$. There exists an *orthogonal transformation* with matrix P which reduces f to the canonical form

$$d_1 X_1^2 + d_2 X_2^2 + d_3 X_3^2$$

where d_1, d_2, d_3 are the *characteristic roots (eigenvalues)* of the real symmetric matrix $\hat{B}$, and X_1, X_2, X_3 are linear combinations of the x's. That is,

$$P\hat{B}P' = \begin{bmatrix} d_1 & 0 & 0 \\ 0 & d_2 & 0 \\ 0 & 0 & d_3 \end{bmatrix} = D$$

and

$$P' = P^{-1}$$

We recall that the characteristic roots of a matrix are the scalars d such that the determinant

$$|\hat{B} - dI| = 0$$

and that all characteristic roots of a real symmetric matrix are real. This provides a straightforward way for reducing f to the canonical form. Since for K factors the determinant $|\hat{B} - dI|$ is a polynomial of degree K in d, when K is large, it is not feasible to expand the determinant and solve for d directly. However, a number of methods are available for finding the orthogonal matrix P such that $P\hat{B}P' = D$ (see [4], [5]). Note that the columns of P are the k characteristic vectors (eigenvectors) of $\hat{B}$.

c) Example of Calculating the Canonical Form of a Second-Degree Equation

Now consider an example. Let the fitted equation be

$$\hat{y} = 10.5 + 0.2x_1 + 0.6x_2 + 4x_3 + 0.1x_1^2 - 0.2x_2^2 + 0.1x_3^2 + 0.6x_1x_2 - 0.2x_2x_3$$

Taking partial derivatives and setting them equal to zero, we have

$$\frac{\partial \hat{y}}{\partial x_1} = 0.2 + 0.2x_1 + 0.6x_2 = 0$$

$$\frac{\partial \hat{y}}{\partial x_2} = 0.6 + 0.6x_1 - 0.4x_2 - 0.2x_3 = 0$$

$$\frac{\partial \hat{y}}{\partial x_3} = 4 - 0.2x_2 + 0.2x_3 = 0$$

Denote the solutions by x_{1S}, x_{2S}, x_{3S}, then

$$x_{1S} = -6 \qquad x_{2S} = \tfrac{5}{3} \qquad x_{3S} = -\tfrac{55}{3}$$

The value of $\hat{y}$ at this point is

$$\hat{y}_S = -26.267$$

If the origin of the system is transferred to (x_{1S}, x_{2S}, x_{3S}) we have

$$f = \hat{y} + 26.267 = 0.1x_1'^2 - 0.2x_2'^2 + 0.1x_3'^2 + 0.6x_1'x_2' - 0.2x_2'x_3'$$

Write

$$\hat{B} = \begin{bmatrix} 0.1 & 0.3 & 0 \\ 0.3 & -0.2 & -0.1 \\ 0 & -0.1 & 0.1 \end{bmatrix}$$

and compute

$$|\hat{B} - d\mathbf{I}| = \begin{vmatrix} 0.1 - d & 0.3 & 0 \\ 0.3 & -0.2 - d & -0.1 \\ 0 & -0.1 & +0.1 - d \end{vmatrix} = -d^3 + 0.13d - 0.012$$

Factoring, we have

$$|\hat{B} - d\mathbf{I}| = (d - 0.1)(d + 0.4)(d - 0.3) = 0$$

Hence the characteristic roots d of $\hat{B}$ are 0.1, 0.3, -0.4. That is

$$D = \begin{bmatrix} 0.1 & & \\ & 0.3 & \\ & & -0.4 \end{bmatrix}$$

To compute the characteristic vectors $\mathbf{p}$ of P, we write $\mathbf{p}\hat{B} = d\mathbf{p}$. Denote $\mathbf{p} = (p_1, p_2, p_3)$. For $d = 0.1$, we have

$$[p_1 \; p_2 \; p_3] \begin{bmatrix} 0.1 & 0.3 & 0 \\ 0.3 & -0.2 & -0.1 \\ 0 & -0.1 & 0.1 \end{bmatrix} = 0.1[p_1 \; p_2 \; p_3]$$

$$0.1p_1 + 0.3p_2 = 0.1p_1$$
$$0.3p_1 - 0.2p_2 - 0.1p_3 = 0.1p_2$$
$$- 0.1p_2 + 0.1p_3 = 0.1p_3$$
$$\mathbf{p} = (1, 0, 3)$$

For $d = 0.3$, we have

$$0.1p_1 + 0.3p_2 = 0.3p_1$$
$$0.3p_1 - 0.2p_2 - 0.1p_3 = 0.3p_2$$
$$- 0.1p_2 + 0.1p_3 = 0.3p_3$$
$$\mathbf{p} = (3, 2, -1)$$

For $d = -0.4$, we have

$$0.1p_1 + 0.3p_2 = -0.4p_1$$
$$0.3p_1 - 0.2p_2 - 0.1p_3 = -0.4p_2$$
$$- 0.1p_2 + 0.1p_3 = -0.4p_3$$
$$\mathbf{p} = (-3, 5, 1)$$

Hence the orthogonal matrix is

$$\begin{bmatrix} 1 & 0 & 3 \\ 3 & 2 & -1 \\ -3 & 5 & 1 \end{bmatrix}$$

Normalizing the vectors, we have

$$\mathbf{P} = \begin{bmatrix} 1/\sqrt{10} & 0 & 3/\sqrt{10} \\ 3/\sqrt{14} & 2/\sqrt{14} & -1/\sqrt{14} \\ -3/\sqrt{35} & 5/\sqrt{35} & 1/\sqrt{35} \end{bmatrix}$$

Hence

$$\begin{bmatrix} 1/\sqrt{10} & 0 & 3/\sqrt{10} \\ 3/\sqrt{14} & 2/\sqrt{14} & -1/\sqrt{14} \\ -3/\sqrt{35} & 5/\sqrt{35} & 1/\sqrt{35} \end{bmatrix} \begin{bmatrix} 0.1 & 0.3 & 0 \\ 0.3 & -0.2 & -0.1 \\ 0 & -0.1 & 0.1 \end{bmatrix}$$

$$\times \begin{bmatrix} 1/\sqrt{10} & 0 & 3/\sqrt{10} \\ 3/\sqrt{14} & 2/\sqrt{14} & -1/\sqrt{14} \\ -3/\sqrt{35} & 5/\sqrt{35} & 1/\sqrt{35} \end{bmatrix}^{-1} = \begin{bmatrix} 0.1 & & \\ & 0.3 & \\ & & -0.4 \end{bmatrix}$$

and

$$\hat{y} + 26.267 = 0.1X_1^2 + 0.3X_2^2 - 0.4X_3^2$$

d) Typical Surfaces Generated by Second-Degree Equations

The nature of typical surfaces generated from a second-degree equation can be appreciated by its canonical forms. For two factors, when both coefficients d_1 and d_2 are negative, the contours of the fitted surface are ellipses. Figure 8.2.1 shows the case when d_1 is smaller in absolute value than d_2, and the contour has the major axes along the X_1 direction. The surface is a hill. When both

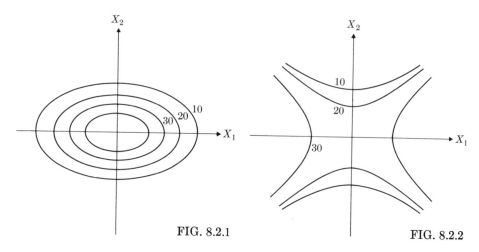

FIG. 8.2.1   FIG. 8.2.2

d_1 and d_2 are positive, the surface will be a basin. When d_1 is negative and d_2 is positive, the contours are hyperbolas. Figure 8.2.2 shows the case when d_1 is smaller in absolute value than d_2. The surface is a saddle. When d_1 is negative and d_2 is zero, the contours become straight lines as shown in Fig. 8.2.3. This may be considered as the limiting situation of either one of the above cases. The surface is the stationary ridge. When d_1 is negative, d_2 is zero, and the center of the system is at infinity. The contours are parabolas as shown in Fig. 8.2.4. The surface is the rising ridge. This may be considered as the limiting case of the above mentioned ellipses or hyperbolas with center at infinity.

With three factors, the contour surfaces can be built up from contour lines of two dimensions by superposition. The contour surfaces are again revealed by the signs of d_1, d_2, and d_3. For example, if the signs are $(-\,-\,-)$, the contour surfaces are ellipsoids. The following is a list of some typical contour surfaces

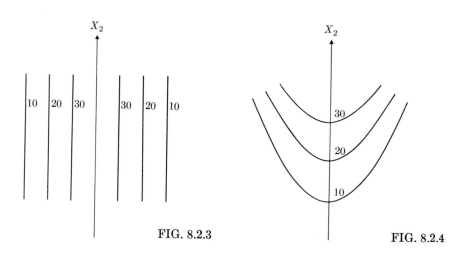

FIG. 8.2.3   FIG. 8.2.4

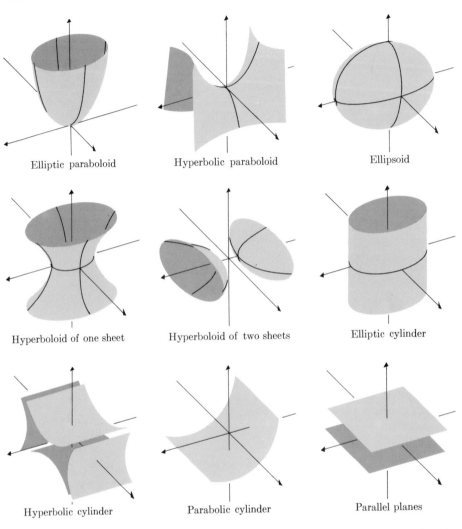

Elliptic paraboloid   Hyperbolic paraboloid   Ellipsoid

Hyperboloid of one sheet   Hyperboloid of two sheets   Elliptic cylinder

Hyperbolic cylinder   Parabolic cylinder   Parallel planes

FIG. 8.2.5

generated by quadratic equations in three variables (see Fig. 8.2.5):

$(- - 0)$,	center at infinity	Elliptic paraboloids
$(+ - 0)$,	center at infinity	Hyperbolic paraboloids
$(- - -)$		Ellipsoids
$(+ + -)$		Hyperboloids of one sheet
$(+ - -)$		Hyperboloids of two sheets
$(- - 0)$		Elliptic cylinders
$(- + 0)$		Hyperbolic cylinders
$(- 0\ 0)$,	center at infinity	Parabolic cylinders
$(- 0\ 0)$		Parallel planes

8.3 RESPONSE SURFACE DESIGNS

a) First-Order Designs

If it may be assumed that within a limited region in the space of the K factors the response surface can be approximated by a plane which takes the equation

$$y_u = b_0 + b_1 x_{1u} + b_2 x_{2u} + b_3 x_{3u} + \cdots + b_K x_{Ku} + e_u \qquad (8.3.1)$$

there is a unique class of designs which will minimize the variances of the estimates of the b's. They are the orthogonal designs including the two-level factorial designs and fractional factorial designs. These designs are easy to carry out. Furthermore, they can be augmented to form designs of second order. In general, they also provide some degrees of freedom for testing *"lack of fit"* to determine if the linear model is adequate. The sum of squares of deviations from the fitted linear equation, that is, $\sum(y_u - \hat{y}_u)^2$ contains two sources of variation: (1) the experimental error, and (2) the inadequacy of the linear model to represent the response surface. If the mean square corresponding to (2) is considerably larger than the mean square for experimental error, inadequacy of the linear model is indicated. A common method of providing an estimate of the experimental error variance is to conduct a number of tests at the factorial combination at which each factor has the midpoint value between the high level and the low level. This point is commonly called the *center of the design*.

For experiments with factors at two levels, we simplify the calculations by conventionally reducing the levels of each factor to standardized levels, with the high level at $+1$ and the lower level at -1. For 2-level factorial design and fractional factorial designs with standardized levels, the estimate of b_i in model (8.3.1) is simply

$$\hat{b}_i = \frac{\sum_u y_u x_{iu}}{\sum_u x_{iu}^2}$$

and the variance of $\hat{b}_i$ is

$$\text{Var}\,[\hat{b}_i] = \frac{\sigma^2}{\sum_u x_{iu}^2}$$

where σ^2 is the error variance. When the center point is replicated n_0 times, σ^2 is estimated from the sum of squares of deviations of the n_0 responses from their mean with $n_0 - 1$ degrees of freedom. These replications at the center will not change the values of the coefficients $\hat{b}_1, \hat{b}_2, \ldots, \hat{b}_K$, but $\hat{b}_0$ becomes the general mean of all the responses. Note also that the sum of squares due to $\hat{b}_i$ is

$$\hat{b}_i \left(\sum_u y_u x_{iu} \right) = \frac{(\sum_u y_u x_{iu})^2}{\sum_u x_{iu}^2}$$

and the sum of squares of deviations from the fitted equation is computed from

$$\sum_u (y_u - \hat{y}_u)^2 = \sum_u y_u^2 - \sum_{i=0}^{K} \hat{b}_i \left(\sum_u y_u x_{iu} \right)$$

The coefficient $b_i (1 \leq i \leq K)$ in (8.3.1) measures the slope of the plane in the direction x_i, that is, the change in y per unit change in x_i. Since we use standardized levels and since x_i changes from a level of -1 unit to a level of $+1$ unit, b_i represents half the average change in y when the factor x_i changes from the lower level to the higher level. This means that the coefficients $b_1, b_2, \ldots, b_K$ are half of the main effects of the factors $x_1, x_2, \ldots, x_K$ defined in Section 7.2. If we fit a more complex model including all cross-product terms, the coefficients of these terms will be half of the interaction effects from 2-factor interactions up to K-factor interactions, respectively. The degrees of freedom provided by a 2^K complete factorial or a fractional replicate for testing "lack of fit" of the model (8.3.1) represent contributions due to the interactions. When replications are made at the center point, an additional degree of freedom is available for measuring "lack of fit." The sum of squares for this single degree of freedom is computed as

$$\frac{n_0 n_1}{n_0 + n_1} (\bar{y}_0 - \bar{y}_1)^2$$

where n_1 is the number of points not at the center, and $\bar{y}_0$, $\bar{y}_1$ are means at the center and at the other points of the design respectively.

Now consider a numerical example. Suppose that the data for a first-order design are given in Table 8.3.1, where the levels of the three quantitative factors x_1, x_2, and x_3 are listed in standardized form. The design consists of a 2^3 factorial and 4 center points.

The sums $\sum_u x_{iu}$ and sums of cross-products $\sum_u x_{iu} x_{i'u}$ $(i \neq i')$ are zero. The other sums are

$$\sum_u x_{iu}^2 = 8.0 \quad (i = 1, 2, 3)$$

$$\sum_u x_{1u} y_u = 20.0$$

$$\sum_u x_{2u} y_u = 25.6$$

$$\sum_u x_{3u} y_u = 11.2$$

$$\sum_u y_u = 360.0$$

TABLE 8.3.1

x_1	x_2	x_3	y
-1	-1	-1	24.3
1	-1	-1	27.3
-1	1	-1	29.1
1	1	-1	33.7
-1	-1	1	25.3
1	-1	1	30.3
-1	1	1	31.3
1	1	1	38.7
0	0	0	30.2
0	0	0	30.4
0	0	0	29.5
0	0	0	29.9

The estimates of b_i are

$$\hat{b}_0 = \frac{360}{12} = 30.0, \qquad \hat{b}_1 = \frac{20}{8} = 2.5$$

$$\hat{b}_2 = \frac{25.6}{8} = 3.2, \qquad \hat{b}_3 = \frac{11.2}{8} = 1.4$$

TABLE 8.3.2

Source	SS	d.f.	MS
b_1	50.00	1	50.00
b_2	81.92	1	81.92
b_3	15.68	1	15.68
Lack of fit	6.24	5	1.25
Error	0.46	3	0.18
Total	154.30	11	

Hence the fitted equation is

$$\hat{y} = 30.0 + 2.5x_1 + 3.2x_2 + 1.4x_3$$

The analysis-of-variance table is shown in Table 8.3.2. The F-ratio for testing "lack of fit" is $1.25/0.18 = 6.94$, which indicates the adequacy of the linear model. If this were an actual experiment, additional steps following the procedure described in Section 8.4 might be taken.

b) Rotatable Designs

The condition of minimum variance of the estimates of individual coefficients, however, does not lead to a unique class of designs for response surfaces of order higher than one. In addition, when designed experiments are conducted mainly for fitting response surfaces, the accuracy of the estimation of the response y is usually of more interest than the accuracy of the estimation of individual coefficients b_i. It is therefore reasonable to consider the variance of the estimated response, Var $[\hat{y}_u]$, at any point on the fitted surface. This variance is a function of the coordinates x_{iu} of the point, and indicates the joint accuracy of the coefficients $\hat{b}_i$. For a given design, the value of this variance function may be larger for some sets of values of $(x_1, x_2, \ldots, x_K)$ and smaller for some other sets of values. In general, it may change along different directions of the x-axes. In other words, it may vary when the surface is oriented through an arbitrary angle about the origin.

In exploratory experiments, the experimenter usually has no rational basis for specifying the accuracy of $\hat{y}$ in any direction along the x-axes. Hence it is reasonable to require that designs for exploring response surfaces have constant Var $[\hat{y}]$ at all points equidistant from the center of the design. This means that the variance of the response estimated by the fitted model is a function only of

$$\rho^2 = \sum_{i=1}^{K} x_i^2$$

A design which satisfies this criterion will leave Var $[\hat{y}]$ unchanged when the design is rotated about the center $(0, 0, \ldots, 0)$, and it is called a *rotatable design*.

A set of points, equally spaced on a circle, or a sphere, or a hypersphere and thus forming the vertices of a regular polygon in a plane, or polyhedron in a

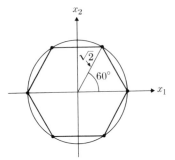

FIG. 8.3.1

TABLE 8.3.3

x_1	x_2
$0.500(\sqrt{2})$	$0.866(\sqrt{2})$
$-0.500(\sqrt{2})$	$0.866(\sqrt{2})$
$-1.000(\sqrt{2})$	0
$-0.500(\sqrt{2})$	$-0.866(\sqrt{2})$
$0.500(\sqrt{2})$	$-0.866(\sqrt{2})$
$1.000(\sqrt{2})$	0

three-dimensional space, or polytope in higher-dimensional spaces, can provide equiradial sets of points which may be combined to form rotatable designs. For example, for 2 factors and 6 experimental points, a rotatable design of first order can be constructed by using the vertices of a hexagon shown in Fig. 8.3.1. The coordinates of the vertices used for the design are given in Table 8.3.3. The 2-level factorial designs and fractional factorial designs discussed in Section 7.3 are also examples of first-order rotatable designs.

For two factors, a second-order rotatable design is obtained if we combine $n_2(>4)$ points, equally spaced on a circle with n_1 points at the center of the circle. In general, the design matrix for a second-order rotatable design in two dimensions can be written as that in Table 8.3.4, where $\theta = 2\pi/n_2$ and α is chosen such that $\sum_u x_{iu}^2 = n_1 + n_2$. For example, if $n_2 = 6$, $n_1 = 6$ and $\alpha = 2$, we get a second-order rotatable design as shown in Table 8.3.5, where the first six experimental points are the coordinates of the vertices of a hexagon inscribed in a circle with radius 2.

In three dimensions, sets of n points evenly spaced on a sphere are given by the vertices of the five regular figures. (See Fig. 8.3.2.) These are the tetra-

TABLE 8.3.4

x_1	x_2
$\alpha \cos \theta$	$\alpha \sin \theta$
$\alpha \cos 2\theta$	$\alpha \sin 2\theta$
$\alpha \cos 3\theta$	$\alpha \sin 3\theta$
$\vdots$	$\vdots$
$\alpha \cos n_2\theta$	$\alpha \sin n_2\theta$
0	0
0	0
$\vdots$	$\vdots$
0	0

TABLE 8.3.5

x_1	x_2
$2(0.500)$	$2(0.866)$
$2(-0.500)$	$2(0.866)$
$2(-1.000)$	$2(0.000)$
$2(-0.500)$	$2(-0.866)$
$2(0.500)$	$2(-0.866)$
$2(1.000)$	$2(0.000)$
0	0
0	0
0	0
0	0
0	0
0	0

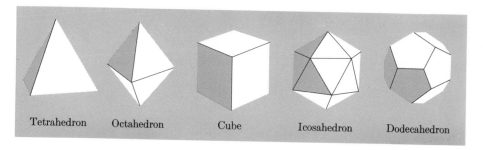

| Tetrahedron | Octahedron | Cube | Icosahedron | Dodecahedron |

FIG. 8.3.2

hedron ($n = 4$), the octahedron ($n = 6$), the cube ($n = 8$), the icosahedron ($n = 12$), and the dodecahedron ($n = 20$). The vertices of the tetrahedron, octahedron, and cube do not individually give rotatable sets of order 2 but they all supply rotatable sets of order 1, and they may be combined to give second-order rotatable designs. However, the dodecahedron and the icosahedron provide a larger number of points and do supply rotatable sets of order 2. In general, an infinite number of three-dimensional second-order rotatable designs can be generated by combining in various ways the vertices of cubes, octahedra, dodecahedra, and icosahedra with or without added center points.

c) Central Composite Second-Order Rotatable Designs

One important class of designs, for example, is obtained by combining the vertices of a cube and of an octahedron concentrically placed and preferably with center points added. The design matrix for a *cube-plus-octahedron rotatable design* is shown in Table 8.3.6.

Rotatable designs in more than three dimensions are constructed from vertices of the regular simplex (K-dimensional analogue of the tetrahedron having $K + 1$ vertices), the cross-polytope (K-dimensional analogue of the octahedron having $2K$ vertices) and the hypercube (K-dimensional analogue of the cube having 2^K vertices). The regular simplex only supplies a first-order rotatable design. However, a second-order rotatable design can always be obtained by combining the cross polytope and hypercube. The *hypercube-plus-cross-polytope second-order rotatable designs*, commonly called *central composite designs*, are very useful in practice. They may be built up in stages. At each stage, valuable information can be obtained, and thus they are suitable for sequential experimentation. The hypercube part of the design supplies experimental points which make up a 2^K factorial design. The cross polytope part of the design provides experimental points at which all the variables except one are held in turn at the "center" (midpoint) levels, the remaining variable is first set at a level above its center value and then at a level below its center value. Since in standard orientation these points lie along the coordinate axes, they may be called axial points. When K is large, a fractional replicate, in which no effects of second order or lower order are confounded, can replace the full hypercube.

TABLE 8.3.6

x_1	x_2	x_3
-1	-1	-1
1	-1	-1
-1	1	-1
1	1	-1
-1	-1	1
1	-1	1
-1	1	1
1	1	1
-1.682	0	0
1.682	0	0
0	-1.682	0
0	1.682	0
0	0	-1.682
0	0	-1.682
0	0	0
0	0	0
0	0	0
0	0	0
0	0	0
0	0	0

For a K-dimensional second-order rotatable design with $n_a = 2K$ axial points, $n_c = 2^{(K-P)}$ points in the $(\frac{1}{2})^P$ replicate of the 2^K factorial, and n_0 center points, the complete list of experimental points is as follows:

1) n_c points (2^K factorial or suitable fraction)

$(\pm 1, \pm 1, \pm 1, \ldots, \pm 1)$

2) n_a axial points

$(\pm \alpha, 0, 0, \ldots, 0)$
$(0, \pm \alpha, 0, \ldots, 0)$
$\vdots$
$(0, 0, 0, \ldots, \pm \alpha)$

3) n_0 center points

$(0, 0, 0, \ldots, 0)$
$(0, 0, 0, \ldots, 0)$
$\vdots$
$(0, 0, 0, \ldots, 0)$

where the scaling is such that the points of the hypercube or its fraction have their coordinates equal to plus or minus unity, and

$$\alpha = n_c^{1/4} = 2^{(K-P)/4}$$

For example, in four dimensions, a second-order rotatable (central composite) design, given in Table 8.3.7, is constructed from the combination of a 2^4 factorial, with 8 axial points and 7 center points. In five dimensions, a second-order rotatable design, shown in Table 8.3.8, consists of a $\frac{1}{2}$-replicate of a 2^5

TABLE 8.3.7

x_1	x_2	x_3	x_4	x_1	x_2	x_3	x_4
−1	−1	−1	−1	−2	0	0	0
1	−1	−1	−1	2	0	0	0
−1	1	−1	−1	0	−2	0	0
1	1	−1	−1	0	2	0	0
−1	−1	1	−1	0	0	−2	0
1	−1	1	−1	0	0	2	0
−1	1	1	−1	0	0	0	−2
1	1	1	−1	0	0	0	2
−1	−1	−1	1	0	0	0	0
1	−1	−1	1	0	0	0	0
−1	1	−1	1	0	0	0	0
1	1	−1	1	0	0	0	0
−1	−1	1	1	0	0	0	0
1	−1	1	1	0	0	0	0
−1	1	1	1	0	0	0	0
1	1	1	1				

TABLE 8.3.8

x_1	x_2	x_3	x_4	x_5	x_1	x_2	x_3	x_4	x_5
−1	−1	−1	−1	1	−2	0	0	0	0
1	−1	−1	−1	−1	2	0	0	0	0
−1	1	−1	−1	−1	0	−2	0	0	0
1	1	−1	−1	1	0	2	0	0	0
−1	−1	1	−1	−1	0	0	−2	0	0
1	−1	1	−1	1	0	0	2	0	0
−1	1	1	−1	1	0	0	0	−2	0
1	1	1	−1	−1	0	0	0	2	0
−1	−1	−1	1	−1	0	0	0	0	−2
1	−1	−1	1	1	0	0	0	0	2
−1	1	−1	1	1	0	0	0	0	0
1	1	−1	1	−1	0	0	0	0	0
−1	−1	1	1	1	0	0	0	0	0
1	−1	1	1	−1	0	0	0	0	0
−1	1	1	1	−1	0	0	0	0	0
1	1	1	1	1	0	0	0	0	0

factorial, with 10 axial points and 6 center points. In six dimensions, a design of the same type, given in Table 8.3.9, is formed from a $\frac{1}{2}$-replicate of a 2^6 factorial, with 12 axial points and 9 center points. Table 8.3.10 gives a summary of some of these designs.

In the analysis of variance, the total sum of squares may be partitioned into four parts: (1) the contribution due to first-order terms, (2) that due to the

TABLE 8.3.9

x_1	x_2	x_3	x_4	x_5	x_6	x_1	x_2	x_3	x_4	x_5	x_6
−1	−1	−1	−1	−1	−1	−1	1	−1	1	1	1
1	−1	−1	−1	−1	1	1	1	−1	1	1	−1
−1	1	−1	−1	−1	1	−1	−1	1	1	1	−1
1	1	−1	−1	−1	−1	1	−1	1	1	1	−1
−1	−1	1	−1	−1	1	−1	1	1	1	1	1
1	−1	1	−1	−1	−1	1	1	1	1	1	1
−1	1	1	−1	−1	−1	−2.378	0	0	0	0	0
1	1	1	−1	−1	1	2.378	0	0	0	0	0
−1	−1	−1	1	−1	1	0	−2.378	0	0	0	0
1	−1	−1	1	−1	−1	0	2.378	0	0	0	0
−1	1	−1	1	−1	−1	0	0	−2.378	0	0	0
1	1	−1	1	−1	1	0	0	2.378	0	0	0
−1	−1	1	1	−1	−1	0	0	0	−2.378	0	0
1	−1	1	1	−1	1	0	0	0	2.378	0	0
−1	1	1	1	−1	1	0	0	0	0	−2.378	0
1	1	1	1	−1	−1	0	0	0	0	2.378	0
−1	−1	−1	−1	1	1	0	0	0	0	0	−2.378
1	−1	−1	−1	1	−1	0	0	0	0	0	2.378
−1	1	−1	−1	1	−1	0	0	0	0	0	0
1	1	−1	−1	1	1	0	0	0	0	0	0
−1	−1	1	−1	1	−1	0	0	0	0	0	0
1	−1	1	−1	1	1	0	0	0	0	0	0
−1	1	1	−1	1	1	0	0	0	0	0	0
1	1	1	−1	1	−1	0	0	0	0	0	0
−1	−1	−1	1	1	−1	0	0	0	0	0	0
1	−1	−1	1	1	1	0	0	0	0	0	0

second-order terms, (3) a "lack of fit" component which measures the deviations of the responses from the fitted surface, and (4) experimental error which is obtained from the center points. The general formulas for sums of squares are shown in Table 8.3.11 where N is the total number of experimental points, and y_s represent the n_0 responses at the center with mean $\bar{y}_0$.

Now suppose that the data for a central composite second-order rotatable design are those given in Table 8.3.12. The design matrix $\mathbf{D}$ and the matrix $\mathbf{X}$ are also shown in the same table with the levels of the 3 factors x_1, x_2, and x_3 in standardized form.

The matrix $\mathbf{X'X}$ and vector $\mathbf{X'Y}$ are shown in Table 8.3.13. The inverse of $\mathbf{X'X}$ is given in Table 8.3.14. The fitted equation is

$$\hat{y} = 10.5 + 0.2x_1 + 0.6x_2 + 4x_3 + 0.1x_1^2 - 0.2x_2^2 + 0.1x_3^2$$
$$+ 0.6x_1x_2 + 0x_1x_3 - 0.2x_2x_3$$

TABLE 8.3.10

Number of factors	2	3	4	5	$5(\frac{1}{2}\text{-rep})$	6	$6(\frac{1}{2}\text{-rep})$	7	$7(\frac{1}{2}\text{-rep})$
n_c = number of points in cube	4	8	16	32	16	64	32	128	64
Number of axial points	4	6	8	10	10	12	12	14	14
Number of center points	5	6	7	10	6	15	9	21	14
Total number of points	13	20	31	52	32	91	53	163	92
$\alpha = n_c^{1/4}$	1.4142	1.6818	2.0000	2.3784	2.0000	2.8284	2.3784	3.3636	2.8284

TABLE 8.3.11

Source	SS	d.f.
First-order terms	$\displaystyle\sum_{i=1}^{K} \hat{b}_i \left(\sum_{u=1}^{N} x_{iu} y_u \right)$	K
Second-order terms	$\displaystyle \hat{b}_0 \left(\sum_{u=1}^{N} y_u \right) + \sum_{i=1}^{K} \hat{b}_{ii} \left(\sum_{u=1}^{N} x_{iu}^2 y_u \right) + \sum_{i<j} \hat{b}_{ju} \left(\sum_{u=1}^{N} x_{iu} x_{ju} y_u \right) - \frac{\left(\sum_{u=1}^{N} y_u\right)^2}{N}$	$\dfrac{K(K+1)}{2}$
Lack of fit	Found by subtraction	$n_c + n_a - \dfrac{K(K+3)}{2}$
Error	$\displaystyle\sum_{s=1}^{n_0} (y_s - \bar{y}_0)^2$	$n_0 - 1$
Total	$\displaystyle\sum_{u=1}^{N} y_u^2 - \frac{\left(\sum_{u=1}^{N} y_u\right)^2}{N}$	$n_c + n_a + n_0 - 1$

TABLE 8.3.12

x_0	D			x_1^2	x_2^2	x_3^2	x_1x_2	x_1x_3	x_2x_3	y
	x_1	x_2	x_3							
1	−1	−1	−1	1	1	1	1	1	1	5.54
1	1	−1	−1	1	1	1	−1	−1	1	5.86
1	−1	1	−1	1	1	1	−1	1	−1	7.06
1	1	1	−1	1	1	1	1	−1	−1	7.54
1	−1	−1	1	1	1	1	1	−1	−1	15.06
1	1	−1	1	1	1	1	−1	1	−1	13.14
1	−1	1	1	1	1	1	−1	−1	1	13.54
1	1	1	1	1	1	1	1	1	1	16.26
1	−1.682	0	0	2.828	0	0	0	0	0	10.45
1	1.682	0	0	2.828	0	0	0	0	0	11.12
1	0	−1.682	0	0	2.828	0	0	0	0	8.93
1	0	1.682	0	0	2.828	0	0	0	0	10.94
1	0	0	−1.682	0	0	2.828	0	0	0	4.05
1	0	0	1.682	0	0	2.828	0	0	0	17.51
1	0	0	0	0	0	0	0	0	0	10.70
1	0	0	0	0	0	0	0	0	0	10.50
1	0	0	0	0	0	0	0	0	0	10.90
1	0	0	0	0	0	0	0	0	0	10.70
1	0	0	0	0	0	0	0	0	0	9.90
1	0	0	0	0	0	0	0	0	0	10.30

TABLE 8.3.13

X'X										X'Y
20	0	0	0	13.658	13.658	13.658	0	0	0	210.00000
0	13.658	0	0	0	0	0	0	0	0	2.72694
0	0	13.658	0	0	0	0	0	0	0	8.18082
0	0	0	13.658	0	0	0	0	0	0	54.63972
13.658	0	0	0	24.008	8	8	0	0	0	145.02420
13.658	0	0	0	8	24.008	8	0	0	0	140.21469
13.658	0	0	0	8	8	24.008	0	0	0	144.99591
0	0	0	0	0	0	0	8	0	0	4.80000
0	0	0	0	0	0	0	0	8	0	0.00000
0	0	0	0	0	0	0	0	0	8	−1.60000

The analysis-of-variance results are given in Table 8.3.15. Both the first- and second-order terms are significant. The "lack-of-fit" term is not significant, and indicates the adequacy of the second-order equation. The calculation of the canonical form of this fitted equation was discussed in the preceding section.

TABLE 8.3.14

$$(\mathbf{X}'\mathbf{X})^{-1}$$

0.166338	0	0	0	−0.056791	−0.056791	−0.056791	0	0	0
0	0.073224	0	0	0	0	0	0	0	0
0	0	0.073224	0	0	0	0	0	0	0
0	0	0	0.073224	0	0	0	0	0	0
−0.056791	0	0	0	0.069389	0.006889	0.006889	0	0	0
−0.056791	0	0	0	0.006889	0.069389	0.006889	0	0	0
−0.056791	0	0	0	0.006889	0.006889	0.069389	0	0	0
0	0	0	0	0	0	0	0.125	0	0
0	0	0	0	0	0	0	0	0.125	0
0	0	0	0	0	0	0	0	0	0.125

TABLE 8.3.15

Source	SS	d.f.	MS
First-order terms	224.01276	3	74.671
Second-order terms	4.15907	6	0.693
Lack of fit	2.52505	5	0.505
Error	0.64000	5	0.128
Total	231.33688	19	

TABLE 8.3.16

Number of factors	2	3	4	5	5($\frac{1}{2}$-rep)	6	6($\frac{1}{2}$-rep)	7	7($\frac{1}{2}$-rep)
Blocks within cube									
n_c: Number of points in cube	4	8	16	32	16	64	32	128	64
Number of blocks in cube	1	2	2	4	1	8	2	16	8
Number of points in each block from cube	4	4	8	8	16	8	16	8	8
Number of added center points in each block	3	2	2	2	6	1	4	1	1
Axial block									
n_a: Number of axial points	4	6	8	10	10	12	12	14	14
Number of added center points	3	2	2	4	1	6	2	11	4
Grand total of points in the design	14	20	30	54	33	90	54	169	90
Value of α for orthogonal blocking	1.4142	1.6330	2.0000	2.3664	2.0000	2.8284	2.3664	3.3333	2.8284
Value of α for rotatability	1.4142	1.6818	2.0000	2.3784	2.0000	2.8284	2.3784	3.3636	2.8284

d) Central Composite Second-Order Rotatable Designs in Incomplete Blocks

The central composite rotatable designs lend themselves conveniently to blocking for increasing precision. The blocking is carried out essentially by grouping points of the cube and axial points into separate blocks and suitably distributing the center points. The cube part may be further divided into smaller blocks if a system of confounding for the two-level factorial or fractional factorial design exists such that all the comparisons confounded correspond to interactions between three or more variables, thus the comparisons confounded will not be associated with the comparisons used to estimate the coefficients of the second-degree polynomial. If blocks are orthogonal to the coefficients in the fitted equation, the calculations in the analysis are simplified. But, exact rotatability and exact orthogonality between quadratic variables and block effects is not always attainable. If this is the case, it is simplest in practice to use a design in which the block effects are exactly orthogonal but the condition of rotatability is slightly sacrificed, and a different α value is used.

Orthogonal blocking will not affect the estimation of the coefficients. In the analysis of variance, the block's sum of squares is computed by

$$\sum_i \frac{B_i^2}{r_i} - \frac{(\sum_{u=1}^N y_u)^2}{N}$$

where B_i is the total of the ith block, r_i is the number of units in the ith block. The sum of squares for experimental error is the pooled sum of squares between center points in the same block. The formulas for other components remain the same. Table 8.3.16 lists blocking arrangements for some rotatable and near rotatable central composite designs.

8.4 THE METHOD OF STEEPEST ASCENT

The method of steepest ascent is basically a sequential procedure of conducting small exploratory experiments and making moves in the space of factors along the direction at right angles to the contours of a fitted surface. We may start with a small design (say, a 2^K factorial or a fraction of a 2^K factorial with center at the best-known conditions of x_i) in a chosen region in the space of factors. The observed data are fitted into a linear model. The linear approximation is tested to determine if it fits the data adequately. Now, if the linear fit is adequate, we move to a new point. The path of moving is determined by

$$\hat{b}_i = \frac{\partial \phi}{\partial x_i}$$

where $\phi = \sum \hat{b}_i x_i$ is obtained by the linear fit. That is, the change in x_i in the path of moving up is proportional to $\hat{b}_i$.

Then, a single factorial combination is tested experimentally. If actual response for this new combination is close to the predicted response from the fitted model, a further ascent is made along the same path. This procedure is continued until such closeness is not the case, that is, when the fitted model no longer represents the actual situation in that region of the surface.

At this time, a new, small design is conducted with its center at the last point on the path. We repeat the previous procedure and finally reach a situation in which the 2^K factorial design gives one of the following:

1) All $\hat{b}_i$'s are small. It means that a plateau is reached. Or,

2) Lack of fit is found. The linear approximation is inadequate, and the curvature of the surface must be considered.

Under the condition of (1), only a few final tests are needed for verifying the results of investigation. If we face the situation of (2), a new design of the second-order rotatable type will be conducted to fit a quadratic equation. The quadratic equation can be simplified, by transformation, into a canonical form as described in Section 8.2.

The nature of the fitted quadratic surface can usually be appreciated by examining its canonical form. The course of further action will depend on this examination. In some cases only confirmatory tests are required, in other situations, another second-order design further along the direction of estimated optimum may be conducted. In the event that the quadratic surface does not fit, then addition of points to fit a cubic surface may account for the inadequacy. Because of their increasing complexity, fourth-degree and higher-degree polynomial equations appear to have very limited practical value. If it is evident that lower-degree polynomials will not provide satisfactory approximation to the response surface, intensive investigation in the vicinity of points with relatively high responses may be recommended.

REFERENCES

1. Box, G. E. P., and J. S. Hunter, "Multifactor Experimental Designs for Exploring Response Surfaces," *Annals of Math. Stat.*, **28**, 1, 195–241 (1957).

2. Box, G. E. P., "The Exploration and Exploitation of Response Surfaces: Some General Considerations and Examples," *Biometrics*, **10**, 16–60 (1954).

3. Box, G. E. P., and P. V. Youle, "The Exploration and Exploitation of Response Surfaces: An Example of the Link between the Fitted Surface and the Basic Mechanism of the System," *Biometrics*, **11**, 287–323 (1955).

4. White, P. A., "The Computation of Eigenvalues and Eigenvectors of a Matrix," *J. Soc. Indust. Appl. Math.*, **6**, 4, 393–437 (1958).

5. Kuo, S. S., *Numerical Methods and Computers*. Addison-Wesley, Reading, Mass., 1965.

9 SPECIAL TOPICS

9.1 GENERAL LINEAR HYPOTHESIS MODEL

In this section we shall outline some results from the theory of general linear hypothesis model. The results are basically generalizations of some of the ideas stated in Sections 0.3 and 0.4.

Consider a random variable y which depends on K known quantities x_1, x_2, ..., x_K and on K unknown parameters b_1, b_2, ..., b_K. To estimate the b_i, a random sample of size n is taken. Assume that the observations y_u can be expressed as linear functions of x_1, x_2, ..., x_K, and that random residual errors e_j are independently distributed with zero mean and equal variance σ^2. Then the model is

$$y_u = b_1 x_{1u} + b_2 x_{2u} + \cdots + b_K x_{Ku} + e_u$$

$$(u = 1, 2, \ldots, n)$$

Or, in more compact form:

$$\mathbf{Y} = \mathbf{XB} + \mathbf{E} \tag{9.1.1}$$

where

$$\mathbf{Y} = \begin{bmatrix} y_1 \\ y_2 \\ \vdots \\ y_n \end{bmatrix}, \qquad \mathbf{X} = \begin{bmatrix} x_{11} & x_{21} & \cdots & x_{K1} \\ x_{12} & x_{22} & \cdots & x_{K2} \\ \vdots & & & \vdots \\ x_{1n} & x_{2n} & \cdots & x_{Kn} \end{bmatrix}$$

$$\mathbf{B} = \begin{bmatrix} b_1 \\ b_2 \\ \vdots \\ b_K \end{bmatrix}, \qquad \mathbf{E} = \begin{bmatrix} e_1 \\ e_2 \\ \vdots \\ e_n \end{bmatrix}$$

The model (9.1.1) is called the general linear hypothesis model of full rank, if rank of $\mathbf{X}$ is equal to K where $K \leqq n$.

Since

$$\mathbf{E'E} = (\mathbf{Y} - \mathbf{XB})'(\mathbf{Y} - \mathbf{XB})$$

and normal equations

$$\frac{\partial}{\partial \mathbf{B}} (\mathbf{E'E}) = 2\mathbf{X'Y} - 2\mathbf{X'X\hat{B}} = 0$$

173

the least squares estimate of **B** is

$$\hat{\mathbf{B}} = (\mathbf{X}'\mathbf{X})^{-1}\mathbf{X}'\mathbf{Y}$$

which is the same as the maximum likelihood estimate if, in addition, we assume that the residual errors are distributed normally.

The unbiased estimate of σ^2 is given by

$$\hat{\sigma}^2 = \frac{(\mathbf{Y} - \mathbf{X}\hat{\mathbf{B}})'(\mathbf{Y} - \mathbf{X}\hat{\mathbf{B}})}{n - K} = \frac{\mathbf{Y}'\mathbf{Y} - \hat{\mathbf{B}}'\mathbf{X}'\mathbf{Y}}{n - K}$$

The Gauss-Markov theorem states that the least squares method gives the minimum variance linear unbiased estimate of **B**.

Furthermore, under the assumption of normality, $\hat{b}_i$ is normally distributed with mean b_i and variance $C_{ii}\sigma^2$, where C_{ii} is the iith element of $(\mathbf{X}'\mathbf{X})^{-1}$; hence $(\hat{b}_i - b_i)/\sigma\sqrt{C_{ii}}$ is distributed normally with zero mean and unit variance and is independent of $(n - K)\hat{\sigma}^2/\sigma^2$, which is distributed as $\chi^2(n - K)$. Consequently, the quantity

$$\frac{\hat{b}_i - b_i}{\sigma\sqrt{C_{ii}}} \sqrt{\frac{\sigma^2}{\hat{\sigma}^2}} = \frac{\hat{b}_i - b_i}{\sqrt{\hat{\sigma}^2 C_{ii}}}$$

follows a t-distribution with $(n - K)$ degrees of freedom, and the confidence limits for b_i are given by

$$\hat{b}_i - t\sqrt{C_{ii}\hat{\sigma}^2} \le b_i \le \hat{b}_i + t\sqrt{C_{ii}\hat{\sigma}^2},$$

where t is the t-value corresponding to $(n - K)$ degrees of freedom at a chosen confidence coefficient $1 - \alpha$.

An important type of test which is often desired by the experimenter is to test the hypothesis that $b_1 = b_2 = \cdots = b_q = 0$ $(q < K)$ in the model equation (9.1.1).

Partitioning **X** and **B** such that

$$\mathbf{X} = [\mathbf{X}_1 \mathbf{X}_2], \qquad \mathbf{B} = \begin{bmatrix} \mathbf{B}_1 \\ \mathbf{B}_2 \end{bmatrix}$$

where

$$\mathbf{X}_1 = \begin{bmatrix} x_{11} & x_{21} & \cdots & x_{q1} \\ x_{12} & x_{22} & \cdots & x_{q2} \\ \vdots & & & \vdots \\ x_{1n} & x_{2n} & \cdots & x_{qn} \end{bmatrix}$$

$$\mathbf{X}_2 = \begin{bmatrix} x_{(q+1)1} & x_{(q+2)1} & \cdots & x_{K1} \\ x_{(q+1)2} & x_{(q+2)2} & \cdots & x_{K2} \\ \vdots & & & \vdots \\ x_{(q+1)n} & x_{(q+2)n} & \cdots & x_{Kn} \end{bmatrix}$$

$$\mathbf{B}_1 = \begin{bmatrix} b_1 \\ b_2 \\ \vdots \\ b_q \end{bmatrix}, \qquad \mathbf{B}_2 = \begin{bmatrix} b_{q+1} \\ b_{q+2} \\ \vdots \\ b_K \end{bmatrix}$$

we can write

$$\mathbf{Y} = \mathbf{XB} + \mathbf{E} = [\mathbf{X_1 X_2}]\begin{bmatrix}\mathbf{B_1}\\\mathbf{B_2}\end{bmatrix} + \mathbf{E}$$

or

$$\mathbf{Y} = \mathbf{X_1 B_1} + \mathbf{X_2 B_2} + \mathbf{E}$$

From the analysis-of-variance point of view we have the following quantities:

1) $\mathbf{Y'Y}$ is the total sum of squares (uncorrected) with n degrees of freedom.

2) $\hat{\mathbf{B}}'\mathbf{X'Y}$ is the sum of squares due to $\mathbf{B}$ with K degrees of freedom, written as

$$SS(\mathbf{B}) = \mathbf{B'X'Y}$$

$\hat{\mathbf{B}}$ is the solution to the normal equations

$$\mathbf{X'X}\hat{\mathbf{B}} = \mathbf{X'Y}$$

3) $\hat{\mathbf{B}}_2'\mathbf{X}_2'\mathbf{Y}$ is the sum of squares due to $\mathbf{B_2}$ and ignoring $\mathbf{B_1}$ with $(K - q)$ degrees of freedom, written as

$$SS(\mathbf{B_2}) = \hat{\mathbf{B}}_2'\mathbf{X}_2'\mathbf{Y}$$

$\hat{\mathbf{B}}_2$ is the solution to the normal equations

$$\mathbf{X}_2'\mathbf{X}_2\hat{\mathbf{B}}_2 = \mathbf{X}_2'\mathbf{Y}$$

which are obtained when only $\mathbf{B_2}$ is used in the model equation.

4) $\hat{\mathbf{B}}'\mathbf{X'Y} - \hat{\mathbf{B}}_2'\mathbf{X}_2'\mathbf{Y}$ is the sum of squares due to $\mathbf{B_1}$ and adjusted for $\mathbf{B_2}$ with q degrees of freedom, written as

$$SS(\mathbf{B_1}/\mathbf{B_2}) = \hat{\mathbf{B}}'\mathbf{X'Y} - \hat{\mathbf{B}}_2'\mathbf{X}_2'\mathbf{Y}$$

5) $\mathbf{Y'Y} - \hat{\mathbf{B}}'\mathbf{X'Y}$ is the sum of squares due to error with $(n - K)$ degrees of freedom.

6) To test the hypothesis $\mathbf{B_1} = 0$, the F-ratio is given by

$$\frac{n - K}{q} \frac{\hat{\mathbf{B}}'\mathbf{X'Y} - \hat{\mathbf{B}}_2'\mathbf{X}_2'\mathbf{Y}}{\mathbf{Y'Y} - \hat{\mathbf{B}}'\mathbf{X'Y}}$$

In general, to test a given hypothesis that some subset of b_i is all equal to zero, it requires that the corresponding b_i be set equal to zero in the normal equations and the remaining equations be solved. This is time-consuming. However, if all b_i in the model are orthogonal, that is, if $\mathbf{X'X}$ is a diagonal matrix, then the sum of squares due to any subset of the b_i adjusted for any other subset is equal to the sum of squares due to the given subset of the b_i ignoring the other subset, and all tests can be easily performed.

9.2 ANALYSIS OF VARIANCE IN EXPERIMENTAL DESIGN BY THE GENERAL LINEAR HYPOTHESIS APPROACH

The linear models used in experimental designs may be considered as special cases of the general linear hypothesis model. That is, in the model

$$y_u = b_1 x_{1u} + b_2 x_{2u} + \cdots + b_K x_{Ku} + e_u$$

b_1 may be regarded as the general mean, $b_2, b_3, \ldots, b_K$, the main effects and interactions, and $x_1 = 1$; the other x_i take the values 0 or 1.

For example, for a two-factor model without interaction, with A at three levels and B at two levels, the usual model is written as

$$y_{11} = \mu + \alpha_1 + \beta_1 + e_{11}$$
$$y_{12} = \mu + \alpha_1 + \beta_2 + e_{12}$$
$$y_{21} = \mu + \alpha_2 + \beta_1 + e_{21}$$
$$y_{22} = \mu + \alpha_2 + \beta_2 + e_{22}$$
$$y_{31} = \mu + \alpha_3 + \beta_1 + e_{31}$$
$$y_{32} = \mu + \alpha_3 + \beta_2 + e_{32}$$

or

$$y_{ij} = \mu + \alpha_i + \beta_j + e_{ij} \quad (i = 1, 2, 3; \quad j = 1, 2)$$

or in matrix notation

$$
\begin{bmatrix} y_{11} \\ y_{12} \\ y_{21} \\ y_{22} \\ y_{31} \\ y_{32} \end{bmatrix}
=
\begin{bmatrix}
1 & 1 & 0 & 0 & 1 & 0 \\
1 & 1 & 0 & 0 & 0 & 1 \\
1 & 0 & 1 & 0 & 1 & 0 \\
1 & 0 & 1 & 0 & 0 & 1 \\
1 & 0 & 0 & 1 & 1 & 0 \\
1 & 0 & 0 & 1 & 0 & 1
\end{bmatrix}
\begin{bmatrix} \mu \\ \alpha_1 \\ \alpha_2 \\ \alpha_3 \\ \beta_1 \\ \beta_2 \end{bmatrix}
+
\begin{bmatrix} e_{11} \\ e_{12} \\ e_{21} \\ e_{22} \\ e_{31} \\ e_{32} \end{bmatrix}
$$

It can be shown that the 6×6 matrix $\mathbf{X}$ has rank 4, which is less than the number of parameters in the model. Therefore, the model is not of full rank.

The linear models in experimental designs are in general not of full rank. This means that the $K \times K$ matrix $\mathbf{X'X}$ has no inverse and the normal equations

$$\mathbf{X'X\hat{B}} = \mathbf{X'Y}$$

do not give unique solutions of $\mathbf{\hat{B}}$.

The general procedure is then to impose side conditions

$$\mathbf{U\hat{B}} = 0$$

such that the matrix

$$\begin{bmatrix} \mathbf{X'X} \\ \mathbf{U} \end{bmatrix}$$

has rank K. Fortunately, meaningful side conditions can often be so chosen that not only the model has full rank but also the solution of

$$\mathbf{X'X\hat{B}} = \mathbf{X'Y}, \qquad \mathbf{U\hat{B}} = 0$$

is simple. For example, in the 3×2 factorial experiment discussed above, we may choose

$$\mathbf{U\hat{B}} = \begin{bmatrix} \hat{\alpha}_1 + \hat{\alpha}_2 + \hat{\alpha}_3 \\ \hat{\beta}_1 + \hat{\beta}_2 \end{bmatrix} = 0$$

The quantities $\mathbf{X'Y}$ and $\hat{\mathbf{B}}'\mathbf{X'Y}$ are important in obtaining the normal equations and in testing hypothesis. Let us examine them.

The elements of matrix $\mathbf{X}$ are all 0's and 1's. The elements of $\mathbf{X'Y}$ are formed by multiplying each column of $\mathbf{X}$ by elements of $\mathbf{Y}$. This is equivalent to getting the overall sum of elements of $\mathbf{Y}$ or partial sums of $\mathbf{Y}$. For example, in the 3×2 factorial experiment, we have

$$\mathbf{X'Y} = \begin{bmatrix} \sum\sum y_{ij} \\ \sum y_{1j} \\ \sum y_{2j} \\ \sum y_{3j} \\ \sum y_{i1} \\ \sum y_{i2} \end{bmatrix}$$

The quantity $\hat{\mathbf{B}}'\mathbf{X'Y}$ is formed by multiplying elements of $\mathbf{X'Y}$ by elements of $\hat{\mathbf{B}}$, respectively, and taking their sum. For example, in the 3×2 experiment, we then have

$$\hat{\mathbf{B}}'\mathbf{X'Y} = \hat{\mu}\sum\sum y_{ij} + \hat{\alpha}_1\sum y_{1j} + \hat{\alpha}_2\sum y_{2j} + \hat{\alpha}_3\sum y_{3j} + \hat{\beta}_1\sum y_{i1} + \hat{\beta}_2\sum y_{i2}$$

We shall now briefly discuss analysis of variance from the point of view of general linear hypothesis model by considering the case of nonreplicated two-way arrangement (no interaction) and thereby indicating the equivalence between these results and those stated in earlier chapters.

The model for a two-way arrangement with one observation in each cell is written as

$$y_{ij} = \mu + \alpha_i + \beta_j + \epsilon_{ij} \quad (i = 1, 2, \ldots, a; \quad j = 1, 2, \ldots, b)$$

where y_{ij} is an observation related to ith level of factor A and jth level of factor B, μ is an unknown general mean, α_i are the unknown main effects of factor A, β_j are the unknown main effects of factor B, and ϵ_{ij} are random errors which are assumed to be independently distributed with zero mean and variance σ^2. For testing hypothesis and interval estimation, ϵ_{ij} will be assumed to be normally distributed.

The normal equations are $\mathbf{X'X}\hat{\mathbf{B}} = \mathbf{X'Y}$ which may be written in detail in the following way:

$$ab\hat{\mu} + b\hat{\alpha}_1 + \cdots + b\hat{\alpha}_a + a\hat{\beta}_1 + \cdots + a\hat{\beta}_b = \sum_i \sum_j y_{ij}$$

$$b\hat{\mu} + b\hat{\alpha}_p + \hat{\beta}_1 + \cdots + \hat{\beta}_b = \sum_j y_{pj} \quad (p = 1, 2, \ldots, a)$$

$$a\hat{\mu} + \hat{\alpha}_1 + \cdots + \hat{\alpha}_a + a\hat{\beta}_q = \sum_i y_{iq} \quad (q = 1, 2, \ldots, b)$$

Imposing the side conditions

$$\mathbf{U}\hat{\mathbf{B}} = \begin{bmatrix} \sum\hat{\alpha}_i \\ \sum\hat{\beta}_j \end{bmatrix} = 0$$

we obtain

$$\hat{\mu} = y_{..}$$
$$\hat{\alpha}_i = y_{i.} - y_{..}$$
$$\hat{\beta}_j = y_{.j} - y_{..}$$

Hence the sum of the squares due to (μ, α, β) is

$$SS(\mu, \alpha, \beta) = \hat{\mathbf{B}}'\mathbf{X}'\mathbf{Y}$$

$$= \hat{\mu} \sum_i \sum_j y_{ij} + \sum_i \hat{\alpha}_i \left(\sum_j y_{ij} \right) + \sum_j \hat{\beta}_j \left(\sum_i y_{ij} \right)$$

$$= \frac{(\sum_i \sum_j y_{ij})^2}{ab} + \left[\frac{\sum_i (\sum_j y_{ij})^2}{b} - \frac{(\sum_i \sum_j y_{ij})^2}{ab} \right]$$

$$+ \left[\frac{\sum_j (\sum_i y_{ij})^2}{a} - \frac{(\sum_i \sum_j y_{ij})^2}{ab} \right]$$

Under the hypothesis $\alpha_1 = \alpha_2 = \cdots = \alpha_a = 0$, we have the normal equations

$$ab\hat{\mu} + a\hat{\beta}_1 + \cdots + a\hat{\beta}_b = \sum_i \sum_j y_{ij}$$

$$a\hat{\mu} + a\hat{\beta}_q = \sum_i y_{iq} \quad (q = 1, 2, \ldots, b)$$

Imposing

$$\Sigma \hat{\beta}_j = 0$$

we have

$$\hat{\mu} = y_{..}, \qquad \hat{\beta}_j = y_{.j} - y_{..}$$

Therefore the sum of squares due to (μ, β) is

$$SS(\mu, \beta) = \hat{\mu} \sum_i \sum_j y_{ij} + \sum_j \hat{\beta}_j \left(\sum_i \right) y_{ij}$$

$$= \frac{(\sum_i \sum_j y_{ij})^2}{ab} + \left[\frac{\sum_j (\sum_i y_{ij})^2}{a} - \frac{(\sum_i \sum_j y_{ij})^2}{ab} \right]$$

Combining them, we have

$$SS(\alpha/\mu, \beta) = SS(\mu, \alpha, \beta) - SS(\mu, \beta)$$

$$= \frac{\sum_i (\sum_j y_{ij})^2}{b} - \frac{(\sum_i \sum_j y_{ij})^2}{ab}$$

$$= \sum_i \sum_j (y_{i.} - y_{..})^2$$

Similarly, we can show that

$$SS(\beta/\mu, \alpha) = \frac{\sum_j (\sum_i y_{ij})^2}{a} - \frac{(\sum_i \sum_j y_{ij})^2}{ab}$$

$$= \sum_i \sum_j (y_{.j} - y_{..})^2$$

The error sum of squares is

$$SS_E = \mathbf{Y'Y} - \mathbf{\hat{B}'X'Y} = \sum_i \sum_j y_{ij}^2 - SS(\mu, \alpha, \beta)$$

$$= \sum_i \sum_j y_{ij}^2 - \frac{\sum_i (\sum_j y_{ij})^2}{b} - \frac{\sum_j (\sum_i y_{ij})^2}{a} + \frac{(\sum_i \sum_j y_{ij})^2}{ab}$$

$$= \sum_i \sum_j (y_{ij} - y_{i\cdot} - y_{\cdot j} + y_{\cdot\cdot})^2$$

Thus we have the identity

$$\sum_i \sum_j y_{ij}^2 = \frac{(\sum_i \sum_j y_{ij})^2}{ab} + SS(\alpha/\mu, \beta) + SS(\beta/\mu, \alpha) + SS_E$$

or the total variation

$$\sum_i \sum_j y_{ij}^2 - \frac{(\sum_i \sum_j y_{ij})^2}{ab} = SS(\alpha/\mu, \beta) + SS(\beta/\mu, \alpha) + SS_E$$

which is the same as that stated in Chapter 1.

9.3 UNBALANCED EXPERIMENTS

In the preceding chapters, we have discussed multifactor experiments with the common stipulation that we have complete balance throughout, that is, equal number of observations in the cells. Occasionally, an experimenter may not be able to control the experiment to achieve this type of complete balance. In such a case, some undesirable results occur. The normal equations no longer have highly symmetrical coefficients and consequently do not give simple and direct solutions. Furthermore, when the solutions $\hat{\alpha}_i$, $\hat{\beta}_j$ are obtained, they are no longer independent, thus the total sum of squares cannot be partitioned into independent components. To test the null hypothesis that some of the effects are zero, we have to follow the procedure discussed in Section 9.1. We shall describe this procedure in some detail by considering two-way arrangements with unequal numbers of observations in the cells as an example. Some general methods of approximation will also be introduced.

a) Two-Way Arrangement with Unequal Numbers of Observations in the Cells

Let the model of no interactions be given by

$$y_{ijk} = \mu + \alpha_i + \beta_j + e_{ijk}$$
$$(k = 0, 1, 2, \ldots, n_{ij}; \quad i = 1, 2, \ldots, a; \quad j = 1, 2, \ldots, b) \tag{9.3.1}$$

where y_{ijk} is the kth observation in the ijth cell; μ, α_i, β_j are unknown parameters; and e_{ijk} are random variables independently and normally distributed with zero mean and variance σ^2. In the ijth cell, there are n_{ij} observations.

If any $n_{ij} = 0$, the cell is empty. The pattern of nonempty cells in the two-way design must not be poorly conditioned in order to estimate μ, α_i, and β_j. If the number of nonempty cells is q, then the q-rowed submatrix in the matrix of (9.1.1) must have rank $(a + b - 1)$.

Minimizing the expression

$$\sum_i \sum_j \sum_k (y_{ijk} - \mu - \alpha_i - \beta_j)$$

by equating to zero its partial derivatives with respect to μ, α_i, and β_j, we get the normal equations

$$\left(\sum_i \sum_j n_{ij}\right) \hat{\mu} + \sum_i \left(\sum_j n_{ij}\right) \hat{\alpha}_i + \sum_j \left(\sum_i n_{ij}\right) \hat{\beta}_j = \sum_i \sum_j \sum_k y_{ijk}$$

$$(9.3.2)$$

$$\left(\sum_j n_{ij}\right) \hat{\mu} + \left(\sum_j n_{ij}\right) \hat{\alpha}_i + \sum_j n_{ij}\hat{\beta}_j = \sum_j \sum_k y_{ijk}$$

$$(i = 1, 2, \ldots, a) \qquad (9.3.3)$$

$$\left(\sum_i n_{ij}\right) \hat{\mu} + \sum_i n_{ij}\hat{\alpha}_i + \left(\sum_i n_{ij}\right) \hat{\beta}_j = \sum_i \sum_k y_{ijk}$$

$$(j = 1, 2, \ldots, b) \qquad (9.3.4)$$

From (9.3.4), we obtain

$$\hat{\beta}_j = -\hat{\mu} + \frac{1}{\sum_i n_{ij}} \sum_i \sum_k y_{ijk} - \frac{1}{\sum_i n_{ij}} \sum_i n_{ij}\hat{\alpha}_i \qquad (9.3.5)$$

Substituting this into (9.3.3), we have

$$\left(\sum_j n_{ij}\right) \hat{\alpha}_i - \sum_j n_{ij}\left(\frac{\sum_{i'} n_{i'j}\hat{\alpha}_{i'}}{\sum_i n_{ij}}\right) = \sum_j \sum_k y_{ijk} - \sum_j n_{ij}\left(\frac{\sum_i \sum_k y_{ijk}}{\sum_i n_{ij}}\right)$$

$$(i = 1, 2, \ldots, a) \qquad (9.3.6)$$

Isolating the quantity involving α_i from the second term at the left of (9.3.6), we obtain

$$\left(\sum_j n_{ij} - \sum_j \frac{n_{ij}^2}{\sum_i n_{ij}}\right) \hat{\alpha}_i - \sum_{i' \neq i} \sum_j \frac{n_{ij}n_{i'j}}{\sum_i n_{ij}} \hat{\alpha}_{i'}$$

$$= \sum_j \sum_k y_{ijk} - \sum_j n_{ij}\left(\frac{\sum_i \sum_k y_{ijk}}{\sum_i n_{ij}}\right) \quad (i = 1, 2, \ldots, a) \qquad (9.3.7)$$

The system of equations of (9.3.7) is augmented by the side condition

$$\sum \hat{\alpha}_i = 0 \qquad (9.3.8)$$

Equations of (9.3.7) and (9.3.8) can be written in matrix form as

$$\mathbf{N\hat{A}} = \mathbf{M}.$$

The solutions $\hat{\alpha}_i$ are then given by $\mathbf{N^{-1}M}$.

To test the hypothesis $\alpha_1 = \alpha_2 = \cdots = \alpha_a$, we need the sum of squares due to (μ, α, β):

$$SS(\mu, \alpha, \beta) = \hat{\mathbf{B}}'\mathbf{X}'\mathbf{Y}$$

$$= \hat{\mu} \sum_i \sum_j \sum_k y_{ijk} + \sum_i \hat{\alpha}_i \left(\sum_j \sum_k y_{ijk} \right) + \sum_j \hat{\beta}_j \left(\sum_i \sum_k y_{ijk} \right)$$

Using (9.3.5), we may eliminate β_j to get

$$SS(\mu, \alpha, \beta) = \sum_i \hat{\alpha}_i \left[\sum_j \sum_k y_{ijk} - \sum_j \left(\frac{n_{ij} \sum_i \sum_k y_{ijk}}{\sum_i n_{ij}} \right) \right] + \sum_j \left[\frac{(\sum_i \sum_k y_{ijk})^2}{\sum_i n_{ij}} \right]$$

To compute $SS(\mu, \beta)$, we use the reduced normal equations

$$\left(\sum_i \sum_j n_{ij} \right) \hat{\mu}^* + \sum_j \left(\sum_i n_{ij} \right) \hat{\beta}_j = \sum_i \sum_j \sum_k y_{ijk}$$

$$\left(\sum_i n_{ij} \right) \hat{\mu}^* + \left(\sum_i n_{ij} \right) \hat{\beta}_j = \sum_i \sum_k y_{ijk} \quad (j = 1, 2, \ldots, b)$$

Use side conditions

$$\sum_j \left(\sum_i n_{ij} \right) \hat{\beta}_j = 0$$

to get solutions

$$\hat{\mu}^* = y_{\ldots} = \frac{1}{\sum_i \sum_j n_{ij}} \sum_i \sum_j \sum_k y_{ijk}$$

$$\hat{\beta}_j = y_{.j.} - y_{\ldots} = \frac{1}{\sum_i n_{ij}} \sum_i \sum_k y_{ijk} - y_{\ldots}$$

and

$$SS(\mu, \beta) = \hat{\mu}^* \sum_i \sum_j \sum_k y_{ijk} + \sum_j \hat{\beta}_j \left(\sum_i \sum_k y_{ijk} \right)$$

$$= \sum_j \left[\frac{(\sum_i \sum_k y_{ijk})^2}{\sum_i n_{ij}} \right]$$

Hence the adjusted sum of squares due to α is

$$SS(\alpha/\mu, \beta) = SS(\mu, \alpha, \beta) - SS(\mu, \beta)$$

$$= \sum_i \hat{\alpha}_i \left[\sum_j \sum_k y_{ijk} - \sum_j n_{ij} \left(\frac{\sum_i \sum_k y_{ijk}}{\sum_i n_{ij}} \right) \right]$$

The error sum of squares may be computed by subtraction. That is,

$$SS_E = \sum_i \sum_j \sum_k y_{ijk}^2 - SS(\mu, \alpha, \beta)$$

To test the hypothesis $\alpha_1 = \alpha_2 = \cdots = \alpha_a$, the F-ratio

$$\frac{(SS(\alpha/\mu, \beta))/(a - 1)}{SS_E/(\sum_i \sum_j n_{ij} - a - b + 1)}$$

is used.

b) Methods of Approximation

Consider a factorial experiment with unequal number of observations in the cells. If there are no empty cells, a simple method of approximation, called the *method of unweighted means*, may be used to get a quick preliminary idea of what the results would be or to replace the lengthy exact solution if one is contented with the approximate solutions.

The procedure of computation is straightforward. The ordinary analysis of variance is applied to the cell means which are treated as single observations. The error mean square is calculated by pooling the sums of squares within cells about the cell means and by finally dividing it by the harmonic mean of the cell frequencies (i.e., multiplying it by the average of the reciprocals of the cell frequencies for the original observations).

Sometimes an experiment is intended to be balanced; however, in the process of collecting data, one or several observations may be missing. The analysis can be reduced to that of balanced experiments by the use of missing-value formulas (discussed in Section 6.6). These formulas are obtained from minimizing the appropriate "error sum of squares" as a function of the unknown missing value. However, they are mostly for a single missing observation and differ from one design to another.

A simple approximate procedure applicable to all designs therefore merits our consideration. Denote any three trial values for the missing observation by y_0, y_1, and y_2, one unit apart, so that $y_1 = y_0 + 1$ and $y_2 = y_1 + 1$; and denote the corresponding error sum of squares computed from the observations with the missing value replaced by y_0, y_1, and y_2, respectively, by E_0, E_1 and E_2. The missing value, y_m, is then given by

$$y_m = y_1 + (E_0 - E_2)/2(E_0 - 2E_1 + E_2)$$

At y_m, the parabola through the three points (y_0, E_0), (y_1, E_1), and (y_2, E_2) attains its minimum. The ordinary analysis-of-variance procedure is then applied to the data supplemented by y_m with the error degrees of freedom reduced by one. For several missing values, this procedure may be used by iteration.

9.4 THE ASSUMPTIONS UNDERLYING THE ANALYSIS OF VARIANCE AND SOME CONSEQUENCES OF DEPARTURES FROM THEM

In deriving statistical methods, frequently some assumptions are introduced to lighten mathematical difficulties of the derivation. These assumptions are often violated in practical problems. A statistical method is called *robust* if the inference drawn from using the method is not seriously invalidated by the violation of its underlying assumptions. We shall reexamine the assumptions underlying analysis-of-variance tests and make some general remarks regarding their robustness.

a) The Assumption of Independence

The assumption of statistical independence of errors is a very important one. The probability for the error of any observation to have a particular value must not depend on the values of the errors for other observations. Investigations have shown that if the errors are serially correlated, the effect on inference about means can be serious.

Correlations among the errors can be largely taken care of by proper randomization. Roughly speaking, the physical act of randomization produces a close approximation to independence of errors.

b) The Assumption of Equal Variances

The experimental errors should have equal variances from one observation to another. More generally, if the analysis of variance is divided into parts, such as in a split-plot design, then within each part the errors should have common variance. If there is heterogeneity of errors and if the number of observations in the cell are equal, the effect on inference about means drawn from applying F-test and S-method of multiple comparisons is very small. However, interval estimates on individual means based on t-test may be seriously distorted.

Furthermore, inequality of variances in the case of unequal cell numbers generally can produce serious distortions to F-test and S-method. This gives another advantage in choosing an experiment with equal cell numbers.

c) The Assumption of Normality

The experimental errors should be normally distributed, and also the random effects in model II and model III should be normally distributed. Studies indicate that nonnormality has little effect on inferences about means such as F-tests on fixed main effects or interactions, confidence interval estimates, and S-methods or T-methods for multiple comparisons. However, nonnormality may produce serious effects on inferences about variances as in confidence interval estimates of the error variance or variance components of random-effect factors, and tests for the homogeneity of variances (for example, the Bartlett's test). The usual technique for reducing nonnormality of the errors is to seek a transformation which will put the data on a different scale such that the errors are approximately normal.

d) The Use of Transformations

Transformations can be used to reduce nonnormality or to reduce inequality of variances. Suppose a random variable y which is a response variable in an experiment has a mean μ, and the variance σ_y^2 of y can be expressed as a function of μ, that is,

$$\sigma_y^2 = f(\mu)$$

We wish to determine a function $\Phi(y)$ to transform y to a new variable Z, that is,

$$Z = \Phi(y)$$

such that the variance of Z will be approximately independent of μ.

By Taylor's theorem, in the neighborhood of

$$y = \mu$$

we have approximately

$$Z = \Phi(\mu) + (y - \mu)\Phi'(\mu)$$

where Φ' is the derivative of Φ. Since

$$E[y - \mu] = 0$$

we have

$$E[Z] = \Phi(\mu)$$

and approximately

$$\sigma_Z^2 = E[(y - \mu)\Phi'(\mu)]^2 = [\Phi'(\mu)]^2\sigma_y^2 = [\Phi'(\mu)]^2 f(\mu)$$

or

$$[\Phi'(\mu)]^2 = \frac{\sigma_Z^2}{f(\mu)}, \qquad \Phi'(\mu) = \frac{\sigma_Z}{[f(\mu)]^{1/2}}$$

Integrating this and replacing μ by y, we get

$$\Phi(y) = \sigma_Z \int [f(y)]^{-(1/2)} \, dy$$

For example, if the distribution of y is binomial and if y is the number of successes in n trials with constant probability p, then

$$E[y] = np, \qquad \sigma_y^2 = np(1 - p)$$

Hence

$$f(\mu) = \mu \left(1 - \frac{\mu}{n}\right)$$

and

$$\Phi(y) = \sigma_Z \int \left[y \left(1 - \frac{y}{n}\right)\right]^{-(1/2)} dy$$

$$= 2\sqrt{n} \, \sigma_Z \, \text{arc sin} \left(\frac{y}{n}\right)^{1/2} + C$$

If we take $C = 0$, and choose

$$\sigma_Z^2 = \frac{1}{4n}$$

the transformation $\Phi(y)$ becomes

$$Z = \Phi(y) = \text{arc sin} \left(\frac{y}{n}\right)^{1/2}$$

where y/n is the observed proportion of successes and the arc sine is in radians; if the arc sine is in degrees, then

$$\sigma_Z^2 = \frac{821}{n}$$

For some populations, the variance is proportional to the mean, that is,

$$\sigma_y^2 = C^2\mu^2$$

which generates the logarithmic transformation

$$Z = \Phi(y) = \log y$$

The empirical transformation

$$Z = \Phi(y) = \log(1 + y)$$

may be used in place of $\log y$ to avoid the difficulty of computing $\log y$ when y is zero. The variance is approximately C^2 if the base of log is e. It is approximately $0.189C^2$ if the base is 10.

If the distribution of y is of the Poisson type with mean μ and variance

$$\sigma_y^2 = f(\mu) = \mu$$

then a square root transformation

$$Z = \Phi(y) = \sqrt{y}$$

may be used. When zeros are occurring among the observations, the transformation

$$Z = \Phi(y) = \sqrt{y + \tfrac{1}{2}}$$

may be used to replace $\sqrt{y}$.

REFERENCES

1. SNEDECOR, G. W., *Statistical Methods*. Iowa State University Press, Ames, Iowa, 1956.

2. "The Analysis of Variance," a special issue of *Biometrics*, **3**, 1–52 (1947).

3. SCHEFFÉ, H., *The Analysis of Variance*. Wiley, New York, 1959.

4. FISHER, R. A., "The Analysis of Variance with Various Binomial Transformations," *Biometrics*, **10**, 130–151 (1954).

10   ANALYSIS OF COVARIANCE

10.1   INTRODUCTION

Randomized blocks, Latin squares, and incomplete blocks are the common devices in experimental design for reducing experimental variation due to the heterogeneity of experimental material or environmental condition. The analysis of covariance is another technique which may be used as an alternative or supplement to the blocking devices of local control. The sources of variation, which cannot be controlled by the design but can be observed and measured along with the response variable, are called covariates or concomitant variables. The responses are adjusted for their regression on the covariates to remove the effects from the experimental error. The measurements of the covariates must not be influenced by the treatments. Usually, these measurements are taken on each experimental unit before the treatments are applied, and they are supposed to predict to some degree the final response on that experimental unit. In such situations, the covariates represent initial calibrations of the responsiveness of the experimental units.

A classical example of using covariance analysis is in the area of nutrition research. Consider that the effect of different diets (or rations) on increase in body weight of experimental animals is studied. Since the weight gain could also depend on the initial weight of the animal, in order to eliminate some of the effects due to different initial weights, the experimenter may wish to divide the animals into homogeneous subgroups according to their initial weights before applying the various diets. However, it is very likely that differences in initial weights within each subgroup still exist; these differences may inflate the estimate of experimental error. A remedy for this type of inadequacy of blocking is provided by a practical alternative which uses the actual values of the initial weights to adjust the values of weight gain.

Another typical example is found in agricultural field trials. Consider that the object of an experiment is to learn the effect of different fertilizers on the yield of a certain crop. The number of plants per plot may be the same at the commencement of the experiment, but will usually vary from plot to plot at the time of harvest. Correction on the yields of single plots on the basis of the corresponding numbers of plants is a usual practice. In this case, the observations on the covariate are not taken before the assignment of treatments; however, we can assume from our knowledge of the nature of the covariate that the concomitant observations are not affected by treatments.

10.2 BASIC THEORY OF THE TECHNIQUE

The basic theory of analysis of covariance may be illustrated by a two-way arrangement with one observation per cell on the response y and one corresponding observation on a covariate z. The adjustments which will be made on the y-values on the basis of corresponding z-values depend on the type of relationship between z and y. If theory or prior knowledge establishes a particular relationship, the adjustments may be made accordingly. In most experimental situations, a completely specified relationship is not available. The usual assumption is that the relationship between z and y is linear, that is,

$$y = \bar{y} + c_1(z - \bar{z})$$
$$= (\bar{y} - c_1\bar{z}) + c_1 z$$
$$= c_0 + c_1 z$$

where $\bar{y}$ and $\bar{z}$ are the means of y and z, and the values of c_0 and c_1 will be estimated from the data. The linear relationship can be modified to a curvilinear relationship of the type

$$y = c_0 + c_1 z + c_2 z^2$$

by regarding z^2 as another covariate and following the procedure of multiple covariance analysis, which will be discussed later.

The mathematical model is written as

$$y_{ij} = \mu + \alpha_i + \beta_j + \gamma(z_{ij} - z_{..}) + \epsilon_{ij} \qquad (10.2.1)$$
$$(i = 1, 2, \ldots, a; \quad j = 1, 2, \ldots, b)$$

where μ is the general mean, α_i are the fixed effects of factor A, β_j are the fixed effects of factor B, γ is the regression coefficient for the dependence of y_{ij} on z_{ij}, $z_{..}$ is the mean of all z_{ij}, and ϵ_{ij} are the errors being independently and normally distributed with zero mean and variance σ^2.

The term for the covariate in the model (10.2.1) is written as $\gamma(z_{ij} - z_{..})$ instead of z_{ij} so that the symbol μ is preserved for the general mean. We may also write the model as

$$y_{ij} = \mu^* + \alpha_i + \beta_j + \gamma z_{ij} + \epsilon_{ij} \qquad (10.2.2)$$

where μ^* is an additive constant and no longer the general mean which is now

$$\mu^* + \gamma z_{..}$$

Following the method of least squares, we shall estimate the unknown parameters in (10.2.1) by minimizing

$$\sum_i \sum_j \{y_{ij} - \hat{\mu} - \hat{\alpha}_i - \hat{\beta}_j - \hat{\gamma}(z_{ij} - z_{..})\} \qquad (10.2.3)$$

with side conditions

$$\sum \hat{\alpha}_i = 0, \qquad \sum \hat{\beta}_j = 0 \tag{10.2.4}$$

To simplify the algebraic manipulations, the following transformations may be used:

$$\hat{\mu} = \hat{\mu}' \tag{10.2.5}$$

$$\hat{\alpha}_i = \hat{\alpha}'_i - \hat{\gamma}(z_{i.} - z_{..}) \tag{10.2.6}$$

$$\hat{\beta}_j = \hat{\beta}'_j - \hat{\gamma}(z_{.j} - z_{..}) \tag{10.2.7}$$

$$z_{ij} = z'_{ij} + z_{i.} + z_{.j} - z_{..} \tag{10.2.8}$$

Consequently, (10.2.3) becomes

$$\sum_i \sum_j (y_{ij} - \hat{\mu}' - \hat{\alpha}'_i - \hat{\beta}'_j - \gamma z'_{ij}) \tag{10.2.9}$$

and

$$\sum \hat{\alpha}'_i = 0, \qquad \sum \hat{\beta}'_j = 0$$

Note that

$$z'_{ij} = z_{ij} - z_{i.} - z_{.j} + z_{..} \tag{10.2.10}$$

and z'_{ij} satisfy the conditions

$$\sum_i z'_{ij} = 0, \qquad \sum_j z'_{ij} = 0 \tag{10.2.11}$$

We introduce the following notations. These notations, which differ somewhat from the conventional ones, may seem to be burdened with symbolism; however, they are systematic and serve the purpose of indicating the connections in computations between analysis of variance and analysis of covariance, and will be useful in later sections.

$$M_{yy,E} = \sum_i \sum_j (y_{ij} - y_{i.} - y_{.j} + y_{..})^2 \tag{10.2.12}$$

$$M_{yz,E} = \sum_i \sum_j (y_{ij} - y_{i.} - y_{.j} + y_{..})(z_{ij} - z_{i.} - z_{.j} + z_{..}) \tag{10.2.13}$$

$$M_{zz,E} = \sum_i \sum_j (z_{ij} - z_{i.} - z_{.j} + z_{..})^2 \tag{10.2.14}$$

$$M_{yy,A} = \sum_i \sum_j (y_{ij} - y_{.j})^2 \tag{10.2.15}$$

$$M_{yz,A} = \sum_i \sum_j (y_{ij} - y_{.j})(z_{ij} - z_{.j}) \tag{10.2.16}$$

$$M_{zz,A} = \sum_i \sum_j (z_{ij} - z_{.j})^2 \tag{10.2.17}$$

$$M_{yy,B} = \sum_i \sum_j (y_{ij} - y_{i.})^2 \qquad (10.2.18)$$

$$M_{yz,B} = \sum_i \sum_j (y_{ij} - y_{i.})(z_{ij} - z_{i.}) \qquad (10.2.19)$$

$$M_{zz,B} = \sum_i \sum_j (z_{ij} - z_{i.})^2 \qquad (10.2.20)$$

A similar notation for the sum of squares and sum of products is used as in the following:

$$S_{yy,E} = \text{Error sum of squares of } y = M_{yy,E}$$

$$S_{zz,E} = \text{Error sum of squares of } z = M_{zz,E}$$

$$S_{yz,E} = \text{Error sum of products of } y \text{ and } z = M_{yz,E}$$

$$S_{yy,A} = b \sum_i (y_{i.} - y_{..})^2 \qquad (10.2.21)$$

$$S_{zz,A} = b \sum_i (z_{i.} - z_{..})^2 \qquad (10.2.22)$$

$$S_{yz,A} = b \sum_i (y_{i.} - y_{..})(z_{i.} - z_{..}) \qquad (10.2.23)$$

$$S_{yy,B} = a \sum_j (y_{.j} - y_{..})^2 \qquad (10.2.24)$$

$$S_{zz,B} = a \sum_j (z_{.j} - z_{..})^2 \qquad (10.2.25)$$

$$S_{yz,B} = a \sum_j (y_{.j} - y_{..})(z_{.j} - z_{..}) \qquad (10.2.26)$$

Since

$$M_{yy,E} = \sum_i \sum_j y_{ij}^2 - b \sum_i y_{i.}^2 - a \sum_j y_{.j}^2 + aby_{..}^2$$

$$M_{yy,A} = \sum_i \sum_j y_{ij}^2 - a \sum_j y_{.j}^2$$

$$S_{yy,A} = b \sum_i y_{i.}^2 - aby_{..}^2$$

then

$$M_{yy,A} = M_{yy,E} + S_{yy,A} \qquad (10.2.27)$$

Similarly,

$$M_{zz,A} = M_{zz,E} + S_{zz,A} \qquad (10.2.28)$$

and similar relations hold for B. Furthermore,

$$M_{yz,E} = \sum_i \sum_j y_{ij}z_{ij} - b \sum_i y_{i.}z_{i.}$$
$$- a \sum_j y_{.j}z_{.j} + aby_{..}z_{..}$$

$$M_{yz,A} = \sum_i \sum_j y_{ij}z_{ij} - a \sum_j y_{.j}z_{.j}$$

$$S_{yz,A} = b \sum_i y_{i.}z_{i.} - aby_{..}z_{..}$$

hence

$$M_{yz,A} = M_{yz,E} + S_{yz,A} \tag{10.2.29}$$

and a similar relation holds for B.

Because of (10.2.5), (10.2.6), and (10.2.7), we can estimate $\hat{\mu}$, $\hat{\alpha}$, $\hat{\beta}$, and $\hat{\gamma}$ by minimizing (10.2.9) and finding $\hat{\mu}'$, $\hat{\alpha}'$, $\hat{\beta}'$, and $\hat{\gamma}'$. Expanding (10.2.9), we get

$$\sum_i \sum_j (y_{ij} - \hat{\mu}' - \hat{\alpha}'_i - \hat{\beta}'_j)^2 - 2\hat{\gamma} \sum_i \sum_j z'_{ij}y_{ij} + \hat{\gamma}^2 \sum_i \sum_j z'^2_{ij} \tag{10.2.30}$$

The other terms vanish because of (10.2.11). Since $\hat{\gamma}$ is separated from the other unknowns, differentiation with respect to $\hat{\gamma}$ immediately gives

$$\hat{\gamma} = \frac{\sum_i \sum_j z'_{ij}y_{ij}}{\sum_i \sum_j z'^2_{ij}} \tag{10.2.31}$$

Since

$$\sum_i \sum_j z'_{ij}y_{ij} = \sum_i \sum_j z'_{ij}(y_{ij} - y_{i.} - y_{.j} + y_{..})$$

so

$$\hat{\gamma} = M_{yz,E}/M_{zz,E} \tag{10.2.32}$$

The estimates of $\hat{\mu}'$, $\hat{\alpha}'_i$, $\hat{\beta}'_j$ must be such that the first term in (10.2.30) is minimized. The ordinary analysis-of-variance procedure applied to y yields directly the familiar results:

$$\hat{\mu}' = y_{..}$$
$$\hat{\alpha}'_i = y_{i.} - y_{..}$$
$$\hat{\beta}'_j = y_{.j} - y_{..}$$

Therefore, because of (10.2.5), (10.2.6), and (10.2.7), the estimates for model (10.2.1) are

$$\hat{\mu} = y_{..} \tag{10.2.33}$$

$$\hat{\alpha}_i = y_{i.} - y_{..} - \hat{\gamma}(z_{i.} - z_{..}) \tag{10.2.34}$$

$$\hat{\beta}_j = y_{.j} - y_{..} - \hat{\gamma}(z_{.j} - z_{..}) \tag{10.2.35}$$

The error sum of squares under the analysis of covariance model (10.2.1) is obtained from (10.2.30). We have

$$SS'_E = \sum_i \sum_j (y_{ij} - \hat{\mu}' - \hat{\alpha}'_i - \hat{\beta}'_j)^2 - 2\gamma M_{yz,E} + \gamma^2 M_{zz,E}$$

$$= \sum_i \sum_j (y_{ij} - y_{i\cdot} - y_{\cdot j} + y_{\cdot\cdot})^2 - 2\gamma M_{yz,E} + \gamma^2 M_{zz,E}$$

$$= M_{yy,E} - \frac{2M_{yz,E}^2}{M_{zz,E}} + \frac{M_{yz,E}^2}{M_{zz,E}}$$

$$= M_{yy,E} - \frac{M_{yz,E}^2}{M_{zz,E}} \tag{10.2.36}$$

Its degrees of freedom is $((a - 1)(b - 1) - 1)$.

To test the hypothesis: $\gamma = 0$, or to construct a confidence interval for $\hat{\gamma}$, we need the variance of $\hat{\gamma}$ which is

$$\sigma_{\hat{\gamma}}^2 = \sigma^2 / M_{zz,E} \tag{10.2.37}$$

where σ^2 is estimated by dividing (10.2.36) by $((a - 1)(b - 1) - 1)$.

The confidence interval of γ is based on the fact that the quantity

$$\frac{\hat{\gamma} - \gamma}{\sigma_{\hat{\gamma}}} \tag{10.2.38}$$

has the t-distribution with $((a - 1)(b - 1) - 1)$ degrees of freedom.

Now consider testing the hypothesis

$$H_A: \alpha_1 = \alpha_2 = \cdots = \alpha_a = 0$$

(The corresponding case for B is quite similar.) We need to estimate $\hat{\gamma}_A$ by minimizing

$$\sum_i \sum_j \{y_{ij} - \hat{\mu}_A - \hat{\beta}_{j,A} - \hat{\gamma}_A(z_{ij} - z_{\cdot\cdot})\}^2 \tag{10.2.39}$$

This gives

$$\hat{\gamma}_A = \frac{M_{yz,A}}{M_{zz,A}} \tag{10.2.40}$$

The error sum of squares under H_A is

$$SS'_A = M_{yy,A} - \hat{\gamma}_A M_{yz,A} \tag{10.2.41}$$

Therefore, for testing H_A, the ratio

$$F = \frac{(SS'_A - SS'_E)/(a - 1)}{SS'_E/(ab - a - b)}$$

is used with degrees of freedom $(a - 1)$ and $(ab - a - b)$.

The means of factor A or B may be adjusted to remove the influence of z. For example, if factor B represents treatments, the adjusted treatment means

TABLE 10.2.1

Age	Diet										
	1		2		3		4		5		6	
	y	z	y	z	y	z	y	z	y	z	y	z
1	2.8	50	1.9	49	0.8	51	0.5	50	2.1	50	0.9	50
2	3.0	51	5.4	53	2.8	53	1.0	50	0.5	48	1.1	48
3	4.5	52	0.9	47	1.9	51	0.1	49	3.2	52	3.2	52
4	2.3	48	0.2	45	3.3	53	0.6	48	2.2	50	2.8	50

are given by

$$adj.y._j = y._j - \gamma(z._j - z..)$$

If

$$H_B: \text{all } \beta_j = 0$$

is rejected, we may wish to investigate the difference d between two adjusted treatment means, $adj.y._j$ and $adj.y._{j'}$. Then we need the variance of d, which is given by

$$\frac{SS'_E}{ab - a - b}\left[\frac{2}{a} + \frac{(z._j - z._{j'})^2}{M_{zz,E}}\right]$$

The computational work may be simplified by using (10.2.27), (10.2.28), (10.2.29), and similar relations. This is especially true when programming the analysis of covariance on a computer, since the quantities

$$y_i. - y..$$
$$y_{ij} - y_i. - y._j + y..$$
$$z_i. - z..$$
$$z_{ij} - z_i. - z._j + z..$$
$$\text{etc.}$$

are directly available from the analysis-of-variance procedure. The extension of the operator calculus described in Chapter 2 to the analysis of covariance is now clearly indicated.

Consider a hypothetical experiment in which weight gain together with initial weight of each experimental animal are recorded. Suppose that the data (say, in pounds) in Table 10.2.1 are weight gains y and initial weights z of 24 experimental animals under 6 different diets. The animals are grouped into 4 blocks by age. The covariance analysis will be used as a supplement to blocking.

The basic quantities S_{yy}, S_{yz}, S_{zz}, M_{yy}, M_{yz}, M_{zz} for A (blocks or age), B (treatments or diet), and E (error)are shown in Table 10.2.2. Note that the

TABLE 10.2.2

Source	d.f.	S_{yy}	S_{zz}	S_{yz}	M_{yy}	M_{zz}	M_{yz}
A (Blocks)	3	2.64	9.00	2.40	30.54	66.50	40.80
B (Treatments)	5	13.90	27.50	6.50	41.80	85.00	44.90
Error	15	27.90	57.50	38.40	27.90	57.50	38.40
Total	23	44.44	94.00	47.30			

quantities under the S_{yy} column and the S_{zz} column are computed in the usual way in analysis of variance, and they are the ordinary sums of squares. The quantities under the S_{yz} column are computed in a similar way with cross-products taken instead of squares. The quantities under the columns of M_{yy}, M_{yz}, M_{zz} for A and B are calculated by using (10.2.27), (10.2.28), (10.2.29), and similar relations.

The regression coefficient γ is estimated as

$$\hat{\gamma} = \frac{M_{yz,E}}{M_{zz,E}} = \frac{38.40}{57.50} = 0.66783$$

The error sum of squares under the analysis-of-covariance model is

$$SS'_E = M_{yy,E} - \frac{M^2_{yz,E}}{M_{zz,E}} = 27.90 - \frac{(38.4)^2}{57.5} = 2.255$$

with 14 degrees of freedom. The t-statistic for testing the hypothesis: $\gamma = 0$, is computed as

$$t = 0.668/\sigma_{\hat{\gamma}} = 0.668 \sqrt{\frac{M_{zz,E}}{0.161}} = 0.668 \sqrt{\frac{57.5}{0.161}} = 12.62$$

Under the hypothesis H_A: all $\alpha_i = 0$, the coefficient γ_A is estimated as

$$\hat{\gamma}_A = \frac{M_{yz,A}}{M_{zz,A}} = \frac{40.8}{66.5} = 0.61353$$

The error sum of squares under H_A is

$$SS'_A = M_{yy,A} - \hat{\gamma}_A M_{yz,A} = 30.54 - (0.61353)(40.8) = 5.508$$

and

$$SS'_A - SS'_E = 3.253$$

Under the hypothesis H_B: all $\beta_j = 0$, the coefficient γ_B is estimated as

$$\hat{\gamma}_B = \frac{M_{yz,B}}{M_{zz,B}} = \frac{44.9}{85} = 0.52824$$

TABLE 10.2.3

Source	d.f.	SS	MS
A (Blocks)	3	3.253	1.084
B (Treatments)	5	15.827	3.165
Error	14	2.255	0.161

The error sum of squares under H_B is

$$SS'_B = M_{yy,B} - \hat{\gamma}_B M_{yz,B}$$

$$= 41.8 - (0.52824)(44.9)$$

$$= 18.083$$

and

$$SS'_B - SS'_E = 15.827$$

The results are summarized in Table 10.2.3.

The reduction on error sum of squares is

$$27.9 - 2.255 = 25.645$$

The degrees of freedom for the error term also reduced from 15 to 14, and the one deducted degree of freedom is used for estimating the coefficient γ. The error mean square is reduced to 0.161. This means a valuable increase in the precision of the experiment. The F-ratio for the significance of treatment effects is $3.165/0.161 = 19.65$, which reveals that the treatment effects, after the elimination of the influence of z, are highly significant. The F-ratio for testing the significance of error reduction due to regression is $25.645/0.161 = 159.18$, which is also highly significant. (Of course, this F-test is equivalent to the t-test on γ with the t-value computed above.)

10.3 MULTIPLE COVARIANCE ON A MULTIFACTOR STRUCTURE

Suppose that in an experiment the response variable y is observed together with h covariates $\mathbf{Z}(z_1, z_2, \ldots, z_h)$ under a balanced arrangement of K factors with design matrix $\mathbf{X}$. A model similar to (10.2.2) may be written in matrix notation as

$$\mathbf{Y} = \mathbf{XB} + \mathbf{Z\Gamma} + \mathbf{E} \qquad (10.3.1)$$

where vector $\mathbf{B}$ has the components $(b_1, b_2, \ldots, b_p)$ corresponding to the effects, interactions, of the multifactor structure; vector $\mathbf{\Gamma}$ has the components $(\gamma_1, \gamma_2, \ldots, \gamma_h)$ corresponding to the regression coefficients on the covariates; and vector $\mathbf{E}$ has the components $(e_1, e_2, \ldots, e_n)$ distributed independently and normally with zero mean and variance σ^2.

To estimate the regression coefficients in (10.3.1), we need to compute the quantities $M_{z_i z_j, E}$ and $M_{y z_i, E}$ similar to those defined in (10.2.12), (10.2.13), and (10.2.14), but with suitable generalizations. These quantities are used to form the following matrix equation:

$$
\begin{bmatrix}
M_{z_1z_1,E} & M_{z_1z_2,E} & \cdots & M_{z_1z_h,E} \\
 & M_{z_2z_2,E} & \cdots & M_{z_2z_h,E} \\
 & & \vdots & \\
 & & & M_{z_hz_h,E}
\end{bmatrix}
\begin{bmatrix}
\hat{\gamma}_1 \\
\hat{\gamma}_2 \\
\vdots \\
\hat{\gamma}_h
\end{bmatrix}
=
\begin{bmatrix}
M_{yz_1,E} \\
M_{yz_2,E} \\
\vdots \\
M_{yz_h,E}
\end{bmatrix}
$$

or,

$$\mathbf{M}_1\hat{\boldsymbol{\Gamma}} = \mathbf{M}_2 \tag{10.3.2}$$

The inverse of the symmetric matrix $\mathbf{M}_1$ multiplied by the $\mathbf{M}_2$ vector gives the solutions of $\hat{\boldsymbol{\Gamma}}$. The estimated covariance matrix of $\hat{\boldsymbol{\Gamma}}$ under (10.3.1) is the inverse of the $\mathbf{M}_1$ matrix times the error mean square under (10.3.1).

Similar to (10.2.36), the analysis-of-covariance error sum of squares is

$$SS'_E = M_{yy,E} - \mathbf{M}'_2\hat{\boldsymbol{\Gamma}} \tag{10.3.3}$$

with $(\prod_{i=1}^K (n_i - 1) - h)$ degrees of freedom, where $M_{yy,E}$ is the error sum of squares for the corresponding analysis of variance and n_i is the number of levels of the ith factor.

For testing a hypothesis H_{b_q}, we follow a procedure analogous to the above calculations. The quantities $M_{z_iz_j,b_q}$ and M_{yz_i,b_q}, similar to those defined in (10.2.16) through (10.2.20), are computed to form

$$\mathbf{M}_{1,b_q}\hat{\boldsymbol{\Gamma}}_{b_q} = \mathbf{M}_{2,b_q} \tag{10.3.4}$$

Note that these quantities may be obtained by adding $M_{z_iz_j,E}$ and $M_{yz_i,E}$ to $S_{z_iz_j,b_q}$ and S_{yz_i,b_q}, similar to those defined in (10.2.22) through (10.2.26).

The solution of the regression coefficients under H_{b_q} is given by

$$\hat{\boldsymbol{\Gamma}}_{b_q} = \mathbf{M}_{1,b_q}^{-1}\mathbf{M}_{2,b_q}$$

These solutions are used to calculate

$$SS'_{b_q} = M_{yy,b_q} - \mathbf{M}'_{2,b_q}\hat{\boldsymbol{\Gamma}}_{b_q}$$

where M_{yy,b_q} may be computed by adding SS_E to S_{yy,b_q}, as indicated by (10.2.27).

Finally, for testing H_{b_q}, the ratio

$$F = \frac{(SS'_{b_q} - SS'_E)/(r - 1)}{SS'_E/(\prod_{i=1}^k (n_i - 1) - h)}$$

is used with $(r - 1)$ and $(\prod_{i=1}^k (n_i - 1) - h)$ degrees of freedom, where r is the number of items in b_q.

The estimates of b_i are obtained from generalizations of (10.2.34) and (10.2.35). That is, if in the analysis of variance procedure b_i is estimated by a linear form in the y-values, say

$$\hat{b}_i = L_i(y)$$

then b_i is estimated, under the analysis of covariance model, by

$$\hat{b}_i = L_i(y) - \sum_{j=1}^{h} \hat{\gamma}_j L_i(z_j)$$

where $L_i(z_j)$ is the same linear form in the z_j values.

The covariance matrix of the $\hat{\gamma}_i$ is $\hat{\sigma}^2 \mathbf{M}_1^{-1}$ which will be used for testing hypothesis or constructing confidence intervals involving only coefficients $\hat{\gamma}_i$.

10.4 COMPUTATIONAL PROCEDURE FOR MULTIPLE COVARIANCE ANALYSIS

The computational procedure for analysis of multiple covariance may be illustrated by the following numerical example of two covariates, z_1 and z_2, in a two-factor, A and B, experiment. The data listed in Table 10.4.1 are artificially generated.

Applying the sequence of operators

$$\Sigma D, \quad D\Sigma, \quad DD$$

described in Section 2.2 to y, z_1, and z_2, we get the deviates in Table 10.4.2.

Now, let us introduce a new operator, denoted by ( )( ), which forms the sum of the products of pairs of deviates from two corresponding sets of deviates and divides by the number of pairs. Then, applying operators ( )^2 and ( )( ) to individual sets of deviates and pairs of corresponding sets of deviates, respectively, and dividing the results by the total number of observations each

TABLE 10.4.1

y	A	B	z_1	z_2
2.51	1	1	1	2
3.50	2	1	3	4
4.55	3	1	5	6
7.59	1	2	7	8
8.51	2	2	9	10
9.52	3	2	11	12
7.05	1	3	2	4
9.08	2	3	6	8
11.02	3	3	10	12
15.07	1	4	14	16
17.02	2	4	18	20
19.02	3	4	22	24
11.54	1	5	3	6
14.54	2	5	9	12
17.51	3	5	15	18
22.57	1	6	21	24
25.52	2	6	27	30
28.56	3	6	33	36

time, we obtain the following quantities:

$$S_{yy,A} = 47.40268$$

$$\begin{bmatrix} S_{z_1z_1,A} & S_{z_1z_2,A} \\ & S_{z_2z_2,A} \end{bmatrix} = \begin{bmatrix} 192.00000 & 192.00000 \\ & 192.00000 \end{bmatrix}$$

$$\begin{bmatrix} S_{yz_1,A} \\ S_{yz_2,A} \end{bmatrix} = \begin{bmatrix} 95.40000 \\ 95.40000 \end{bmatrix}$$

$$S_{yy,B} = 904.48201$$

$$\begin{bmatrix} S_{z_1z_1,B} & S_{z_1z_2,B} \\ & S_{z_2z_2,B} \end{bmatrix} = \begin{bmatrix} 1188.00000 & 1260.00000 \\ & 1344.00000 \end{bmatrix}$$

$$\begin{bmatrix} S_{yz_1,B} \\ S_{yz_2,B} \end{bmatrix} = \begin{bmatrix} 990.84000 \\ 1074.90000 \end{bmatrix}$$

$$S_{yy,E} = 7.98800 = M_{yy,E}$$

$$\mathbf{M}_1 = \begin{bmatrix} S_{z_1z_1,E} & S_{z_1z_2,E} \\ & S_{z_2z_2,E} \end{bmatrix} = \begin{bmatrix} 32.00000 & 32.00000 \\ & 32.00000 \end{bmatrix}$$

$$\mathbf{M}_2 = \begin{bmatrix} S_{yz_1,E} \\ S_{yz_2,E} \end{bmatrix} = \begin{bmatrix} 15.98000 \\ 15.98000 \end{bmatrix}$$

Adding the quantities related to E into the corresponding quantities related to A or B, we get

$$M_{yy,A} = 55.39068$$

$$\mathbf{M}_{1,A} = \begin{bmatrix} M_{z_1z_1,A} & M_{z_1z_2,A} \\ & M_{z_2z_2,A} \end{bmatrix} = \begin{bmatrix} 224.00000 & 224.00000 \\ & 224.00000 \end{bmatrix}$$

$$\mathbf{M}_{2,A} = \begin{bmatrix} M_{yz_1,A} \\ M_{yz_2,A} \end{bmatrix} = \begin{bmatrix} 111.38000 \\ 111.38000 \end{bmatrix}$$

$$M_{yy,B} = 912.47000$$

$$\mathbf{M}_{1,B} = \begin{bmatrix} M_{z_1z_1,B} & M_{z_1z_2,B} \\ & M_{z_2z_2,B} \end{bmatrix} = \begin{bmatrix} 1220.00000 & 1292.00000 \\ & 1376.00000 \end{bmatrix}$$

$$\mathbf{M}_{2,B} = \begin{bmatrix} M_{yz_1,B} \\ M_{yz_2,B} \end{bmatrix} = \begin{bmatrix} 1006.82000 \\ 1090.88000 \end{bmatrix}$$

$$\mathbf{M}_{1,A}^{-1} = \begin{bmatrix} 0.00446 & 0.0 \\ & 0.0 \end{bmatrix}$$

$$\mathbf{M}_{1,B}^{-1} = \begin{bmatrix} 0.14552 & -0.13663 \\ & 0.12902 \end{bmatrix}$$

The three sets of regression coefficients are estimated below:

$$\hat{\mathbf{\Gamma}}_A = \mathbf{M}_{1,A}^{-1}\mathbf{M}_{2,A} = [\ \ 0.49723 \quad 0.0]$$
$$\hat{\mathbf{\Gamma}}_B = \mathbf{M}_{1,B}^{-1}\mathbf{M}_{2,B} = [-2.54151 \quad 3.17915]$$
$$\hat{\mathbf{\Gamma}} = \mathbf{M}_1^{-1}\mathbf{M}_2 \quad\ = [\ \ 0.49937 \quad 0.0]$$

TABLE 10.4.2

y	z_1	z_2	A	B
−35.690001	−72.000000	−72.000000	1	
−0.170000	0.	0.	2	
35.860000	72.000000	72.000000	3	
−171.319996	−162.000000	−180.000000		1
−80.959997	−54.000000	−72.000000		2
−71.779999	−108.000000	−108.000000		3
71.980000	108.000000	108.000000		4
26.860001	−54.000000	−36.000000		5
225.220001	270.000000	288.000000		6
17.510001	36.000000	36.000000	1	1
−0.190000	0.	0.	2	1
−17.320001	−36.000000	−36.000000	3	1
18.590000	36.000000	36.000000	1	2
−0.370000	0.	0.	2	2
−18.220000	−36.000000	−36.000000	3	2
−0.309999	−0.	−0.	1	3
0.709999	0.	0.	2	3
−0.400000	0.	0.	3	3
0.290000	−0.	−0.	1	4
−0.129999	0.	0.	2	4
−0.159998	0.	0.	3	4
−18.129998	−36.000000	−36.000000	1	5
0.350001	0.	0.	2	5
17.780000	36.000000	36.000000	3	5
−17.950003	−36.000000	−36.000000	1	6
−0.370001	0.	0.	2	6
18.319998	36.000000	36.000000	3	6

The error sum of squares for the analysis of covariance is

$$SS'_E = M_{yy,E} - \mathbf{M}'_2\hat{\boldsymbol{\Gamma}} = 0.00800$$

with 8 degrees of freedom. This gives a mean square of 0.00100. Similarly we have

$$SS'_A = M_{yy,A} - \mathbf{M}'_{2,A}\hat{\boldsymbol{\Gamma}}_A = 0.00898$$

and

$$SS'_A - SS'_E = 0.00098$$

with 2 degrees of freedom. This gives a mean square of 0.00049. Also we have

$$SS'_B = M_{yy,B} - \mathbf{M}'_{2,B}\hat{\boldsymbol{\Gamma}}_B = 3.24400$$

and

$$SS'_B - SS'_E = 3.23600$$

with 5 degrees of freedom. This gives a mean square of 0.64720. The results are summarized in Table 10.4.3.

TABLE 10.4.3

Source	d.f.	SS	MS
A	2	0.00098	0.00049
B	5	3.23600	0.64720
Error	8	0.00800	0.00100

The t-values

$$t_i = \frac{\hat{\gamma}_i}{\sqrt{v_{ii}\hat{\sigma}^2}} \quad (i = 1, 2)$$

where v_{ii} is the ith diagonal element of $\mathbf{M}_1^{-1}$ and $\hat{\sigma}^2$ is the error mean square, are computed as 89.33975 and 0.0.

REFERENCES

1. "The Analysis of Covariance," a special issue of *Biometrics*, **13**, 261–405 (1957).

2. RAO, C. R., "On the Linear Combination of Observations and the General Theory of Least Squares," *Sankhyā*, **7**, 237–255 (1946).

3. SCHEFFÉ, H., *The Analysis of Variance*. Wiley, New York, 1959.

11 NONFACTORIAL EXPERIMENTS

11.1 INTRODUCTION

In some experiments the combinatorial arrangement of the treatments may not be in a factorial form or the factorial structure is not of primary importance. The experimenter may be interested principally in increasing precision in one direction or another, yet, due to intrinsic limitations in the experiment, the principles of randomized blocks and Latin squares cannot be employed. In other instances, the experimenter may desire maximum precision in comparing pairs of treatments or in estimating residual effects when treatments are tested in sequence. All these situations call for special experimental designs. The literature on nonfactorial designs is extensive. We shall only attempt to give a brief description of some of the more useful designs.

11.2 DESIGNS FOR ONE-WAY ELIMINATION OF ERROR

The design of randomized blocks is a method for increasing precision. However, each block must contain a complete replication of all the treatments. Often, this condition cannot be satisfied, because either each block does not supply sufficient experimental units or it is not feasible to carry out one replication of all treatments in a block. Several types of designs are available to resolve this difficulty.

a) Balanced Incomplete Block (BIB) Designs

The plan in Table 11.2.1 is an example of balanced incomplete block design in which 7 treatments are arranged in 7 blocks of 4 units.

Each treatment occurs 4 times, and every pair of treatments occurs together twice in this plan. In general, a balanced incomplete block design satisfies the following conditions:

TABLE 11.2.1

Blocks	Treatments
(1)	3 5 6 7
(2)	1 4 6 7
(3)	1 2 5 7
(4)	1 2 3 6
(5)	2 3 4 7
(6)	1 3 4 5
(7)	2 4 5 6

1) Each block contains the same number of experimental units.

2) Each treatment appears the same number of times.

3) Each pair of treatments appears together in the same block the same number of times.

Denote the number of treatments by t, number of blocks by b, number of units per block by k, number of replications by r, and the number of times each pair of treatments appears together by λ. We take

$$\lambda > 0, \quad k < t$$

Clearly,

$$bk = tr \tag{11.2.1}$$

Now consider any given treatment and the pairs of treatments containing it. Counting the number of such pairs by using (1) and (3), we obtain

$$r(k - 1) = \lambda(t - 1) \tag{11.2.2}$$

The five basic parameters t, b, k, r, and λ are interconnected by (11.2.1) and (11.2.2). However, (11.2.1) and (11.2.2) are not the only necessary conditions for the existence of a balanced incomplete block design. In fact, the determination of precise ranges of values of these five integers for which a balanced incomplete block design exists is still an unsolved mathematical problem. The fact that any pair of treatments appears together the same λ times ensures that every pair of treatments may be compared with the same precision (i.e., with one error variance), and simplifies the analysis for adjusting the treatment means for differences between the blocks.

The model for a balanced incomplete block design is the same as that for a complete randomized block design, that is

$$y_{ij} = \mu + \alpha_i + \beta_j + \epsilon_{ij} \tag{11.2.3}$$

where α_i denote fixed block effects, β_j denote fixed treatment effects, and ϵ_{ij} are independently $N(0, \sigma^2)$. Not all possible combinations of i and j occur in the experiment. The model has side conditions

$$\sum_i \alpha_i = 0, \qquad \sum_j \beta_j = 0$$

It is seen that the model assumes zero interactions between blocks and treatments.

To get the estimates of treatment effects, consider a particular treatment, say, the qth. From (11.2.3), the total for this qth treatment is

$$\sum_{i(q)} y_{iq} = r\mu + \sum_{i(q)} \alpha_i + r\beta_q + \sum_{i(q)} \epsilon_{iq} \tag{11.2.4}$$

where the summations $\sum_{i(q)}$ are carried over all blocks containing the qth treatment. The total for the ith block is

$$\sum_{j(i)} y_{ij} = k\mu + k\alpha_i + \sum_{j(i)} \beta_j + \sum_{j(i)} \epsilon_{ij} \tag{11.2.5}$$

where the summations $\sum_{j(i)}$ are taken over all treatments included in the ith block. Summing (11.2.5) over all blocks containing the qth treatment, we get

$$\sum_{i(q)} \sum_{j(i)} y_{ij} = rk\mu + k \sum_{i(q)} \alpha_i + \sum_{i(q)} \sum_{j(i)} \beta_j + \sum_{i(q)} \sum_{j(i)} \epsilon_{ij} \tag{11.2.6}$$

Now consider the term $\sum_{i(q)} \sum_{j(i)} \beta_j$. Since $\sum_j \beta_j = 0$, which can be written as

$$\sum_{j \neq q} \beta_j + \beta_q = 0$$

we have

$$\sum_{i(q)} \sum_{j(i)} \beta_j = r\beta_q + \lambda \sum_{j \neq q} \beta_j = (r - \lambda)\beta_q \qquad (11.2.7)$$

Subtracting Eq. (11.2.6) from k times Eq. (11.2.4) and using (11.2.7), we obtain

$$k \sum_{i(q)} y_{iq} - \sum_{i(q)} \sum_{j(i)} y_{ij} = (kr - r + \lambda)\beta_q + k \sum_{i(q)} \epsilon_{iq} - \sum_{i(q)} \sum_{j(i)} \epsilon_{ij}$$

Hence an unbiased estimate of β_q is

$$\hat{\beta}_q = \frac{1}{kr - r + \lambda} \left[k \sum_{i(q)} y_{iq} - \sum_{i(q)} \sum_{j(i)} y_{ij} \right]$$

which may be written as

$$\hat{\beta}_q = \frac{k(t - 1)}{t(k - 1)r} \left[T_{.q} - \sum_{i(q)} y_{i.} \right]$$

where $T_{.q}$ is the sum of qth treatment and $y_{i.}$ is the mean of ith block. The $\hat{\beta}_q$ effect is free from block effects.

The estimate of the qth adjusted treatment mean is

$$y_{..} + \hat{\beta}_q$$

where $y_{..}$ is the general mean of the whole experiment. The variance of $(y_{..} + \hat{\beta}_q)$ is

$$\frac{\sigma^2}{r} \left[\frac{1}{t} + \frac{k(t - 1)^2}{(k - 1)t^2} \right]$$

The variance of the difference between two adjusted treatment means is

$$\frac{2\sigma^2 k(t - 1)}{r(k - 1)t}$$

The block sum of squares, ignoring treatments, is computed in the same way as in complete randomized block experiment. This crude sum of squares is merely used as an aid to calculate the error mean squares. The analysis-of-variance table is shown in Table 11.2.2, where $T_{i.}$ and $T_{.j}$ are the totals of ith block and jth treatment, respectively, and $T_{..}$ is the grand total of all bk observations. Usually the hypothesis of interest is that all $\beta_j = 0$. The F-statistic for testing this hypothesis is the ratio between the treatment mean square and the error mean square.

The particular balanced incomplete block design given in Table 11.2.1 has an additional property that the number of blocks and number of treatments

TABLE 11.2.2

Source	SS	d.f.
Blocks	$\dfrac{1}{k}\sum_{i=1}^{b} T_{i.}^2 - \dfrac{1}{bk} T_{..}^2$	$b-1$
Treatments (adjusted)	$\dfrac{k(t-1)}{t(k-1)r}\sum_{j=1}^{t}\left[T_{.j} - \sum_{i(j)} y_{i.}\right]^2$	$t-1$
Error	By subtraction	$bk - t - b + 1$
Total	$\sum\sum y_{ij}^2 - \dfrac{1}{bk} T_{..}^2$	$bk - 1$

are equal, that is

$$b = t$$

By (11.2.1), we have

$$k = r$$

In such special cases, the design is sometimes called a *symmetrical balanced incomplete block design.* For a symmetrical balanced incomplete block design, the block effects can be adjusted by a method similar to that for adjusting treatment effects. The sums of squares have the following relation:

(adjusted block SS) + (crude treatment SS)

$$= \text{(crude block } SS) + \text{(adjusted treatment } SS) \qquad (11.2.8)$$

The crude treatment sum of squares (ignoring blocks) is, of course, given by

$$\frac{1}{r}\sum_{j} T_{.j}^2 - \frac{1}{bk} T_{..}^2$$

The adjusted block sum of squares (eliminating treatments) is given by

$$\frac{r(b-1)}{b(r-1)k}\sum_{i=1}^{b}\left[T_{i.} - \sum_{j(i)} y_{.j}\right]^2$$

which may also be calculated by subtraction if relation (11.2.8) is used. The adjusted block effects can be tested against the error term.

We have only discussed the analysis of balanced incomplete block designs for the fixed model. When blocks are chosen randomly from a large population and block effects are assumed to be random variables, the method of analysis is more complicated and requires the so-called "recovery of interblock information" procedure which may be found in Yates [3] and Scheffé [4].

Consider a balanced incomplete block design. If the number of treatments is an exact square and the number of units per block is the corresponding square

TABLE 11.2.3

Blocks	Replication I	Blocks	Replication II
(1)	1 2 3	(4)	1 4 7
(2)	4 5 6	(5)	2 5 8
(3)	7 8 9	(6)	3 6 9

Blocks	Replication III	Blocks	Replication IV
(7)	1 5 9	(10)	1 8 6
(8)	7 2 6	(11)	4 2 9
(9)	4 8 3	(12)	7 5 3

root, then the design is called a *balanced lattice*. Table 11.2.3 gives an example of a balanced lattice for 9 treatments in 12 blocks of 3 units. Note that in a balanced lattice the blocks can be grouped into sets, and each treatment appears only once within each set; that is, each set is a complete replication.

For the model of a balanced lattice experiment, a term denoting replication effects may be added into (11.2.3). The analysis-of-variance table is similar to that in Table 11.2.2 and has an additional sum of squares for replications which is computed in the usual way and removed from the block sum of squares.

TABLE 11.2.4

Blocks	Treatments
(1)	1 2 3
(2)	1 6 4
(3)	1 7 5
(4)	6 8 3
(5)	6 9 5
(6)	7 8 4
(7)	7 9 3
(8)	2 8 5
(9)	2 9 4

b) Partially Balanced Incomplete Block (PBIB) Design

For certain numbers of treatments, balanced incomplete block designs exist only with a very large number of replications. Furthermore, it may be desirable occasionally to make some treatment comparisons more precise than others. Under these circumstances, *partially balanced incomplete block designs* which do not have complete symmetry but allow some reduction in the number of replications may be used.

Table 11.2.4 shows such a design for 9 treatments arranged in 9 blocks of 3 units. Here we have

$$t = 9, \quad k = 3$$
$$r = 3, \quad b = 9$$

TABLE 11.2.5

| | | Relation to 3 | |
		1st Associate	2nd Associate
Relation to 8	1st Associate	2 6 7	4 5
	2nd Associate	1 9	

and the design satisfies conditions (1) and (2) for a balanced incomplete block design. However, pairs of treatments do not appear the same number of times. Consider treatment 3. It appears together with treatments 1 and 2 in block (1); 6 and 8 in block (4); and 7 and 9 in block (7); but it does not appear in the same block with treatments 4 and 5. Similarly, if we consider any other treatment, we find that there are six treatments which appear with it in the same block and two which do not. Pairs of treatments appearing together in the same block are called *first associates* and pairs not appearing together are called *second associates*. The design is said to have two associate classes.

Now consider a pair of treatments which are first associates, say, 3 and 8. For treatment 3, treatments 1, 2, 6, 7, and 9 appear with it in the same block, but 4 and 5 do not. For treatment 8, treatments 6, 7, 4, 2, and 5 appear with it in the same block, but 1 and 9 do not. Combining these relationships, we have Table 11.2.5. Counting the numbers of treatments in the table, we have

$$\begin{pmatrix} 3 & 2 \\ 2 & 0 \end{pmatrix}$$

which remains the same for any pair of treatments which are first associates.

Similar considerations for any pair of treatments which are second associates yield a different set of numbers:

$$\begin{pmatrix} 6 & 0 \\ 0 & 1 \end{pmatrix}$$

A partially balanced incomplete block design with two associate classes satisfies the following conditions.

1) The t-treatments are arranged in b blocks and each block contains $k(<t)$ units.

2) Each treatment appears in r blocks.

3) Two treatments are either first associates or second associates.

4) Each treatment has exactly n_i ith associates $(i = 1, 2)$.

5) Two treatments which are ith associates appear together in exactly λ_i blocks $(i = 1, 2)$.

6) Let p_{jk}^i be the number of treatments common to the jth associate of a given treatment T and kth associate of another treatment T', where T and T' are ith associates. Then p_{jk}^i remain the same for any pair of ith associates $(i, j, k = 1, 2)$.

Using the notations defined above, we have the following parameters for the design in Table 11.2.4:

$$t = 9, \quad k = 3$$

$$r = 3, \quad b = 9$$

$$\lambda_1 = 1, \quad \lambda_2 = 0$$

$$n_1 = 6, \quad n_2 = 2$$

$$p_{jk}^1 = \begin{pmatrix} 3 & 2 \\ 2 & 0 \end{pmatrix}$$

$$p_{jk}^2 = \begin{pmatrix} 6 & 0 \\ 0 & 1 \end{pmatrix}$$

We shall briefly discuss the analysis of a PBIB design for the fixed model. For more detailed discussions, especially when block effects are considered as random, see Bose and Shimamoto [5], and Rao [6].

The model for a PBIB design is the same as that for a BIB design, that is,

$$y_{ij} = \mu + \alpha_i + \beta_j + \epsilon_{ij} \tag{11.2.9}$$

where α_i and β_j are fixed block and treatment effects, and ϵ_{ij} are independently $N(0, \sigma^2)$. Note that for a given $i(i = 1, 2, \ldots, b)$ there are only k different values of j.

We need the following notations:

$T_{i.}$ = the total of the k observations in the ith block.

$T_{.j}$ = the total of the r observations for the jth treatment.

Q_j = the adjusted response for the jth treatment, where Q_j is obtained by subtracting from $T_{.j}$ the sum of block averages for those blocks which contain the jth treatment.

$S_1(Q_j)$ = the total of the adjusted response for all the first associates of the jth treatment.

G = the grand total of all bk observations.

Furthermore, we define

$$\Delta = \frac{1}{\kappa^2} \{(a + \lambda_1)(a + \lambda_2) + (\lambda_1 - \lambda_2)[a(f - g) + f\lambda_2 - g\lambda_1]\}$$

$$c_1 = \frac{1}{k\Delta} [\lambda_1(a + \lambda_2) + (\lambda_1 - \lambda_2)(f\lambda_2 - g\lambda_1)]$$

$$c_2 = \frac{1}{k\Delta} [\lambda_2(a + \lambda_1) + (\lambda_1 - \lambda_2)(f\lambda_2 - g\lambda_1)]$$

where

$$a = r(k - 1), \quad f = p_{12}^1, \quad g = p_{12}^2$$

TABLE 11.2.6

Source	SS	d.f.
Blocks	$SS_1 = \dfrac{1}{k} \sum\limits_{i=1}^{b} T_{i.}^2 - \dfrac{G^2}{bk}$	$b - 1$
Treatments (adjusted)	$SS_2 = \sum\limits_{j=1}^{t} \hat{\beta}_j Q_j$	$t - 1$
Error	SS_E (by subtraction)	$bk - b - t + 1$
Total	$\sum y_{ij}^2 - \dfrac{G^2}{bk}$	$bk - 1$

TABLE 11.2.7

Source	SS	d.f.
Replication groups	$\sum\limits_{c=1}^{r'} \dfrac{R_c^2}{nt} - \dfrac{G^2}{bk}$	$r' - 1$
Blocks within replication	$\sum\limits_{i=1}^{b} \dfrac{T_{i.}^2}{k} - \sum\limits_{c=1}^{r'} \dfrac{R_c^2}{nt}$	$b - r'$
Treatments (adjusted)	$\sum \hat{\beta}_j Q_j$	$t - 1$
Error	By subtraction	$bk - b - t + 1$
Total	$\sum y_{ij}^2 - \dfrac{G^2}{bk}$	$bk - 1$

The estimate of treatment effect β_j is

$$\hat{\beta}_j = \frac{1}{r(k-1)} [(k - c_2)Q_j + (c_1 - c_2)S_1(Q_j)]$$

For any two treatments, jth and j'th, which are ith associates ($i = 1, 2$), the variance of $\hat{\beta}_j - \hat{\beta}_{j'}$ is

$$\text{Var}\,[\hat{\beta}_j - \hat{\beta}_{j'}] = \frac{2\sigma^2(k - c_i)}{r(k-1)}$$

The analysis-of-variance table is given in Table 11.2.6. The F-statistic for testing the hypothesis (all $\beta_j = 0$) is given by

$$\frac{SS_2/(t-1)}{SS_E/(bk - b - t + 1)}$$

In some designs, the blocks may be grouped into r' replication groups. Within each replication group, each treatment is replicated n times. In using such arrangements, the experimental material is so divided that the blocks in the same replication are relatively more homogeneous. The model in (11.2.9) is now modified as

$$y_{ij} = \mu + r_c + \alpha'_i + \beta_j + \epsilon_{ij}$$

where r_c are fixed replication effects and α'_i are fixed block effects within replication. Putting

$$r_c + \alpha'_i = \alpha_i$$

we see that the estimates of treatment effects remain the same as before. The analysis-of-variance table is also modified and shown in Table 11.2.7, where R_c denotes the sum of the block totals in the cth replication. The F-test on treatment effects is performed as usual.

c) Lattice Designs

The balanced lattice design described in (a) usually requires a large number of replications. A reduction of the number of replications may be accomplished by partial balance. Several types of partially balanced lattices have been introduced for this purpose.

A lattice with two replications is called a *simple lattice* in which the number of treatments is k^2, number of units per block is k, and number of blocks is $2k$. An example for $k = 4$ is shown in Table 11.2.8.

TABLE 11.2.8

Blocks	Replication I				Blocks	Replication II			
(1)	1	2	3	4	(5)	1	5	9	13
(2)	5	6	7	8	(6)	2	6	10	14
(3)	9	10	11	12	(7)	3	7	11	15
(4)	13	14	15	16	(8)	4	8	12	16

The lack of complete balance is indicated by the fact that, for example, treatment 1 appears in the same block with treatments 2, 3, 4, 5, 9, and 13 but not with the others. Hence two error variances are required for testing differences between pairs of treatments.

A lattice design with k^2 treatments arranged in $3k$ blocks of k units and 3 replications for each treatment is called a *triple lattice*. Table 11.2.9 contains an example for $k = 5$.

A lattice design with k^2 treatments arranged in $4k$ blocks of k units and 4 replications for each treatment is called a *quadruple lattice*. Table 11.2.10 shows an example for $k = 7$.

The asymmetrical nature of triple lattices and quadruple lattices is similar to that of the simple lattices.

TABLE 11.2.9

Blocks	Replication I				
(1)	1	2	3	4	5
(2)	6	7	8	9	10
(3)	11	12	13	14	15
(4)	16	17	18	19	20
(5)	21	22	23	24	25
Blocks	Replication II				
(6)	1	6	11	16	21
(7)	2	7	12	17	22
(8)	3	8	13	18	23
(9)	4	9	14	19	24
(10)	5	10	15	20	25
Blocks	Replication III				
(11)	1	7	13	19	25
(12)	21	2	8	14	20
(13)	16	22	3	9	15
(14)	11	17	23	4	10
(15)	6	12	18	24	5

TABLE 11.2.10

Blocks	Replication I							Blocks	Replication II						
(1)	1	2	3	4	5	6	7	(8)	1	8	15	22	29	36	43
(2)	8	9	10	11	12	13	14	(9)	2	9	16	23	30	37	44
(3)	15	16	17	18	19	20	21	(10)	3	10	17	24	31	38	45
(4)	22	23	24	25	26	27	28	(11)	4	11	18	25	32	39	46
(5)	29	30	31	32	33	34	35	(12)	5	12	19	26	33	40	47
(6)	36	37	38	39	40	41	42	(13)	6	13	20	27	34	41	48
(7)	43	44	45	46	47	48	49	(14)	7	14	21	28	35	42	49
Blocks	Replication III							Blocks	Replication IV						
(15)	1	9	17	25	33	41	49	(22)	1	37	24	11	47	34	21
(16)	43	2	10	18	26	34	42	(23)	15	2	38	25	12	48	35
(17)	36	44	3	11	19	27	35	(24)	29	16	3	39	26	13	49
(18)	29	37	45	4	12	20	28	(25)	43	30	17	4	40	27	14
(19)	22	30	38	46	5	13	21	(26)	8	44	31	18	5	41	28
(20)	15	23	31	39	47	6	14	(27)	22	9	45	32	19	6	42
(21)	8	16	24	32	40	48	7	(28)	36	23	10	46	33	20	7

Lattices with some higher numbers of replications for k^2 treatments are available. *Cubic lattices* for k^3 treatments and *rectangular lattices* for $k(k + 1)$ treatments in blocks of k units also have been introduced. For detailed discussions on lattice designs, see Cochran and Cox [1].

d) Simple Chain Block Designs

A *simple chain block design* may be used in experimental situations in which

1) the number of treatments is large and may considerably exceed the size of block;

2) within the blocks, comparisons are relatively precise;

3) elimination of effect due to blocks is desired.

TABLE 11.2.11

	Blocks			
(1)	(2)	(3)	(4)	(5)
A	C	E	G	I
B	D	F	H	J
C'	E'	G'	I'	A'
D'	F'	H'	J'	B'
k	l	m	n	o
p	q			

The principle of simple chain block designs may be illustrated by an example in Table 11.2.11 for 17 treatments in blocks of 6 or 5 units. The letters denote the treatments. Capital letters refer to treatments having two replications; small letters refer to treatments with a single replication.

The design has a basic linking property. Treatments C and D appear in blocks 1 and 2 and form the link between these two blocks; E and F, G and H, I and J, and A and B form the links between blocks 2 and 3, 3 and 4, 4 and 5, and 5 and 1, respectively. Therefore, the design may be regarded as a chain. The linking property is used to compute the block effects. Each treatment is then adjusted for the effects of the block or blocks in which it lies.

The design is flexible. The basic groups such as A, B may have 1, 2, 3 or more letters (or treatments). However, all basic groups should have the same number. Additional treatments with a single replication like k, l, m may be included—subject only to the limitation imposed by the size of the block. For additional information on chain block designs, see Cochran and Cox [1], and Youden and Connor [9].

11.3 DESIGNS FOR TWO-WAY ELIMINATION OF ERROR

The Latin square design is a method for eliminating the effect of variation in two directions corresponding to the rows and columns of the square (as well as for studying the main effects of three factors which are of interest in themselves). However, when the number of available experimental units in one direction or both is less than the number of treatments, the Latin square designs cannot be used and the need for certain incomplete block designs arises. Several types of designs for two-way elimination of error will be described briefly below.

a) Incomplete Latin Squares

These designs are constructed by rearranging some balanced incomplete blocks or by omitting certain columns or rows in an ordinary Latin square. Most of these designs were developed by Youden; hence they are also called *Youden squares*. A Youden square for 7 treatments is shown in Table 11.3.1.

TABLE 11.3.1

Rows (blocks)	Columns (replications)			
	I	II	III	IV
(1)	3	5	6	7
(2)	4	6	7	1
(3)	5	7	1	2
(4)	6	1	2	3
(5)	7	2	3	4
(6)	1	3	4	5
(7)	2	4	5	6

The Youden square is a balanced incomplete block design when rows are regarded as blocks. For the example in Table 11.3.1, we have

$$r = k = 4, \qquad t = b = 7, \qquad \lambda = 2$$

In general, in a Youden square, every treatment appears once in each column and every pair of treatments appears together the same number of times in a row. In addition,

$$r = k = \text{number of columns}$$
$$t = b = \text{number of rows}$$

Column effects are eliminated automatically from treatment comparisons, and row effects may be removed by adjusting treatment means.

Table 11.3.2 contains a Youden square which is formed by deleting the last column of a 5×5 Latin square.

The model for a Youden square experiment is the same as that for a Latin square experiment, that is,

$$y_{iju} = \mu + \alpha_i + \beta_j + \gamma_u + \epsilon_{iju}$$

where α_i, β_j, and γ are fixed row (block), treatment, and column effects, re-

TABLE 11.3.2

Rows (blocks)	Columns (replications)			
	I	II	III	IV
(1)	1	2	3	4
(2)	2	1	5	3
(3)	3	4	1	5
(4)	4	5	2	1
(5)	5	3	4	2

spectively, and ϵ_{iju} are independently $N(0, \sigma^2)$. In addition, we assume

$$\sum \alpha_i = 0, \qquad \sum \beta_j = 0, \qquad \sum \gamma_u = 0$$

Note that (i, j, u) takes on only the bk values specified by the design.

The analysis of variance for a Youden square follows the same procedure for a BIB design (see Section 11.2a), with an additional sum of squares for columns calculated in the usual way. The sums of squares and degrees of freedom are shown in Table 11.3.3 where the notations of a BIB design are used. The treatment mean square is divided by the error mean square to form the F-ratio for testing the significance of the treatment effect. Similar F-tests can be performed on the row effect and the column effect.

TABLE 11.3.3

Source	SS	d.f.
Rows (crude)	$SS_1 = \dfrac{1}{k} \displaystyle\sum_{i=1}^{b} T_{i..}^2 - \dfrac{1}{bk} T_{...}^2$	
Treatments (adjusted)	$SS_2 = \dfrac{k(t-1)}{t(k-1)r} \left[\displaystyle\sum_{j=1}^{t} T_{.j.} - \displaystyle\sum_{i(j)} y_{i..} \right]^2$	$t - 1$
Treatments (crude)	$SS_3 = \dfrac{1}{r} \displaystyle\sum_{j=1}^{t} T_{.j.}^2 - \dfrac{1}{bk} T_{...}^2$	
Rows (adjusted)	$SS_4 = \dfrac{r(b-1)}{b(r-1)k} \left[\displaystyle\sum_{i=1}^{b} T_{i..} - \displaystyle\sum_{j(i)} y_{.j.} \right]^2$	$b - 1$
Columns	$SS_5 = \dfrac{1}{k} \displaystyle\sum_{u=1}^{k} T_{..u}^2 - \dfrac{1}{bk} T_{...}^2$	$k - 1$
Error	$SS_E = SS_6 - SS_1 - SS_2 - SS_5$ $\quad = SS_6 - SS_3 - SS_4 - SS_5$	$bk - t - b - k + 2$
Total	$SS_6 = \sum\sum y_{iju}^2 - \dfrac{1}{bk} T_{...}^2$	$bk - 1$

TABLE 11.3.4

Square I				Square II				Square III			
1	5	9	13	1	2	3	4	1	11	16	6
2	6	10	14	6	5	8	7	12	2	5	15
3	7	11	15	11	12	9	10	14	8	3	9
4	8	12	16	16	15	14	13	7	13	10	4

Square IV				Square V			
1	7	12	14	1	10	15	8
8	2	13	11	9	2	7	16
10	16	3	5	13	6	3	12
15	9	6	4	5	14	11	4

b) Balanced Lattice Squares

If available homogeneous experimental units are numbered less than treatments in two directions (rows and columns), neither Latin squares nor Youden squares can be used. A group of designs called *balanced lattice squares may* remove this difficulty. Table 11.3.4 gives an example for 16 treatments arranged in five 4 × 4 squares.

In a design of balanced lattice squares, the number of treatments must be a square, k^2, each replication consists of the k^2 treatments arranged in a $k \times k$ square, and each pair of treatments appears together in the same row or column of a square an equal number of times, λ, in all the squares. In the example above, we have $\lambda = 2$. The differences among squares (replications) are eliminated, and treatment means may be adjusted for row and column effects. For more information on balanced lattice squares, see Cochran and Cox [1].

c) Generalized Chain Block Designs

Some of the simple chain block designs can be generalized in such a fashion that elimination of error is achieved not only for columns but also for rows. Table 11.3.5 gives a *generalized chain block design* for 8 treatments.

If the columns are regarded as blocks, this is a typical chain block design, and the chain goes 1, 3, 2, 4, 1. Again, if the rows are regarded as blocks, the

TABLE 11.3.5

Rows	Columns			
	(1)	(2)	(3)	(4)
(I)	A	B	C	D
(II)	E	F	G	H
(III)	G'	H'	B'	A'
(IV)	C'	D'	F'	E'

chain goes I, IV, II, III, I. Thus the arrangement is a chain block design for both rows and columns, and treatment means may be corrected to remove the effects of the columns and rows. For detailed discussions on generalized chain block designs, see Mandel [12].

11.4 DESIGNS FOR SPECIAL PURPOSES

a) Designs Balanced for Residual Effects

When different treatments are applied in sequence to the same object such as machines, farming plots, or laboratory animals, there may be residual effect of any treatment carrying over to the succeeding period when another treatment is applied. If separation of any two successive periods of experimentation by an interval of time is not feasible, a special type of arrangement may be needed. Designs which allow each treatment to be preceded by each of the other treatments an equal number of times may accomplish this special purpose. These designs are called *balanced with respect to residual effects*.

TABLE 11.4.1

Periods	4 treatments in sequences			
	(1)	(2)	(3)	(4)
(I)	1	2	3	4
(II)	2	3	4	1
(III)	4	1	2	3
(IV)	3	4	1	2

TABLE 11.4.2

Periods	5 treatments in sequences									
	(1)	(2)	(3)	(4)	(5)	(6)	(7)	(8)	(9)	(10)
(I)	1	2	3	4	5	1	2	3	4	5
(II)	2	3	4	5	1	3	4	5	1	2
(III)	4	5	1	2	3	2	3	4	5	1
(IV)	5	1	2	3	4	5	1	2	3	4
(V)	3	4	5	1	2	4	5	1	2	3

If the number of treatments is even, a suitable choice of a Latin square forms such a design. If the number of treatments is odd, two Latin squares must be used. Table 11.4.1 gives the design for 4 treatments. Table 11.4.2 shows the design for 5 treatments. For the analysis of these designs, see Cochran and Cox [1].

b) Designs for Paired Observations

Sometimes because of the very nature of an experiment, the block size is limited to two experimental units, such as the use of identical twins in biomedical research. Balanced incomplete block designs can be formed by taking all possible pairs of the t-treatments in $\frac{1}{2}t(t-1)$ blocks with $(t-1)$ replications for each treatment.

TABLE 11.4.3

(1 2)	(1 5)	(1 7)	(1 10)
(2 3)	(2 6)	(2 8)	
(3 4)	(3 7)	(3 9)	
(4 5)	(4 8)	(4 10)	
(5 6)	(5 9)		
(6 7)	(6 10)		
(7 8)			
(8 9)			
(9 10)			

With large values of t, partially balanced incomplete block designs with reduced number of blocks may be more desirable. Table 11.4.3 shows an example for 10 treatments with 4 replications per treatment; the treatments require only 20 blocks instead of 45. More information about such designs can be found in Zoellner and Kempthorne [13].

REFERENCES

1. COCHRAN, W. G., and G. M. COX, *Experimental Designs*, 2nd Ed. Wiley, New York, 1957.

2. FEDERER, W. T., *Experimental Design*. MacMillan, New York, 1955.

3. YATES, F., "The Recovery of Interblock Information in Balanced Incomplete Block Designs," *Annals Eugenics*, **10**, 317–325 (1940).

4. SCHEFFÉ, H., *The Analysis of Variance*. Wiley, New York, 1959.

5. BOSE, R. C., and T. SHIMAMOTO, "Classification and Analysis of Partially Balanced Incomplete Block Designs with Two Associate Classes," *J. Amer. Stat. Assoc.*, **47**, 151–184 (1952).

6. RAO, C. R., "General Methods of Analysis for Incomplete Block Designs," *J. Amer. Stat. Assoc.*, **42**, 541–561 (1947).

7. BOSE, R. C., W. H. CLATWORTHY, and S. S. SHRIKHANDE, "Tables of Partially Balanced Designs with Two Associate Classes," North Carolina Agricultural Experiment Station, Technical Bulletin No. 107, 1954.

8. CLATWORTHY, W. H., "Contributions on Partially Balanced Incomplete Block Designs with Two Associate Classes," National Bureau of Standards, Applied Math Series 47, 1956.

9. YOUDEN, W. J., and W. S. CONNOR, "The Chain Block Design," *Biometrics*, **9**, 127–140 (1953).

10. YOUDEN, W. J., "Use of Incomplete Block Replications in Estimating Tobacco-Mosaic Virus," *Contr. Boyce Thompson Inst.*, **9**, 41–48 (1937).

11. YOUDEN, W. J., "Experimental Designs to Increase Accuracy of Greenhouse Studies," *Contr. Boyce Thompson Inst.*, **11**, 219–228 (1940).

12. MANDEL, J., "Chain Block Designs with Two-Way Elimination of Heterogeneity," *Biometrics*, **10**, 251–272 (1954).

13. ZOELLNER, J. A., and O. KEMPTHORNE, "Incomplete Block Designs with Blocks of Two Plots," Agricultural Experiment Station, Iowa State University, Research Bulletin No. 418, 1954.

GENERAL REFERENCES

1. FISHER, R. A., *The Design of Experiments*, 7th Ed. Hafner, New York, 1960.
2. YATES, F., "The Design and Analysis of Factorial Experiments," Imperial Bureau of Soil Science, Harpenden, England, 1937.
3. COCHRAN, W. G., and G. M. Cox, *Experimental Designs*, 2nd Ed. Wiley, New York, 1957.
4. FEDERER, W. T., *Experimental Design*. MacMillan, New York, 1955.
5. KEMPTHORNE, O., *The Design and Analysis of Experiments*. Wiley, New York, 1952.
6. Cox, D. R., *Planning of Experiments*. Wiley, New York, 1958.
7. SCHEFFÉ, H., *The Analysis of Variance*. Wiley, New York, 1959.
8. MANN, H. B., *Analysis and Design of Experiments*. Dover, New York, 1949.

TABLES

1. FISHER, R. A., and F. YATES, *Statistical Tables for Biological Agricultural and Medical Research*, 6th Ed. Hafner, New York, 1963.
2. PEARSON, E. S., and H. O. HARTLEY, *Biometrika Tables for Statisticians*. Cambridge University Press, 1958.
3. OWEN, D. B., *Handbook of Statistical Tables*. Addison-Wesley, Reading, Massachusetts, 1962.
4. KITAGAWA, T., and M. MITOME, *Tables for the Design of Factorial Experiments*. Baifukan, Tokyo, 1953.
5. STATISTICAL ENGINEERING LABORATORY OF NATIONAL BUREAU OF STANDARDS, "Fractional Factorial Experiment Designs for Factors at Two Levels," National Bureau of Standards, Applied Math Series 48, 1957.
6. CONNOR, W. S., and M. ZELEN, "Fractional Factorial Experiment Designs for Factors at Three Levels," National Bureau of Standards, Applied Math Series 54, 1959.
7. CONNOR, W. S., and S. YOUNG, "Fractional Factorial Designs for Experiments with Factors at Two and Three Levels," National Bureau of Standards, Applied Math Series 58, 1961.

A COMPUTER PROGRAM FOR THE ANALYSIS OF COMMON FACTORIAL EXPERIMENTS

A) Introduction

A general program is coded in FORTRAN language for the analysis of common factorial experiments on the IBM 7094 with the following restrictions:

Maximum number of factors = 12

Maximum number of observations = 4096

The program makes explicit use of the operator calculus and mapping schemes described in Chapter 2, and consists of a main program and several subroutines.

a) In the main program, input and output are handled.

b) Subroutine CMEAN computes means for a given group of factorial combinations specified by an input parameter card.

c) Subroutine TRAN applies transformations to experimental data.

d) Subroutine GENTUP generates a sequence of ordered K-tuples.

e) Subroutine CONTR controls the sequence of operators.

f) Subroutine SUMOP performs operator Σ.

g) Subroutine DOP performs operator D.

h) Subroutine SQADD performs operator $(\ )^2$.

i) Subroutine DEG computes degrees of freedom.

B) Input

a) Codes for transformation of data

1   means no transformation

2   means $Y = \log X$ where X = original value, and Y = transformed value

3   means $Y = \log (X + 1.0)$

4   means $Y = (X + 0.5)^{1/2}$

5   means $Y = \sin^{-1}\left(\dfrac{X + 3/8}{N + 3/4}\right)^{1/2}$

    where N = total number of observations

6   means $Y = \frac{1}{2}\log \dfrac{1 + X}{1 - X}$

b) Parameter cards for computing groups of means:

These cards are used to control the computation of any group of means desired. For example, for a 2^6 experiment, a card with a sequence of 100000 will yield the means for factor A at the low level as well as A at the high level; a sequence of 110000 will yield the means for

   i) A at the low level and B at the low level
  ii) A at the high level and B at the low level
 iii) A at the low level and B at the high level
 iv) A at the high level and B at the high level

c) Input data

The input data must follow a particular order. This may be illustrated by an example. Consider a $3 \times 2 \times 3$ complete factorial, and let the 18 observed data points be $X_1, X_2, X_3, \ldots, X_{18}$. Assume that $X_1, X_2, X_3, \ldots, X_{18}$ are read in consecutively; then $X_1, X_2, X_3, \ldots, X_{18}$ must have the following sequence of related factorial combinations:

$$
\begin{array}{ccc}
1 & 1 & 1 \\
2 & 1 & 1 \\
3 & 1 & 1 \\
1 & 2 & 1 \\
2 & 2 & 1 \\
3 & 2 & 1 \\
1 & 1 & 2 \\
2 & 1 & 2 \\
3 & 1 & 2 \\
1 & 2 & 2 \\
2 & 2 & 2 \\
3 & 2 & 2 \\
1 & 1 & 3 \\
2 & 1 & 3 \\
3 & 1 & 3 \\
1 & 2 & 3 \\
2 & 2 & 3 \\
3 & 2 & 3 \\
\end{array}
$$

Note that the factorial combinations are not to be read in as input data.

d) Input cards

    Let

          M = number of factors

       NP = number of parameter cards for computing means

Use the table on the following page.

```
310 LP1=LP1+1
    IF(LP1-1)320,320,330
320 KR2(I)=1
    KR1(LP1)=1
    L1(LP1)=L(I)
    GO TO 340
330 L1(LP1)=L(I)
    KR1(LP1)=KR1(LP1-1)*L1(LP1-1)
    KR2(I)=KR1(LP1)
    GO TO 340
340 CONTINUE
    KT1=KR1(LP1)*L1(LP1)
    KT2=KT1-1
    DO 370 I=1,M
    IF(LP(I))360,360,370
360 KR2(I)=KT1
370 CONTINUE
375 CALL CMEAN(M,KT,LP,LV,L,K,KR,X,SUM,NCELL,CELL,SMEAN,ST,DIFF,GMEAN,
   1LOCAT)
    WRITE OUTPUT TAPE 6,380,SUM,SMEAN,DIFF,ST,NCELL,(LP(I2),I2=1,M)
380 FORMAT(1H0,5X,F13.4,2X,F13.4,2X,F13.4,2X,F11.4,3X,I4,6X,13I4)
    DO 382 I=1,M
382 K1(I)=1
    DO 400 J1=1,KT2
    CALL GENTUP(M,L,LP,K1,KR2)
    CALL CMEAN(M,KT,LP,LV,L,K,KR,X,SUM,NCELL,CELL,SMEAN,ST,DIFF,GMEAN,
   1LOCAT)
    WRITE OUTPUT TAPE 6,390,SUM,SMEAN,DIFF,ST,NCELL,(LP(I2),I2=1,M)
390 FORMAT(1H ,5X,F13.4,2X,F13.4,2X,F13.4,2X,F11.4,3X,I4,6X,13I4)
400 CONTINUE
410 CONTINUE
    WRITE OUTPUT TAPE 6,75
    WRITE OUTPUT TAPE 6,78,GMEAN
    WRITE OUTPUT TAPE 6,80
    WRITE OUTPUT TAPE 6,78,GSD
411 GO TO(418,412,418),KODE
412 KBT=L(1)
    CALL BTEST(KBT,KT,BST)
    IF(BST)418,418,414
414 WRITE OUTPUT TAPE 6,415
415 FORMAT(1H0,7X,60HBARTLETT STATISTIC FOR TESTING HOMOGENEITY OF CEL
   1L VARIANCES)
    WRITE OUTPUT TAPE 6,78,BST
418 GO TO(419,430),KDEV
419 WRITE OUTPUT TAPE 6,420
420 FORMAT(1H1,6X,14HSUM OF SQUARES,7X,3HD F,8X,11HMEAN SQUARE,8X,8HDE
   1VIATES,8X,21HSOURCE IDENTIFICATION)
    GO TO 445
430 WRITE OUTPUT TAPE 6,440
440 FORMAT(1H1,6X,14HSUM OF SQUARES,7X,3HD F,8X,11HMEAN SQUARE,24X,21H
   1SOURCE IDENTIFICATION)
445 DO 450 I=1,M
    LVS(I)=1
    KS(I)=1
450 LS(I)=2
    KRS(1)=1
    DO 455 I=2,M
455 KRS(I)=KRS(I-1)*LS(I-1)
    KTC=KRS(M)*LS(M)
    CALL CONTR(M,LVS,NSKIP,KT,L,X,Y,KTS,LVID,MDG,SSQ,SMDG,SQM,SKTS,LO
   1CAT)
    WRITE OUTPUT TAPE 6,470,SSQ,MDG,SQM,(LVID(I3),I3=1,M)
470 FORMAT(1H0,5X,F15.6,5X,I4,5X,F15.6,22X,13I3)
    GO TO(474,480),KDEV
474 DO 475 J5=1,KTS
475 WRITE OUTPUT TAPE 6,476,Y(J5)
476 FORMAT(1H ,49X,F16.6)
480 SSQ1=0.0
    MDG1=0.0
```

```
      SQM1=0.0
      DO 4475 J3=2,KTC
      CALL GENTUP(M,LS,LVS,KS,KRS)
      CALL CONTR(M,LVS,NSKIP,KT,L,X,Y,KTS,LVID,MDG,SSQ,SMDG,SQM,SKTS,LO
     1CAT)
      WRITE OUTPUT TAPE 6,470,SSQ,MDG,SQM,(LVID(I3),I3=1,M)
      IF(LVID(1)-1)4250,4200,4250
 4200 SSQ1=SSQ1+SSQ
      MDG1=MDG1+MDG
 4250 GO TO(4280,4475),KDEV
 4280 WRITE OUTPUT TAPE 6,4300,Y(1),(LVID(I3),I3=1,M)
 4300 FORMAT(1H ,49X,F16.6,6X,13I3)
      LVID1=0
      DO 4340 I=1,M
      IF(LVID(I))4340,4340,4310
 4310 LVID1=LVID1+1
      IF(LVID1-1)4320,4320,4330
 4320 KR2(I)=1
      KR1(LVID1)=1
      L1(LVID1)=L(I)
      GO TO 4340
 4330 L1(LVID1)=L(I)
      KR1(LVID1)=KR1(LVID1-1)*L1(LVID1-1)
      KR2(I)=KR1(LVID1)
      GO TO 4340
 4340 CONTINUE
      KT1=KR1(LVID1)*L1(LVID1)
      KT2=KT1-1
      DO 4370 I=1,M
      IF(LVID(I))4360,4360,4370
 4360 KR2(I)=KT1
 4370 CONTINUE
      DO 4465 I=1,M
 4465 K1(I)=1
      DO 4470 J5=2,KTS
      CALL GENTUP(M,L,LVID,K1,KR2)
      WRITE OUTPUT TAPE 6,4300,Y(J5),(LVID(I3),I3=1,M)
 4470 CONTINUE
 4475 CONTINUE
 4480 GO TO(4495,4481,5010),KODE
 4481 WRITE OUTPUT TAPE 6,4482
 4482 FORMAT(1H0,6X,10HERROR TERM)
 4483 SMDG1=MDG1
      SQM1=SSQ1/SMDG1
 4485 WRITE OUTPUT TAPE 6,4490,SSQ1,MDG1,SQM1
 4490 FORMAT(1H0,5X,F15.6,5X,I4,5X,F15.6)
 4495 IF(NOTE)1,1,5005
 5005 DO 5008 I=1,NOTE
      READ INPUT TAPE 7,5007
 5007 FORMAT(55H                                                       )
      WRITE OUTPUT TAPE 6,28
 5008 WRITE OUTPUT TAPE 6,5007
      GO TO 1
 5010 IF(NEST)4495,4495,5020
 5020 KYCLE=KYCLE+1
      IF(KYCLE-1)5040,5025,5040
 5025 KT=KT/L(M)
      M=M-1
      WRITE OUTPUT TAPE 6,5035
 5035 FORMAT(1H1,7X,46HANALYSIS OF SUBSETS OF DATA IN A NESTED DESIGN)
 5040 LOCAT=(KYCLE-1)*KT+1
      IF(KEEP+1-LOCAT)5060,5060,5050
 5050 GO TO 411
 5060 NEST=NEST-1
      KYCLE=0
      IF(NEST)4495,4495,5070
 5070 LOCAT=1
      GO TO 4480
 4496 WRITE OUTPUT TAPE 6,4497
 4497 FORMAT(1H1,6X,50HERROR IN INPUT DATA ANALYSIS TERMINATED BY PROGRAM)
```

```
*COMPILE,PRINT SAP,PUNCH OBJECT                              CMEAN001
C          SUBROUTINE COMPUTES MEAN FOR A GIVEN GROUP
C          M=NUMBER OF FACTORS IN THE DESIGN
C          KT=TOTAL NUMBER OF OBSERVATIONS
C          LP=LEVEL COMBINATION DENOTING THE GROUP
C          X=EXPERIMENTAL DATA
       SUBROUTINE CMEAN(M,KT,LP,LV,L,K,KR,X,SUM,NCELL,CELL,SMEAN,ST,DIFF,
      1GMEAN,LOCAT)
       DIMENSION ALF(13),TITLE(13,12),FMT(12),X(4096),Y(4096),K(13),K1(13
      1),KR(13),KR1(13),KR2(13),KRS(13),KS(13),L(13),L1(13),LV(13),LP(13)
      2,LS(13),LVS(13),LVID(13),NSKIP(13)
       COMMON ALF,TITLE,FMT,X,Y,K,K1,KR,KR1,KR2,KRS,KS,L,L1,LV,LP,LS,LVS,
      1LVID,NSKIP
       SUM=0.0
       NCELL=0
       SMEAN=0.0
       SS=0.0
       ST=0.0
       DO 130 I=1,M
       K(I)=1
 130   LV(I)=1
       KR(1)=1
       DO 135 I=2,M
 135   KR(I)=KR(I-1)*L(I-1)
       KT=KR(M)*L(M)
       DO 150 I=1,M
       IF(LP(I))141,141,143
 141   GO TO 150
 143   IF(LP(I)-LV(I))145,150,145
 145   GO TO 155
 150   CONTINUE
 151   SUM=X(LOCAT)
       SS=SS+X(LOCAT)**2
       NCELL=1
       INEST1=LOCAT+1
       INEST2=LOCAT+KT-1
 155   DO 230 J=INEST1,INEST2
       CALL GENTUP(M,L,LV,K,KR)
       DO 180 I=1,M
       IF(LP(I))160,160,170
 160   GO TO 180
 170   IF(LP(I)-LV(I))171,180,171
 171   GO TO 230
 180   CONTINUE
 190   SUM=SUM+X(J)
 200   SS=SS+X(J)**2
       NCELL=NCELL+1
 230   CONTINUE
 235   IF(NCELL)245,245,240
 240   CELL=NCELL
       SMEAN=SUM/CELL
       ST=((CELL*SS-SUM**2)**.5)/CELL
 245   DIFF=GMEAN-SMEAN
       RETURN
*COMPILE,PRINT SAP,PUNCH OBJECT                              CONTRO01
C          SUBROUTINE CONTROLS THE SEQUENCES OF OPERATORS BY USING
C          BINARY SEQUENCES
C          M=NUMBER OF FACTORS
C          KT=TOTAL NUMBER OF OBSERVATIONS
C          LVS=A SEQUENCE OF ONES AND TWOS
       SUBROUTINE CONTR(M,LVS,NSKIP,KT,L,X,Y,KTS,LVID,MDG,SSQ,SMDG,SQM,SK
      1TS,LOCAT)
       DIMENSION ALF(13),TITLE(13,12),FMT(12),X(4096),Y(4096),K(13),K1(13
      1),KR(13),KR1(13),KR2(13),KRS(13),KS(13),L(13),L1(13),LV(13),LP(13)
      2,LS(13),LVS(13),LVID(13),NSKIP(13)
       COMMON ALF,TITLE,FMT,X,Y,K,K1,KR,KR1,KR2,KRS,KS,L,L1,LV,LP,LS,LVS,
      1LVID,NSKIP
       TKT=KT
       KTS=KT
```

```
         NSKIP(1)=1
         DO 2050 I=2,M
         IF(LVS(I-1)-1)2020,2030,2020
 2020 NSKIP(I)=NSKIP(I-1)*L(I-1)
         GO TO 2050
 2030 NSKIP(I)=NSKIP(I-1)
         GO TO 2050
 2050 CONTINUE
         DO 2055 J=1,KT
 2054 JNEST=J+LOCAT-1
 2055 Y(J)=X(JNEST)
         DO 2080 I=1,M
         LSC=LVS(I)
         I=I
         GO TO(2060,2070),LSC
 2060 CALL SUMOP(M,KTS,L,NSKIP,Y,I)
         GO TO 2080
 2070 CALL DOP(M,KTS,L,NSKIP,Y,I)
         GO TO 2080
 2080 CONTINUE
         CALL DEG(M,LVS,L,MDG)
         CALL SQADD(KTS,Y,SSQ,SKTS)
         DO 2090 I=1,M
 2090 LVID(I)=LVS(I)-1
         SSQ=SSQ/TKT
         SMDG=MDG
         SQM=SSQ/SMDG
         RETURN
*COMPILE,PRINT SAP,PUNCH OBJECT                                          GENT 001
C          SUBROUTINE GENERATES A SEQUENCE OF ORDERED M-TUPLES
C          M=NUMBER OF FACTORS
C          L(I)=LEVELS OF FACTORS,GIVEN
C          LV(I)=LEVELS OF FACTORS,VARIABLE
C          K(I)=COUNTER OF REPETITIONS OF LEVELS
C          KR(I)=NUMBER OF REPETITIONS OF LEVELS
         SUBROUTINE GENTUP(M,L,LV,K,KR)
         DIMENSION ALF(13),TITLE(13,12),FMT(12),X(4096),Y(4096),K(13),K1(13
      1),KR(13),KR1(13),KR2(13),KRS(13),KS(13),L(13),L1(13),LV(13),LP(13)
      2,LS(13),LVS(13),LVID(13),NSKIP(13)
         COMMON ALF,TITLE,FMT,X,Y,K,K1,KR,KR1,KR2,KRS,KS,L,L1,LV,LP,LS,LVS,
      1LVID,NSKIP
         DO 110 I=1,M
         IF(K(I)-KR(I))90,95,95
   90 K(I)=K(I)+1
         GO TO 110
   95 LV(I)=LV(I)+1
         K(I)=1
         IF(LV(I)-L(I))110,110,100
  100 LV(I)=1
         GO TO 110
  110 CONTINUE
  120 RETURN
*COMPILE,PRINT SAP,PUNCH OBJECT                                          TRAN 001
C          SUBROUTINE APPLIES SPECIFIED TRANSFORMATIONS TO DATA
C          KT=TOTAL NUMBER OF OBSERVATIONS
C          KTRAN=CODES OF TRANSFORMATIONS
         SUBROUTINE TRAN(KT,KTRAN)
         DIMENSION ALF(13),TITLE(13,12),FMT(12),X(4096),Y(4096),K(13),K1(13
      1),KR(13),KR1(13),KR2(13),KRS(13),KS(13),L(13),L1(13),LV(13),LP(13)
      2,LS(13),LVS(13),LVID(13),NSKIP(13)
         COMMON ALF,TITLE,FMT,X,Y,K,K1,KR,KR1,KR2,KRS,KS,L,L1,LV,LP,LS,LVS,
      1LVID,NSKIP
         TKT=KT
         GO TO(3210,3220,3230,3240,3250,3260),KTRAN
 3210 RETURN
 3220 DO 3225 J=1,KT
 3225 X(J)=LOGF(X(J))
         RETURN
 3230 DO 3235 J=1,KT
 3235 X(J)=LOGF(X(J)+1.0)
```

```
      RETURN
 3240 DO 3245 J=1,KT
 3245 X(J)=(X(J)+.5)**.5
      RETURN
 3250 DO 3255 J=1,KT
      X(J)=((X(J)+.375)/(TKT+.75))**.5
 3255 X(J)=ATANF(X(J)/(1.0-X(J)**2.0)**.5)
      RETURN
 3260 DO 3265 J=1,KT
 3265 X(J)=.5*(LOGF((1.0+X(J))/(1.0-X(J))))
      RETURN
*COMPILE,PRINT SAP,PUNCH OBJECT                              SUMOP001
C     SUBROUTINE COMPUTES SUM OVER ALL LEVELS OF A FACTOR
C     WHILE KEEPING THE LEVELS OF OTHER FACTORS CONSTANT
C     L(I)=LEVELS OF FACTORS,GIVEN
C     NSKIP=NUMBER OF DATA POINTS TO BE SKIPPED WHEN A SUM IS COMPUTED
      SUBROUTINE SUMOP(M,KTS,L,NSKIP,Y,I)
      DIMENSION ALF(13),TITLE(13,12),FMT(12),X(4096),Y(4096),K(13),K1(13
     1),KR(13),KR1(13),KR2(13),KRS(13),KS(13),L(13),L1(13),LV(13),LP(13)
     2,LS(13),LVS(13),LVID(13),NSKIP(13)
      COMMON ALF,TITLE,FMT,X,Y,K,K1,KR,KR1,KR2,KRS,KS,L,L1,LV,LP,LS,LVS,
     1LVID,NSKIP
      J2=1
      M1=1
      J7=0
  900 SOP=0.0
  910 M2=M1+(NSKIP(I)*(L(I)-1))
      M3=NSKIP(I)
      DO 1000 J=M1,M2,M3
 1000 SOP=SOP+Y(J)
      Y(J2)=SOP
      J2=J2+1
      IF(NSKIP(I)-1)1010,1010,1020
 1010 M1=M1+L(I)
      IF(M1-KTS)900,900,1060
 1020 M1=M1+1
 1021 J7=J7+1
      IF(NSKIP(I)-J7)1030,1030,1040
 1030 M1=NSKIP(I)*L(I)+M1-NSKIP(I)
      J7=0
 1040 IF(M1-KTS)1050,1050,1060
 1050 GO TO 900
 1060 KTS=KTS/L(I)
      RETURN
*COMPILE,PRINT SAP,PUNCH OBJECT                              DOP  001
C     SUBROUTINE MULTIPLIES EACH DATA POINT BY THE LEVEL OF A FACTOR AND
C     SUBTRACT THE SUM OF THESE POINTS FROM EACH POINT WHILE KEEPING
C     THE LEVELS OF OTHER FACTORS CONSTANT
C     L(I)=LEVELS OF FACTORS
C     NSKIP=NUMBER OF DATA POINTS TO BE SKIPPED WHEN A SUM IS COMPUTED
      SUBROUTINE DOP(M,KTS,L,NSKIP,Y,I)
      DIMENSION ALF(13),TITLE(13,12),FMT(12),X(4096),Y(4096),K(13),K1(13
     1),KR(13),KR1(13),KR2(13),KRS(13),KS(13),L(13),L1(13),LV(13),LP(13)
     2,LS(13),LVS(13),LVID(13),NSKIP(13)
      COMMON ALF,TITLE,FMT,X,Y,K,K1,KR,KR1,KR2,KRS,KS,L,L1,LV,LP,LS,LVS,
     1LVID,NSKIP
      MD1=1
      J8=0
 1200 SDOP=0.0
 1210 MD2=MD1+(NSKIP(I)*(L(I)-1))
      MD3=NSKIP(I)
      DO 1220 J4=MD1,MD2,MD3
 1220 SDOP=SDOP+Y(J4)
      DL=L(I)
      DO 1230 J4=MD1,MD2,MD3
 1230 Y(J4)=Y(J4)*DL-SDOP
      IF(NSKIP(I)-1)1240,1240,1250
 1240 MD1=MD1+L(I)
      IF(MD1-KTS)1200,1200,1290
 1250 MD1=MD1+1
```

```
 1251 J8=J8+1
 1255 IF(NSKIP(I)-J8)1260,1260,1270
 1260 MD1=NSKIP(I)*L(I)+MD1-NSKIP(I)
      J8=0
 1270 IF(MD1-KTS)1280,1280,1290
 1280 GO TO 1200
 1290 RETURN
*COMPILE,PRINT SAP,PUNCH OBJECT                                    DEG  001
C     SUBROUTINE COMPUTES DEGREES OF FREEDOM FOR EACH MAIN
C     EFFECT OR INTERACTION
C     LVS=A SEQUENCE OF ONES AND TWOS
C     L(I)=LEVELS OF THE FACTORS
C     M=NUMBER OF FACTORS
      SUBROUTINE DEG(M,LVS,L,MDG)
      DIMENSION ALF(13),TITLE(13,12),FMT(12),X(4096),Y(4096),K(13),K1(13
     1),KR(13),KR1(13),KR2(13),KRS(13),KS(13),L(13),L1(13),LV(13),LP(13)
     2,LS(13),LVS(13),LVID(13),NSKIP(13)
      COMMON ALF,TITLE,FMT,X,Y,K,K1,KR,KR1,KR2,KRS,KS,L,L1,LV,LP,LS,LVS,
     1LVID,NSKIP
      MDG=1
      DO 3030 I=1,M
      IF(LVS(I)-1)3010,3010,3020
 3010 MDG=MDG
      GO TO 3030
 3020 MDG=MDG*(L(I)-1)
 3030 CONTINUE
      RETURN
*COMPILE,PRINT SAP,PUNCH OBJECT                                   SQADD001
C     SUBROUTINE SQUARES EACH ELEMENT IN A SET,AND DIVIDE
C     THEIR SUM BY THE NUMBER OF ELEMENTS IN THE SET
      SUBROUTINE SQADD(KTS,Y,SSQ,SKTS)
      DIMENSION ALF(13),TITLE(13,12),FMT(12),X(4096),Y(4096),K(13),K1(13
     1),KR(13),KR1(13),KR2(13),KRS(13),KS(13),L(13),L1(13),LV(13),LP(13)
     2,LS(13),LVS(13),LVID(13),NSKIP(13)
      COMMON ALF,TITLE,FMT,X,Y,K,K1,KR,KR1,KR2,KRS,KS,L,L1,LV,LP,LS,LVS,
     1LVID,NSKIP
      SKTS=KTS
      SSQ=0.0
      DO 3120 J5=1,KTS
 3120 SSQ=SSQ+Y(J5)**2
      SSQ=SSQ/SKTS
      RETURN
*COMPILE,PRINT SAP,PUNCH OBJECT                                   BTEST001
C     SUBROUTINE PERFORMS BARTLETT TEST OF HOMOGENEITY OF VARIANCES
      SUBROUTINE BTEST(KBT,KT,BST)
      DIMENSION ALF(13),TITLE(13,12),FMT(12),X(4096),Y(4096),K(13),K1(13
     1),KR(13),KR1(13),KR2(13),KRS(13),KS(13),L(13),L1(13),LV(13),LP(13)
     2,LS(13),LVS(13),LVID(13),NSKIP(13)
      COMMON ALF,TITLE,FMT,X,Y,K,K1,KR,KR1,KR2,KRS,KS,L,L1,LV,LP,LS,LVS,
     1LVID,NSKIP
      KKKBT=KT/KBT
      TBK=KBT
      TBKKK=KKKBT
      KKBT1=1
      KKBT2=KBT
      AMV=0.0
      GMLOG=0.0
      DO 7040 J=1,KKKBT
      BSUM=0.0
      BVAR=0.0
      BSS=0.0
      DO 7000 I=KKBT1,KKBT2
      BSUM=BSUM+X(I)
 7000 BSS=BSS+X(I)**2
      BVAR=(TBK*BSS-BSUM**2)/TBK**2
 7010 IF(BVAR)7020,7020,7030
 7020 BST=0.0
      RETURN
 7030 Y(J)=BVAR
      KKBT1=KKBT1+KBT
```

```
      KKBT2=KKBT2+KBT
7040  CONTINUE
      DO 7060 J=1,KKKBT
      AMV=AMV+Y(J)/TBKKK
      Y(J)=LOGF(Y(J))
7060  GMLOG=GMLOG+Y(J)/TBKKK
      AMV=LOGF(AMV)
      BST1=TBKKK*(TBK-1.0)*(AMV-GMLOG)
      BST2=1.0+(TBKKK+1.0)/(3.0*TBKKK*(TBK-1.0))
      BST=BST1/BST2
      RETURN
*DATA
```

E) Example

a) Input listing

```
    3    6    1    1    1    1    0    0
X1
X2
X3
    2    2    3
          DATA ARTIFICIALLY GENERATED
(4F6.0)
        4        0       -2       -2
        4        0        0        4
        4        6        2       -8
    1    0    0
    0    1    0
    0    0    1
    1    1    0
    1    0    1
    0    1    1
```

b) Output listing

```
ANALYSIS OF VARIANCE

FACTOR   A   IS   X1

FACTOR   B   IS   X2

FACTOR   C   IS   X3


DATA ARTIFICIALLY GENERATED

DATA FROM EXPERIMENT
            4.000000          1    1    1
            0.                2    1    1
           -2.000000          1    2    1
           -2.000000          2    2    1
            4.000000          1    1    2
            0.                2    1    2
            0.                1    2    2
            4.000000          2    2    2
            4.000000          1    1    3
            6.000000          2    1    3
            2.000000          1    2    3
           -8.000000          2    2    3
```

SUM	MEAN	DE FR G MEAN	STD DEV	FREQ	GROUP		
12.0000	2.0000	-1.0000	2.3094	6	1	0	0
0.	0.	1.0000	4.4721	6	2	0	0
18.0000	3.0000	-2.0000	2.2361	6	0	1	0
-6.0000	-1.0000	2.0000	3.7859	6	0	2	0
0.	0.	1.0000	2.4495	4	0	0	1
8.0000	2.0000	-1.0000	2.0000	4	0	0	2
4.0000	1.0000	-0.0000	5.3852	4	0	0	3

12.0000	4.0000	-3.0000	0.	3	1	1	0
6.0000	2.0000	-1.0000	2.8284	3	2	1	0
-0.	-0.	1.0000	1.6330	3	1	2	0
-6.0000	-2.0000	3.0000	4.8990	3	2	2	0
2.0000	1.0000	-0.0000	3.0000	2	1	0	1
-2.0000	-1.0000	2.0000	1.0000	2	2	0	1
4.0000	2.0000	-1.0000	2.0000	2	1	0	2
4.0000	2.0000	-1.0000	2.0000	2	2	0	2
6.0000	3.0000	-2.0000	1.0000	2	1	0	3
-2.0000	-1.0000	2.0000	7.0000	2	2	0	3
4.0000	2.0000	-1.0000	2.0000	2	0	1	1
-4.0000	-2.0000	3.0000	0.	2	0	2	1
4.0000	2.0000	-1.0000	2.0000	2	0	1	2
4.0000	2.0000	-1.0000	2.0000	2	0	2	2
10.0000	5.0000	-4.0000	1.0000	2	0	1	3
-6.0000	-3.0000	4.0000	5.0000	2	0	2	3

GRAND MEAN
        1.0000

GRAND STANDARD DEVIATION
        3.6968

SUM OF SQUARES	D F	MEAN SQUARE	DEVIATES	SOURCE IDENTIFICATION		
12.000000	1	12.000000		0	0	0
			12.000000			
12.000000	1	12.000000		1	0	0
			12.000000	1	0	0
			-12.000000	2	0	0
48.000000	1	48.000000		0	1	0
			24.000000	0	1	0
			-24.000000	0	2	0
0.	1	0.		1	1	0
			0.	1	1	0
			-0.	2	1	0
			-0.	1	2	0
			0.	2	2	0
8.000000	2	4.000000		0	0	1
			-12.000000	0	0	1
			12.000000	0	0	2
			0.	0	0	3
8.000000	2	4.000000		1	0	1
			0.	1	0	1
			-0.	2	0	1
			-12.000000	1	0	2
			12.000000	2	0	2
			12.000000	1	0	3
			-12.000000	2	0	3
32.000000	2	16.000000		0	1	1
			0.	0	1	1
			-0.	0	2	1
			-24.000000	0	1	2
			24.000000	0	2	2
			24.000000	0	1	3
			-24.000000	0	2	3
56.000000	2	28.000000		1	1	1
			12.000000	1	1	1
			-12.000000	2	1	1
			-12.000000	1	2	1
			12.000000	2	2	1
			24.000000	1	1	2
			-24.000000	2	1	2
			-24.000000	1	2	2
			24.000000	2	2	2
			-36.000000	1	1	3
			36.000000	2	1	3
			36.000000	1	2	3
			-36.000000	2	2	3

A COMPUTER PROGRAM FOR THE ANALYSIS OF LATIN SQUARE AND GRAECO-LATIN SQUARE EXPERIMENTS

A) Introduction

A program is coded in FORTRAN language for the analysis of Latin Square and Graeco-Latin Square experiments on the IBM 7094 with the restriction that the order (or size) of the square must be less than or equal to 22.

The program consists of a main program and two subroutines.

a) In the main program, input and output are handled and sums of squares and mean squares are computed.

b) Subroutine TRAN applies transformations to experimental data.

Codes for transformation of data are the following:

1 means no transformation
2 means $y = \log x$ where $x =$ original value, and $y =$ transformed value
3 means $y = \log (x + 1.0)$
4 means $y = (x + 0.5)^{1/2}$
5 means $y = \sin^{-1} \left(\dfrac{x + 3/8}{N + 3/4} \right)^{1/2}$
   where $N =$ total number of observations
6 means $y = \frac{1}{2} \log \dfrac{1 + x}{1 - x}$

c) Subroutine CMEAN computes means for a given group.

B) Input Cards

A few symbols used in the program may be noted here.

$$\text{KODE} = \begin{cases} 1 & \text{for Latin Square} \\ 2 & \text{for Graeco-Latin} \end{cases}$$

$$\text{NP} = \text{Number of title cards in the input}$$

$$\text{KT} = \text{Total number of observations}$$

$$\text{KTRAN} = \text{Code for transformation of data}$$

$$\text{KBYK} = \text{Size of the square}$$

Observations are followed by indices indicating forms (or order) within rows, columns, and letters. Use 1, 2, 3, ... for indexing and observe the convention of having rows first, columns second, Latin letters third, and Greek letters fourth.

Card No.	Column	Format	Information
1	1–4	$i4$	KODE
	5–8	$i4$	NP
	9–12	$i4$	KT
	13–16	$i4$	KTRAN
2 to $NP + 1$	9–55	$46H$	Title Cards
$NP + 2$	1–2	$i2$	KBYK
$NP + 3$	1–72	$12A6$	Format card for data cards
$NP + 4$ to last	1–72	(as specified above)	Observations followed by indices

C) Output

The output mainly consists of

a) sums, means and standard deviations for each possible grouping;

b) analysis-of-variance table.

D) Fortran Listing

```
COMPILE,PRINT SAP,PUNCH OBJECT                                    LATIN001
C     ANALYSIS OF LATIN SQUARE AND GRAECO-LATIN SQUARE EXPERIMENTS
      DIMENSION X(500),IND(500,10),FMT(12),LP(10),SUMM(100),SQUAR(100)
      COMMON X,IND,FMT,LP,SUMM,SQUAR
   10 READ INPUT TAPE 7,20,KODE,NP,KT,KTRAN
   20 FORMAT(4I4)
      WRITE OUTPUT TAPE 6,30
   30 FORMAT(1H1,7X,20HANALYSIS OF VARIANCE)
      DO 40 I=1,NP
      READ INPUT TAPE 7,35
   35 FORMAT(55H                                                        )
   36 FORMAT(1H0)
      WRITE OUTPUT TAPE 6,36
   40 WRITE OUTPUT TAPE 6,35
      GO TO(3000,4000),KODE
 4000 WRITE OUTPUT TAPE 6,4010
 4010 FORMAT(1H0,7X,31HDATA FROM A GRAECO-LATIN SQUARE)
      GO TO 3011
 3000 WRITE OUTPUT TAPE 6,3010
 3010 FORMAT(1H0,7X,35HDATA FROM A LATIN SQUARE EXPERIMENT)
 3011 READ INPUT TAPE 7,3015,KBYK
 3015 FORMAT(I2)
      READ INPUT TAPE 7,3020,(FMT(J),J=1,12)
 3020 FORMAT(12A6)
      GO TO(3025,3027),KODE
 3025 NF=3
      GO TO 3029
 3027 NF=4
 3029 DO 3030 I=1,KT
 3030 READ INPUT TAPE 7,FMT,X(I),(IND(I,J),J=1,NF)
      CALL TRAN(KT,KTRAN)
      DO 3050 I=1,KT
```

```
3050 WRITE OUTPUT TAPE 6,3060,X(I),(IND(I,J),J=1,NF)
3060 FORMAT(1H ,10X,F13.6,10X,4I5)
     GMEAN=0.0
     GSD=0.0
     GSUM=0.0
     GSS=0.0
     SKT=KT
     DO 3070 I=1,KT
     GSUM=GSUM+X(I)
     GSS=GSS+X(I)**2
3070 GMEAN=GMEAN+X(I)/SKT
     GSD=((SKT*GSS-GSUM**2)**.5)/SKT
     WRITE OUTPUT TAPE 6,3090
3090 FORMAT(1H1,14X,3HSUM,12X,4HMEAN,3X,12HDE FR G MEAN,6X,7HSTD DEV,4X
    1,4HFREQ,8X,5HGROUP)
3115 DO 3140 I=1,NF
     SQUAR(I)=0.0
     DO 3120 J=1,NF
3120 LP(J)=0
     DO 3135 II=1,KBYK
     LP(I)=LP(I)+1
     CALL CMEAN(NF,KT,LP,X,IND,SUM,NCELL,CELL,SMEAN,ST,DIFF,GMEAN)
     WRITE OUTPUT TAPE 6,3130,SUM,SMEAN,DIFF,ST,NCELL,(LP(I2),I2=1,NF)
3130 FORMAT(1H ,5X,F13.4,2X,F13.4,2X,F13.4,2X,F11.4,4X,I3,7X,4I3)
     SUMM(I1)=SUM
     SQUAR(I)=SQUAR(I)+SUMM(I1)**2
3135 CONTINUE
3140 CONTINUE
     WRITE OUTPUT TAPE 6,3200
3200 FORMAT(1H0,7X,10HGRAND MEAN)
     WRITE OUTPUT TAPE 6,3210,GMEAN
3210 FORMAT(1H ,8X,F15.6)
     WRITE OUTPUT TAPE 6,3220
3220 FORMAT(1H0,7X,24HGRAND STANDARD DEVIATION)
     WRITE OUTPUT TAPE 6,3210,GSD
     CBYC=KBYK
     CORR=(GSUM**2)/(CBYC**2)
     KBYK1=KBYK-1
     KBYK2=KBYK-2
     KBYK3=KBYK1*KBYK2
     KBYK4=KBYK**2-1
     KBYK5=KBYK-3
     KBYK6=KBYK1*KBYK5
     TOTAL=GSS-CORR
     ROW=SQUAR(1)/CBYC-CORR
     ROWM=ROW/(CBYC-1.0)
     COL=SQUAR(2)/CBYC-CORR
     COLM=COL/(CBYC-1.0)
     TREAT=SQUAR(3)/CBYC-CORR
     TREATM=TREAT/(CBYC-1.0)
     GO TO(3240,3250),KODE
3240 ERROR=TOTAL-ROW-COL-TREAT
     ERRM=ERROR/((CBYC-1.0)*(CBYC-2.0))
     GO TO 3290
3250 GREEK=SQUAR(4)/CBYC-CORR
     GREEKM=GREEK/(CBYC-1.0)
     ERROR=TOTAL-ROW-COL-TREAT-GREEK
     ERRM=ERROR/((CBYC-1.0)*(CBYC-3.0))
     GO TO 3290
3290 WRITE OUTPUT TAPE 6,3300
3300 FORMAT(1H1,6X,14HSUM OF SQUARES,7X,3HD F,8X,11HMEAN SQUARE,24X,21H
    1SOURCE IDENTIFICATION)
     LP(1)=1
     LP(2)=0
     LP(3)=0
     LP(4)=0
     WRITE OUTPUT TAPE 6,3310,ROW,KBYK1,ROWM,(LP(I),I=1,NF)
3310 FORMAT(1H0,5X,F15.6,5X,I4,5X,F15.6,22X,13I3)
     LP(1)=0
```

```
        LP(2)=1
        LP(3)=0
        LP(4)=0
        WRITE OUTPUT TAPE 6,3310,COL,KBYK1,COLM,(LP(I),I=1,NF)
        LP(1)=0
        LP(2)=0
        LP(3)=1
        LP(4)=0
        WRITE OUTPUT TAPE 6,3310,TREAT,KBYK1,TREATM,(LP(I),I=1,NF)
        GO TO(3318,3400),KODE
 3318   WRITE OUTPUT TAPE 6,3320
 3320   FORMAT(1H0,6X,10HERROR TERM)
        WRITE OUTPUT TAPE 6,3330,ERROR,KBYK3,ERRM
 3330   FORMAT(1H0,5X,F15.6,5X,I4,5X,F15.6)
        WRITE OUTPUT TAPE 6,3340
 3340   FORMAT(1H0,6X,5HTOTAL)
        WRITE OUTPUT TAPE 6,3350,TOTAL,KBYK4
 3350   FORMAT(1H0,5X,F15.6,5X,I4)
        GO TO 10
 3400   LP(1)=0
        LP(2)=0
        LP(3)=0
        LP(4)=1
        WRITE OUTPUT TAPE 6,3310,GREEK,KBYK1,GREEKM,(LP(I),I=1,NF)
        WRITE OUTPUT TAPE 6,3320
        WRITE OUTPUT TAPE 6,3330,ERROR,KBYK6,ERRM
 3335   WRITE OUTPUT TAPE 6,3340
        WRITE OUTPUT TAPE 6,3350,TOTAL,KBYK4
        GO TO 10
*COMPILE,PRINT SAP,PUNCH OBJECT                                  TRAN0001
C          SUBROUTINE APPLIES SPECIFIED TRANSFORMATIONS TO DATA
C          KT=TOTAL NUMBER OF OBSERVATIONS
C          KTRAN=CODES OF TRANSFORMATIONS
        SUBROUTINE TRAN(KT,KTRAN)
        DIMENSION X(500),IND(500,10),FMT(12),LP(10),SUMM(100),SQUAR(100)
        COMMON X,IND,FMT,LP,SUMM,SQUAR
        TKT=KT
        GO TO(3210,3220,3230,3240,3250,3260),KTRAN
 3210   RETURN
 3220   DO 3225 J=1,KT
 3225   X(J)=LOGF(X(J))
        RETURN
 3230   DO 3235 J=1,KT
 3235   X(J)=LOGF(X(J)+1.0)
        RETURN
 3240   DO 3245 J=1,KT
 3245   X(J)=(X(J)+.5)**.5
        RETURN
 3250   DO 3255 J=1,KT
        X(J)=((X(J)+.375)/(TKT+.75))**.5
 3255   X(J)=ATANF(X(J)/(1.0-X(J)**2.0)**.5)
        RETURN
 3260   DO 3265 J=1,KT
 3265   X(J)=.5*(LOGF((1.0+X(J))/(1.0-X(J))))
        RETURN
*COMPILE,PRINT SAP,PUNCH OBJECT                                  MEAN0001
C       SUBROUTINE COMPUTES MEAN FOR A GIVEN GROUP
        SUBROUTINE CMEAN(M,KT,LP,X,IND,SUM,NCELL,CELL,SMEAN,ST,DIFF,GMEAN)
        DIMENSION X(500),IND(500,10),FMT(12),LP(10),SUMM(100),SQUAR(100)
        COMMON X,IND,FMT,LP,SUMM,SQUAR
        SUM=0.0
        SS=0.0
        ST=0.0
        NCELL=0
        SMEAN=0.0
        DO 1130 I=1,KT
        DO 1080 J=1,M
        IF(LP(J))1060,1060,1070
```

```
1060 GO TO 1080
1070 IF(LP(J)-IND(I,J))1071,1080,1071
1071 GO TO 1130
1080 CONTINUE
1090 SUM=SUM+X(I)
     NCELL=NCELL+1
     SS=SS+X(I)**2
1130 CONTINUE
     IF(NCELL)1150,1150,1140
1140 CELL=NCELL
     SMEAN=SUM/CELL
     ST=((CELL*SS-SUM**2)**.5)/CELL
1150 DIFF=GMEAN-SMEAN
     RETURN
```

E) Example

a) Input listing

```
1    4   16   1
     ROWS
     COLUMNS
     TREATMENTS
     DATA ARTIFICIALLY GENERATED
 4
(F6.0,6X,3I1)
      34         111
      31         122
      15         133
      28         144
      28         212
      37         221
      17         234
      10         243
      12         313
      21         324
      33         331
      26         342
      26         414
      23         423
      23         432
      36         441
```

b) Output listing

```
ANALYSIS OF VARIANCE
ROWS
COLUMNS
TREATMENTS
DATA ARTIFICIALLY GENERATED

DATA FROM A LATIN SQUARE EXPERIMENT
        34.000000          1    1    1
        31.000000          1    2    2
        15.000000          1    3    3
        28.000000          1    4    4
        28.000000          2    1    2
        37.000000          2    2    1
        17.000000          2    3    4
        10.000000          2    4    3
        12.000000          3    1    3
        21.000000          3    2    4
        33.000000          3    3    1
        26.000000          3    4    2
        26.000000          4    1    4
        23.000000          4    2    3
        23.000000          4    3    2
        36.000000          4    4    1
```

SUM	MEAN	DE FR G MEAN	STD DEV	FREQ	GROUP		
108.0000	27.0000	-2.0000	7.2457	4	1	0	0
92.0000	23.0000	2.0000	10.3199	4	2	0	0
92.0000	23.0000	2.0000	7.6485	4	3	0	0
108.0000	27.0000	-2.0000	5.3385	4	4	0	0
100.0000	25.0000	0.	8.0623	4	0	1	0
112.0000	28.0000	-3.0000	6.4031	4	0	2	0
88.0000	22.0000	3.0000	7.0000	4	0	3	0
100.0000	25.0000	0.	9.4340	4	0	4	0
140.0000	35.0000	-10.0000	1.5811	4	0	0	1
108.0000	27.0000	-2.0000	2.9155	4	0	0	2
60.0000	15.0000	10.0000	4.9497	4	0	0	3
92.0000	23.0000	2.0000	4.3012	4	0	0	4

GRAND MEAN
    25.000000

GRAND STANDARD DEVIATION
    8.093206

SUM OF SQUARES	D F	MEAN SQUARE	SOURCE IDENTIFICATION		
64.000000	3	21.333333	1	0	0
72.000000	3	24.000000	0	1	0
832.000000	3	277.333332	0	0	1
ERROR TERM					
80.000000	6	13.333333			
TOTAL					
1048.000000	15				

APPENDIX III

A COMPUTER PROGRAM FOR THE ANALYSIS OF FRACTIONAL FACTORIAL EXPERIMENTS WITH FACTORS AT TWO LEVELS

A) Introduction

A program is coded in FORTRAN language for the analysis of a 2^{-P} replicate of a 2^K factorial experiment on the IBM 7094 with the following restrictions:

a) $K \leq 16$

b) $2^{K-P} \leq 256$

The program consists of a main program and a few subroutines.

a) In the main program, input and output are handled and aliases sets are computed.

b) Subroutine CMEAN computes means for a given group of factorial combinations specified by an input parameter card.

c) Subroutine TRAN applies transformations to experimental data.

d) Subroutine GENTUP generates a sequence of ordered M-tuples.

e) Subroutine CONTR controls the sequence of operators.

f) Subroutine SUMOP performs operator Σ.

g) Subroutine DOP performs operator D.

h) Subroutine SQADD performs operator $(\ )^2$.

i) Subroutine DEG computes degrees of freedom.

237

B) Input

a) Codes for transformation of data.

   1 means no transformation

   2 means $Y = \log X$ where $X =$ original value, and $Y =$ transformed value

   3 means $Y = \log (X + 1.0)$

   4 means $Y = (X + 0.5)^{1/2}$

   5 means $Y = \sin^{-1} \left(\dfrac{X + 3/8}{N + 3/4} \right)^{1/2}$

     where $N =$ total number of observations

   6 means $Y = \frac{1}{2} \log \dfrac{1 + X}{1 - X}$

b) Parameter cards for computing groups of means:

These cards are used to control the computation of any group of means desired. For example, for a 6-factor experiment, a card with a sequence of 1 0 0 0 0 0 will yield the means and other associated statistics for factor A at the low level as well as A at the high level; a sequence of 1 1 0 0 0 0 will yield those for

   i) A at the low level and B at the low level

  ii) A at the high level and B at the low level

 iii) A at the low level and B at the high level

 iv) A at the high level and B at the high level

C) Defining Contrast Cards and Aliases

The defining contrast cards are punched in zeros and ones. For example, the experiment given in Table 7.3.5 has the following four defining contrasts:

$$I = ABCE = ABDF = CDEF$$

and they are represented by

$$
\begin{array}{cccccc}
0 & 0 & 0 & 0 & 0 & 0 \\
1 & 1 & 1 & 0 & 1 & 0 \\
1 & 1 & 0 & 1 & 0 & 1 \\
0 & 0 & 1 & 1 & 1 & 1
\end{array}
$$

D) Input Cards

Let $M =$ number of factors

   $NP =$ number of parameter cards for computing means

   $KT =$ number of observations

   $KC =$ number of defining contrasts

Card No.	Column	Format	Information
1	1–4	$i4$	Number of factors
	5–8	$i4$	Number of parameter cards
	9–12	$i4$	Number of observations
	13–16	$i4$	Number of defining contrast cards
	17–20	$i4$	Code for transformation of data
	21–24	$i4$	0 for not punching aliases sets
			1 for punching aliases sets
	25–28	$i4$	Highest order of aliases desired
	29–32	$i4$	0 for not printing aliases
			1 for printing aliases
	33–36	$i4$	0 for not printing deviates
			1 for printing deviates
2 to $M+1$	2–72	$12A6$	Names of factors
$M+2$	1–48	$16i3$	Number of levels of the factors
$M+3$	9–55	$46H$	Name of dependent variable
$M+4$	1–72	$12A6$	Format card for data cards
$M+5$ to	1–72	(as speci-	Observations followed by factorial
$M+5+KT$		fied above)	levels denoted by ones and twos
$M+5+KT+1$ to	1–64	$16i4$	Parameter cards for group means
$M+5+KT+1+NP$			
$M+KT+NP+7$ to	1–64	$16i4$	Defining contrasts
$M+KT+NP+7+KC$			
Last card	1–3	$i3$	Number of factors to be ignored temporarily

The data cards have to be arranged in a certain order. For example, the 16 combinations for the design given in Table 7.3.5 will be ordered in the following fashion:

1)	1	1	1	1	1	1	5)	1	1	2	1	2	1
2)	2	2	1	1	1	1	6)	2	2	2	1	2	1
3)	2	1	2	2	1	1	7)	2	1	1	2	2	1
4)	1	2	2	2	1	1	8)	1	2	1	2	2	1
9)	2	1	2	1	1	2	13)	2	1	1	1	2	2
10)	1	2	2	1	1	2	14)	1	2	1	1	2	2
11)	1	1	1	2	1	2	15)	1	1	2	2	2	2
12)	2	2	1	2	1	2	16)	2	2	2	2	2	2

Here, factors A and C are ignored temporarily, and the desired order is represented by factors $BDEF$.

E) Output

The output mainly consists of

a) sums, means, deviations of means from grand mean, standard deviations, and frequencies for all the specified groups
b) aliases sets (optional)
c) analysis-of-variance table (see Section 7.5)

F) Fortran Listing

```
*COMPILE,PRINT SAP,PUNCH OBJECT                                          FRACT001
C       ANALYSIS OF VARIANCE PROGRAM FOR FRACTIONAL FACTORIAL DESIGNS
        DIMENSION ALF(16),TITLE(16,12),FMT(12),X(256),IND(256,16),LP(16),K
       1R1(16),KR2(16),L(16),L1(16),K1(16),K(16),KR(16),LV(16),LC(16),KA(1
       26),Y(256),KRS(16),KS(16),LS(16),LVID(16),NSKIP(16),LVS(16)
        COMMON ALF,TITLE,FMT,X,IND,LP,KR1,KR2,L,L1,K1,K,KR,LV,LC,KA,Y,KRS,
       1KS,LS,LVID,NSKIP,LVS
B       ALF(1)=602160606060
B       ALF(2)=602260606060
B       ALF(3)=602360606060
B       ALF(4)=602460606060
B       ALF(5)=602560606060
B       ALF(6)=602660606060
B       ALF(7)=602760606060
B       ALF(8)=603060606060
B       ALF(9)=603160606060
B       ALF(10)=604160606060
B       ALF(11)=604260606060
B       ALF(12)=604360606060
B       ALF(13)=604460606060
B       ALF(14)=604560606060
B       ALF(15)=604660606060
B       ALF(16)=604760606060
     1  READ INPUT TAPE 7,2,M,NP,KT,KC,KTRAN,KP,NA,NALIAS,KDEV
     2  FORMAT(9I4)
        DO 3 J=1,M
     3  READ INPUT TAPE 7,4,(TITLE(J,I),I=1,12)
     4  FORMAT(12A6)
        WRITE OUTPUT TAPE 6,5
     5  FORMAT(1H1,7X,20HANALYSIS OF VARIANCE)
        DO 6 J=1,M
     6  WRITE OUTPUT TAPE 6,7,ALF(J),(TITLE(J,I),I=1,12)
     7  FORMAT(1H0,7X,6HFACTOR,1X,A3,4H IS ,12A6)
    10  READ INPUT TAPE 7,20,(L(I),I=1,M)
    20  FORMAT(16I3)
        READ INPUT TAPE 7,30
    30  FORMAT(55H                                                        )
    32  FORMAT(1H0)
        WRITE OUTPUT TAPE 6,32
        WRITE OUTPUT TAPE 6,30
        READ INPUT TAPE 7,35,(FMT(J),J=1,12)
    35  FORMAT(12A6)
        DO 50 I=1,KT
    50  READ INPUT TAPE 7,FMT,X(I),(IND(I,J),J=1,M)
    55  CALL TRAN(KT,KTRAN)
        WRITE OUTPUT TAPE 6,60
    60  FORMAT(1H0,7X,20HDATA FROM EXPERIMENT)
        DO 70 I=1,KT
    70  WRITE OUTPUT TAPE 6,80,X(I),(IND(I,J),J=1,M)
    80  FORMAT(1H ,10X,F13.6,10X,16I5)
    82  GMEAN=0.0
    83  GSD=0.0
        GSS=0.0
        GSUM=0.0
        SKT=KT
        DO 85 I=1,KT
        GSUM=GSUM+X(I)
        GSS=GSS+X(I)**2
    85  GMEAN=GMEAN+X(I)/SKT
        GSD=((SKT*GSS-GSUM**2)**.5)/SKT
        WRITE OUTPUT TAPE 6,87
    87  FORMAT(1H0,7X,10HGRAND MEAN)
    88  FORMAT(1H0,7X,24HGRAND STANDARD DEVIATION)
        WRITE OUTPUT TAPE 6,89,GMEAN
    89  FORMAT(1H ,8X,F15.6)
        WRITE OUTPUT TAPE 6,88
```

```
      WRITE OUTPUT TAPE 6,89,GSD
      WRITE OUTPUT TAPE 6,90
   90 FORMAT(1H1,14X,3HSUM,12X,4HMEAN,3X,12HDE FR G MEAN,6X,7HSTD DEV,4X
     1,4HFREQ,8X,5HGROUP)
      DO 410 I1=1,NP
      READ INPUT TAPE 7,110,(LP(I),I=1,M)
  110 FORMAT(16I4)
      LP1=0
      DO 340 I=1,M
      IF(LP(I))340,340,310
  310 LP1=LP1+1
      IF(LP1-1)320,320,330
  320 KR2(I)=1
      KR1(LP1)=1
      L1(LP1)=L(I)
      GO TO 340
  330 L1(LP1)=L(I)
      KR1(LP1)=KR1(LP1-1)*L1(LP1-1)
      KR2(I)=KR1(LP1)
      GO TO 340
  340 CONTINUE
      KT1=KR1(LP1)*L1(LP1)
      KT2=KT1-1
      DO 370 I=1,M
      IF(LP(I))360,360,370
  360 KR2(I)=KT1
  370 CONTINUE
      CALL CMEAN(M,KT,LP,X,IND,SUM,NCELL,CELL,SMEAN,ST,DIFF,GMEAN)
      WRITE OUTPUT TAPE 6,380,SUM,SMEAN,DIFF,ST,NCELL,(LP(I2),I2=1,M)
  380 FORMAT(1H0,5X,F13.4,2X,F13.4,2X,F13.4,2X,F11.4,4X,I3,7X,16I3)
      DO 382 I=1,M
  382 K1(I)=1
      DO 400 J1=1,KT2
      CALL GENTUP(M,L,LP,K1,KR2)
      CALL CMEAN(M,KT,LP,X,IND,SUM,NCELL,CELL,SMEAN,ST,DIFF,GMEAN)
      WRITE OUTPUT TAPE 6,390,SUM,SMEAN,DIFF,ST,NCELL,(LP(I2),I2=1,M)
  390 FORMAT(1H ,5X,F13.4,2X,F13.4,2X,F13.4,2X,F11.4,4X,I3,7X,16I3)
  400 CONTINUE
  410 CONTINUE
      DO 630 I3=1,KC
      DO 430 I=1,M
      LVS(I)=1
      LS(I)=2
  430 KS(I)=1
      KRS(1)=1
      DO 435 I=2,M
  435 KRS(I)=KRS(I-1)*LS(I-1)
      KTC=KRS(M)*LS(M)
      READ INPUT TAPE 7,110,(LC(I),I=1,M)
      IF (NALIAS) 521,521,499
  499 WRITE OUTPUT TAPE 6,500
  500 FORMAT(1H1,7X,17HDEFINING CONTRAST)
      WRITE OUTPUT TAPE 6,510,I3,(LC(I),I=1,M)
  510 FORMAT(1H ,7X,I4,10X,16I4)
      WRITE OUTPUT TAPE 6,520
  520 FORMAT(1H0,7X,11HALIASES SET)
  521 DO 620 I=1,KTC
      NT=0
      DO 536 J=1,M
      IF(LVS(J)-2)536,535,536
  535 NT=NT+1
  536 CONTINUE
      IF(NT-NA)539,539,616
  539 DO 600 J=1,M
  540 IF(LC(J)+LVS(J)-1)560,560,570
  560 KA(J)=0
      GO TO 600
  570 IF(LC(J)+LVS(J)-2)580,580,590
```

```
   580 KA(J)=1
       GO TO 600
   590 KA(J)=0
   600 CONTINUE
       IF (NALIAS) 616,616,605
   605 WRITE OUTPUT TAPE 6,610,I,(KA(J),J=1,M)
   610 FORMAT(1H ,7X,I4,10X,16I4)
       IF(KP)616,616,614
   614 WRITE OUTPUT TAPE 5,615,I3,I,(KA(J),J=1,M)
   615 FORMAT(I4,2X,I4,5X,16I2)
   616 CALL GENTUP(M,LS,LVS,KS,KRS)
   620 CONTINUE
   630 CONTINUE
       READ INPUT TAPE 7,4010,N
  4010 FORMAT(I3)
       M1=M-N
       IF(M1)1,1,4015
  4015 KR(1)=1
       DO 4030 I=2,M1
  4030 KR(I)=KR(I-1)*L(I-1)
       KT=KR(M1)*L(M1)
       DO 4100 I=1,KT
       DO 4100 J=1,M
  4100 IND(I,J)=IND(I,J)-1
       IF(KDEV)4110,4110,4410
  4110 WRITE OUTPUT TAPE 6,4120
  4120 FORMAT(1H1,6X,14HSUM OF SQUARES,7X,3HD F,8X,11HMEAN SQUARE,24X,21H
      1SOURCE IDENTIFICATION)
       GO TO 4430
  4410 WRITE OUTPUT TAPE 6,4420
  4420 FORMAT(1H1,6X,14HSUM OF SQUARES,7X,3HD F,8X,11HMEAN SQUARE,8X,8HDE
      1VIATES,8X,21HSOURCE IDENTIFICATION)
  4430 DO 4450 I=1,M1
       LVS(I)=1
       KS(I)=1
  4450 LS(I)=2
       KRS(1)=1
       DO 4455 I=2,M1
  4455 KRS(I)=KRS(I-1)*LS(I-1)
       KTC=KRS(M1)*LS(M1)
       CALL CONTR(M1,LVS,NSKIP,KT,L,X,Y,KTS,LVID,MDG,SSQ,SMDG,SQM,SKTS)
       WRITE OUTPUT TAPE 6,4470,SSQ,MDG,SQM,(IND(1,J),J=1,M)
  4470 FORMAT(1H0,5X,F15.6,5X,I4,5X,F15.6,22X,16I3)
       IF(KDEV)4477,4477,4474
  4474 DO 4475 J5=1,KTS
  4475 WRITE OUTPUT TAPE 6,4476,Y(J5)
  4476 FORMAT(1H ,49X,F16.6)
  4477 DO 4490 J3=2,KTC
       CALL GENTUP(M1,LS,LVS,KS,KRS)
       CALL CONTR(M1,LVS,NSKIP,KT,L,X,Y,KTS,LVID,MDG,SSQ,SMDG,SQM,SKTS)
       WRITE OUTPUT TAPE 6,4470,SSQ,MDG,SQM,(IND(J3,J4),J4=1,M)
       IF(KDEV)4490,4490,4478
  4478 DO 4480 J5=1,KTS
  4480 WRITE OUTPUT TAPE 6,4476,Y(J5)
  4490 CONTINUE
       GO TO 1
*COMPILE,PRINT SAP,PUNCH OBJECT                                    TRAN 001
C        SUBROUTINE APPLIES SPECIFIED TRANSFORMATIONS TO DATA
C        KT=TOTAL NUMBER OF OBSERVATIONS
C        KTRAN=CODES OF TRANSFORMATIONS
       SUBROUTINE TRAN(KT,KTRAN)
       DIMENSION ALF(16),TITLE(16,12),FMT(12),X(256),IND(256,16),LP(16),K
      1R1(16),KR2(16),L(16),L1(16),K1(16),K(16),KR(16),LV(16),LC(16),KA(1
      26),Y(256),KRS(16),KS(16),LS(16),LVID(16),NSKIP(16),LVS(16)
       COMMON ALF,TITLE,FMT,X,IND,LP,KR1,KR2,L,L1,K1,K,KR,LV,LC,KA,Y,KRS,
      1KS,LS,LVID,NSKIP,LVS
       TKT=KT
       GO TO(3210,3220,3230,3240,3250,3260),KTRAN
```

```
3210 RETURN
3220 DO 3225 J=1,KT
3225 X(J)=LOGF(X(J))
     RETURN
3230 DO 3235 J=1,KT
3235 X(J)=LOGF(X(J)+1.0)
     RETURN
3240 DO 3245 J=1,KT
3245 X(J)=(X(J)+.5)**.5
     RETURN
3250 DO 3255 J=1,KT
     X(J)=((X(J)+.375)/(TKT+.75))**.5
3255 X(J)=ATANF(X(J)/(1.0-X(J)**2.0)**.5)
     RETURN
3260 DO 3265 J=1,KT
3265 X(J)=.5*(LOGF((1.0+X(J))/(1.0-X(J))))
     RETURN
*COMPILE,PRINT SAP,PUNCH OBJECT                              CMEAN001
C       SUBROUTINE COMPUTES MEAN FOR A GIVEN GROUP
        SUBROUTINE CMEAN(M,KT,LP,X,IND,SUM,NCELL,CELL,SMEAN,ST,DIFF,GMEAN)
        DIMENSION ALF(16),TITLE(16,12),FMT(12),X(256),IND(256,16),LP(16),K
       1R1(16),KR2(16),L(16),L1(16),K1(16),K(16),KR(16),LV(16),LC(16),KA(1
       26),Y(256),KRS(16),KS(16),LS(16),LVID(16),NSKIP(16),LVS(16)
        COMMON ALF,TITLE,FMT,X,IND,LP,KR1,KR2,L,L1,K1,K,KR,LV,LC,KA,Y,KRS,
       1KS,LS,LVID,NSKIP,LVS
        SUM=0.0
        SS=0.0
        ST=0.0
        NCELL=0
        SMEAN=0.0
        DO 1130 I=1,KT
        DO 1080 J=1,M
        IF(LP(J))1060,1060,1070
1060    GO TO 1080
1070    IF(LP(J)-IND(I,J))1071,1080,1071
1071    GO TO 1130
1080    CONTINUE
1090    SUM=SUM+X(I)
        NCELL=NCELL+1
        SS=SS+X(I)**2
1130    CONTINUE
        IF(NCELL)1150,1150,1140
1140    CELL=NCELL
        SMEAN=SUM/CELL
        ST=((CELL*SS-SUM**2)**.5)/CELL
1150    DIFF=GMEAN-SMEAN
        RETURN
*COMPILE,PRINT SAP,PUNCH OBJECT                              GENT 001
C       SUBROUTINE GENERATES A SEQUENCE OF ORDERED M-TUPLES
        SUBROUTINE GENTUP(M,L,LV,K,KR)
        DIMENSION ALF(16),TITLE(16,12),FMT(12),X(256),IND(256,16),LP(16),K
       1R1(16),KR2(16),L(16),L1(16),K1(16),K(16),KR(16),LV(16),LC(16),KA(1
       26),Y(256),KRS(16),KS(16),LS(16),LVID(16),NSKIP(16),LVS(16)
        COMMON ALF,TITLE,FMT,X,IND,LP,KR1,KR2,L,L1,K1,K,KR,LV,LC,KA,Y,KRS,
       1KS,LS,LVID,NSKIP,LVS
        DO 2110 I=1,M
        IF(K(I)-KR(I))2090,2095,2095
2090    K(I)=K(I)+1
        GO TO 2110
2095    LV(I)=LV(I)+1
        K(I)=1
        IF(LV(I)-L(I))2110,2110,2100
2100    LV(I)=1
        GO TO 2110
2110    CONTINUE
2120    RETURN
*COMPILE,PRINT SAP,PUNCH OBJECT                              CONTR001
C       SUBROUTINE CONTROLS THE SEQUENCES OF OPERATORS BY USING
```

```
C      BINARY SEQUENCES
C      M=NUMBER OF FACTORS
C      KT=TOTAL NUMBER OF OBSERVATIONS
C      LVS=A SEQUENCE OF ONES AND TWOS
       SUBROUTINE CONTR(M,LVS,NSKIP,KT,L,X,Y,KTS,LVID,MDG,SSQ,SMDG,SQM,SK
      1TS)
       DIMENSION ALF(16),TITLE(16,12),FMT(12),X(256),IND(256,16),LP(16),K
      1R1(16),KR2(16),L(16),L1(16),K1(16),K(16),KR(16),LV(16),LC(16),KA(1
      26),Y(256),KRS(16),KS(16),LS(16),LVID(16),NSKIP(16),LVS(16)
       COMMON ALF,TITLE,FMT,X,IND,LP,KR1,KR2,L,L1,K1,K,KR,LV,LC,KA,Y,KRS,
      1KS,LS,LVID,NSKIP,LVS
       TKT=KT
       KTS=KT
       NSKIP(1)=1
       DO 2050 I=2,M
       IF(LVS(I-1)-1)2020,2030,2020
 2020  NSKIP(I)=NSKIP(I-1)*L(I-1)
       GO TO 2050
 2030  NSKIP(I)=NSKIP(I-1)
       GO TO 2050
 2050  CONTINUE
       DO 2055 J=1,KT
 2055  Y(J)=X(J)
       DO 2080 I=1,M
       LSC=LVS(I)
       I=I
       GO TO(2060,2070),LSC
 2060  CALL SUMOP(M,KTS,L,NSKIP,Y,I)
       GO TO 2080
 2070  CALL DOP(M,KTS,L,NSKIP,Y,I)
       GO TO 2080
 2080  CONTINUE
       CALL DEG(M,LVS,L,MDG)
       CALL SQADD(KTS,Y,SSQ,SKTS)
       DO 2090 I=1,M
 2090  LVID(I)=LVS(I)-1
       SSQ=SSQ/TKT
       SMDG=MDG
       SQM=SSQ/SMDG
       RETURN
*COMPILE,PRINT SAP,PUNCH OBJECT                              SUMOP001
C      SUBROUTINE COMPUTES SUM OVER ALL LEVELS OF A FACTOR
C      WHILE KEEPING THE LEVELS OF OTHER FACTORS CONSTANT
C      L(I)=LEVELS OF FACTORS,GIVEN
C      NSKIP=NUMBER OF DATA POINTS TO BE SKIPPED WHEN A SUM IS COMPUTED
       SUBROUTINE SUMOP(M,KTS,L,NSKIP,Y,I)
       DIMENSION ALF(16),TITLE(16,12),FMT(12),X(256),IND(256,16),LP(16),K
      1R1(16),KR2(16),L(16),L1(16),K1(16),K(16),KR(16),LV(16),LC(16),KA(1
      26),Y(256),KRS(16),KS(16),LS(16),LVID(16),NSKIP(16),LVS(16)
       COMMON ALF,TITLE,FMT,X,IND,LP,KR1,KR2,L,L1,K1,K,KR,LV,LC,KA,Y,KRS,
      1KS,LS,LVID,NSKIP,LVS
       J2=1
       M1=1
       J7=0
  900  SOP=0.0
  910  M2=M1+(NSKIP(I)*(L(I)-1))
       M3=NSKIP(I)
       DO 1000 J=M1,M2,M3
 1000  SOP=SOP+Y(J)
       Y(J2)=SOP
       J2=J2+1
       IF(NSKIP(I)-1)1010,1010,1020
 1010  M1=M1+L(I)
       IF(M1-KTS)900,900,1060
 1020  M1=M1+1
 1021  J7=J7+1
       IF(NSKIP(I)-J7)1030,1030,1040
 1030  M1=NSKIP(I)*L(I)+M1-NSKIP(I)
       J7=0
```

```
 1040 IF(M1-KTS)1050,1050,1060
 1050 GO TO 900
 1060 KTS=KTS/L(I)
      RETURN
*COMPILE,PRINT SAP,PUNCH OBJECT                                    DOP  001
C        SUBROUTINE MULTIPLIES EACH DATA POINT BY THE LEVEL OF A FACTOR AND
C        SUBTRACT THE SUM OF THESE POINTS FROM EACH POINT WHILE KEEPING
C        THE LEVELS OF OTHER FACTORS CONSTANT
C        L(I)=LEVELS OF FACTORS
C        NSKIP=NUMBER OF DATA POINTS TO BE SKIPPED WHEN A SUM IS COMPUTED
      SUBROUTINE DOP(M,KTS,L,NSKIP,Y,I)
      DIMENSION ALF(16),TITLE(16,12),FMT(12),X(256),IND(256,16),LP(16),K
     1R1(16),KR2(16),L(16),L1(16),K1(16),K(16),KR(16),LV(16),LC(16),KA(1
     26),Y(256),KRS(16),KS(16),LS(16),LVID(16),NSKIP(16),LVS(16)
      COMMON ALF,TITLE,FMT,X,IND,LP,KR1,KR2,L,L1,K1,K,KR,LV,LC,KA,Y,KRS,
     1KS,LS,LVID,NSKIP,LVS
      MD1=1
      J8=0
 1200 SDOP=0.0
 1210 MD2=MD1+(NSKIP(I)*(L(I)-1))
      MD3=NSKIP(I)
      DO 1220 J4=MD1,MD2,MD3
 1220 SDOP=SDOP+Y(J4)
      DL=L(I)
      DO 1230 J4=MD1,MD2,MD3
 1230 Y(J4)=Y(J4)*DL-SDOP
      IF(NSKIP(I)-1)1240,1240,1250
 1240 MD1=MD1+L(I)
      IF(MD1-KTS)1200,1200,1290
 1250 MD1=MD1+1
 1251 J8=J8+1
 1255 IF(NSKIP(I)-J8)1260,1260,1270
 1260 MD1=NSKIP(I)*L(I)+MD1-NSKIP(I)
      J8=0
 1270 IF(MD1-KTS)1280,1280,1290
 1280 GO TO 1200
 1290 RETURN
*COMPILE,PRINT SAP,PUNCH OBJECT                                    DEG  001
C        SUBROUTINE COMPUTES DEGREES OF FREEDOM FOR EACH MAIN
C        EFFECT OR INTERACTION
C        LVS=A SEQUENCE OF ONES AND TWOS
C        L(I)=LEVELS OF THE FACTORS
C        M=NUMBER OF FACTORS
      SUBROUTINE DEG(M,LVS,L,MDG)
      DIMENSION ALF(16),TITLE(16,12),FMT(12),X(256),IND(256,16),LP(16),K
     1R1(16),KR2(16),L(16),L1(16),K1(16),K(16),KR(16),LV(16),LC(16),KA(1
     26),Y(256),KRS(16),KS(16),LS(16),LVID(16),NSKIP(16),LVS(16)
      COMMON ALF,TITLE,FMT,X,IND,LP,KR1,KR2,L,L1,K1,K,KR,LV,LC,KA,Y,KRS,
     1KS,LS,LVID,NSKIP,LVS
      MDG=1
      DO 3030 I=1,M
      IF(LVS(I)-1)3010,3010,3020
 3010 MDG=MDG
      GO TO 3030
 3020 MDG=MDG*(L(I)-1)
 3030 CONTINUE
      RETURN
*COMPILE,PRINT SAP,PUNCH OBJECT                                    SQADD001
C        SUBROUTINE SQUARES EACH ELEMENT IN A SET,AND DIVIDE
C        THEIR SUM BY THE NUMBER OF ELEMENTS IN THE SET
      SUBROUTINE SQADD(KTS,Y,SSQ,SKTS)
      DIMENSION ALF(16),TITLE(16,12),FMT(12),X(256),IND(256,16),LP(16),K
     1R1(16),KR2(16),L(16),L1(16),K1(16),K(16),KR(16),LV(16),LC(16),KA(1
     26),Y(256),KRS(16),KS(16),LS(16),LVID(16),NSKIP(16),LVS(16)
      COMMON ALF,TITLE,FMT,X,IND,LP,KR1,KR2,L,L1,K1,K,KR,LV,LC,KA,Y,KRS,
     1KS,LS,LVID,NSKIP,LVS
      SKTS=KTS
      SSQ=0.0
      DO 3120 J5=1,KTS
```

```
3120 SSQ=SSQ+Y(J5)**2
     SSQ=SSQ/SKTS
     RETURN
*DATA
```

G) Example

a) Input listing

```
   6    6   16    4    1    0    2    0    0
X1
X2
X3
X4
X5
X6
   2    2    2    2    2    2
          DATA ARTIFICIALLY GENERATED
(F6.2,6X,6I1)
   1.52        111111
   2.03        221111
   0.58        212211
   1.03        122211
   1.57        112121
   2.03        222121
   0.52        211221
   1.02        121221
   3.53        212112
   4.09        122112
   2.53        111212
   3.01        221212
   3.55        211122
   4.00        121122
   2.59        112222
   3.03        222222
   1    0    0    0    0    0
   0    1    0    0    0    0
   0    0    1    0    0    0
   0    0    0    1    0    0
   0    0    0    0    1    0
   0    0    0    0    0    1
   0    0    0    0    0    0
   1    1    1    0    1    0
   1    1    0    1    0    1
   0    0    1    1    1    1
   2
```

b) Output listing

ANALYSIS OF VARIANCE

FACTOR   A   IS   X1

FACTOR   B   IS   X2

FACTOR   C   IS   X3

FACTOR   D   IS   X4

FACTOR   E   IS   X5

FACTOR   F   IS   X6

DATA ARTIFICIALLY GENERATED

DATA FROM EXPERIMENT

1.520000	1	1	1	1	1	1
2.030000	2	2	1	1	1	1
0.580000	2	1	2	2	1	1
1.030000	1	2	2	2	1	1
1.570000	1	1	2	1	2	1
2.030000	2	2	2	1	2	1
0.520000	2	1	1	2	2	1
1.020000	1	2	1	2	2	1
3.530000	2	1	2	1	1	2
4.090000	1	2	2	1	1	2
2.530000	1	1	1	2	1	2
3.010000	2	2	1	2	1	2
3.550000	2	1	1	1	2	2
4.000000	1	2	1	1	2	2
2.590000	1	1	2	2	2	2
3.030000	2	2	2	2	2	2

GRAND MEAN
2.289375

GRAND STANDARD DEVIATION
1.145832

SUM	MEAN	DE FR G MEAN	STD DEV	FREQ	GROUP					
18.3500	2.2937	-0.0044	1.1524	8	1	0	0	0	0	0
18.2800	2.2850	0.0044	1.1393	8	2	0	0	0	0	0
16.3900	2.0487	0.2406	1.1167	8	0	1	0	0	0	0
20.2400	2.5300	-0.2406	1.1239	8	0	2	0	0	0	0
18.1800	2.2725	0.0169	1.1452	8	0	0	1	0	0	0
18.4500	2.3062	-0.0169	1.1462	8	0	0	2	0	0	0
22.3200	2.7900	-0.5006	1.0329	8	0	0	0	1	0	0
14.3100	1.7887	0.5006	1.0284	8	0	0	0	2	0	0
18.3200	2.2900	-0.0006	1.1471	8	0	0	0	0	1	0
18.3100	2.2887	0.0006	1.1446	8	0	0	0	0	2	0
10.3000	1.2875	1.0019	0.5550	8	0	0	0	0	0	1
26.3300	3.2912	-1.0019	0.5571	8	0	0	0	0	0	2

SUM OF SQUARES	D F	MEAN SQUARE	SOURCE IDENTIFICATION					
83.859802	1	83.859802	0	0	0	0	0	0
0.926406	1	0.926406	1	1	0	0	0	0
4.010006	1	4.010006	1	0	1	1	0	0
0.000756	1	0.000756	0	1	1	1	0	0
0.000006	1	0.000006	0	0	1	0	1	0
0.001406	1	0.001406	1	1	1	0	1	0
0.000056	1	0.000056	1	0	0	1	1	0
0.001806	1	0.001806	0	1	0	1	1	0
16.060056	1	16.060056	1	0	1	0	0	1
0.000006	1	0.000006	0	1	1	0	0	1
0.000006	1	0.000006	0	0	0	1	0	1
0.000306	1	0.000306	1	1	0	1	0	1
0.000056	1	0.000056	1	0	0	0	1	1
0.001406	1	0.001406	0	1	0	0	1	1
0.004556	1	0.004556	0	0	1	1	1	1
0.000056	1	0.000056	1	1	1	1	1	1

INDEX